NCLEX-RN® 101:
How to Pass!

Ninth Edition

LORETTA MANNING, MSN, RN, GNP
President, I CAN Publishing®, Inc.

SYLVIA RAYFIELD, MN, RN, CNS
Sylvia Rayfield & Associates, Inc.

I CAN Publishing®, Inc. ◆ Duluth, GA
www.icanpublishing.com

Technical Assistance: Kathy Gallun, Tampa, FL; Jennifer Robinson, Duluth, GA; Mary Jo Zazueta, Traverse City, MI; and Linda Fisher, Duluth, GA

Cartoon Illustrations: C. J. Miller, BSN, RN, Iowa City, IA

Cover Design/Image Illustrations: Teresa Davidson, Greensboro, NC

Quotes from Michael Dooley or tut are from Totally Unique Thoughts. You can visit their website— http://www.tut.com—where all the latest, totally unique graphics and thoughts can be found.

ISBN: 978-0-9903542-2-2
Library of Congress Control Number: 2015958694

Printed in the United States of America

Nursing procedures and/or practice described in this book should be applied by the nurse, or health-care practitioner, under appropriate supervision according to established professional standards of care. These standards should be used with regard to the unique circumstances that apply in each practice situation. Every effort has been taken to validate and confirm the accuracy of information presented and to describe generally accepted practices. However, the authors, editors, and publisher cannot accept any responsibility for errors or omissions or for consequences from application of the information in this book and make no warranty, express or implied, with respect to the contents of this book.

Every effort has been exerted by the authors and publisher to ensure that drug selection and dosage set forth in this text are in accord with current recommendations and practice at the time of publication. However, in view of ongoing research, the constant flow of information relating to government regulations, drug therapy, and drug reactions, the reader is urged to check the manufacturer's information on the package insert of each drug for any change in indications and dosage and for added warnings and precautions. This is particularly important when the recommended agent is a new or infrequently used drug.

This book is written to be used as a test question review book for the NCLEX-RN® and the CGFNS™ examination. It is not intended for use as a primary resource for procedures, treatments, medications, or to serve as a complete textbook for nursing care.

Copies of this book may be obtained directly from:

I CAN Publishing®, Inc.
2650 Chattahoochee Drive, Suite 100
Duluth, GA 30097

1-866-428-5589
www.icanpublishing.com

THE BIG DIFFERENCE
FOR THIS BOOK

Comparable to NCLEX® and CGFNS™

Clinical Decision-Making Strategies

Addresses the nursing activities in the New NCLEX-RN® Test Plan

Rationales for correct and incorrect answers

Easy ways to pinpoint your needs

WE CARE!!

Contents

Contents

Contributors

Karen E. Alexander, PhD, RN, CNOR
Program Director, RN to BSN Program
Assistant Professor Nursing
University of Houston–Clear Lake
Houston, Texas

Marie Bremner, DSN, RN, CS
Professor of Nursing
Kennesaw State University
Kennesaw, Georgia

Michelle Staton Briley, BSN, RN
Nurse Consultant
Greenville, North Carolina

Darlene M. Burke, MS, MA, RN
Faculty, MiraCosta College
Oceanside, California
Consultant, Professional Source Nurse
　Consulting
Carlsbad, California

JoCarol Claborn, MS, RN
Independent Consultant
Lubbock, Texas

Carol Anne Claxton-Baker, MBA/HA,
　BSN, BS, RN
Director of Health Services
The Oaks, Pruitt Healthcare
Athens, Georgia

Robin P. Cunningham, MSN, RN,
　LNCC, CNE
Lecturer, Simulation Learning
　Center Coordinator
University of North Carolina—Wilmington
Wilmington, North Carolina

Linda Delunas, PhD, RN
Assistant Professor
Indiana University Northwest
Gary, Indiana

Dr. Judy J. Duvall, EdD, RN
Assistant Professor
Whitson-Hester School of Nursing
Tennessee Technological University
Cookeville, Tennessee

Linda Fisher RN, BSN, MN
Healthcare Science Instructor
Maxwell High School of Technology
Lawrenceville, Georgia

Darlene Franklin RN MSN
Assistant Professor of Nursing Emeritus
Whitson-Hester School of Nursing
Tennessee Technological University
International Nursing Consultant
Sylvia Rayfield & Associates
I CAN Publishing®, Inc.
Cookeville, Tennessee

Kathy Gallun MSN, RN
Educational Consultant
Sylvia Rayfield and Associates
I CAN Publishing®, Inc.
Tampa, Florida

Sandra Galura PhD, RN, CCRN, CPAN
Academic Programs Director
Florida Hospital Center for Clinical Educa-
　tion and Staff Development
Orlando, Florida

Melissa J. Geist, EdD, APRN-BC, CNE
Associate Professor of Nursing
Whitson-Hester School of Nursing
Tennessee Technological University
Cookeville, Tennessee

Sharon Shook Kallam, RN, BSN, MSN
Nursing Education Consultant
RN Supervisor
Hugh Chatham Nursing Center
Elkin, North Carolina

Susan L.W. Krupnick, MSN, RN,
　CARN, CS
Psychiatric Nursing
University of Pennsylvania
Philadelphia, Pennsylvania

Jana Lyner, BSN, RN
Faculty
Pensacola Junior College
Pensacola, Florida

Sylvia McDonald, RN, MEd, MSN
Consultant
Sylvia Rayfield & Associates, Inc.
and I CAN Publishing® Inc.
Jefferson, Georgia

Kimi McMahan Walker, RN, MSN-Ed
Nursing Instructor and
　Clinical Coordinator
Southwestern Community College
Sylva, North Carolina

C. J. Miller, BSN, RN
Illustrator
Iowa City, Iowa

Linda Murray, BSN, RN, CNOR, FCN
Knoxville District, School Nurse
Monmouth, Illinois

Bruce A. Scott, MSN, APRN, BC
San Joaquin Delta College
Stockton, California
Clinical Nurse, Orthopedics
University of California, Davis Medical
　Center
Sacramento, California

Deb Bagnasco Stanford, MSN, RN
Clinical Assistant Professor
UNC Greensboro, North Carolina

Linda J. Stirk MS, RN, CNE
Nursing Faculty
Blue Ridge Community College
Flat Rock, North Carolina

Charlotte Taylor, MSN, RN
Psychiatric Nursing
University of Arkansas
Monticello, Arkansas

Libby Turnipseed, LNCC, CNLCP,
　MSCC, CRNP
Turnipseed & Associates, LLC
Rainbow City, Alabama

Mayola L. Villarruel, DNP, ANP-BC,
　NEA-BC
Director Patient Care Services
Community Hospital
Munster, Indiana

Larry Zager, MSN, BSN
Leadership and Education Consultant
Ridgeway, South Carolina

Lydia R. Zager MSN, RN, NEA-BC
Clinical Professor
College of Nursing
University of South Carolina
Columbia, South Carolina

JoAnn Zerwekh, EdD, MSN, RN
Nursing Education Consultants
President/CEO
Chandler, AZ

Acknowledgments

We wish to express our love and appreciation to our families, associates, and good friends who have offered their support during the preparation of this book.

Loretta's husband, Randy Manning, what can I say? Your support, tolerance, wit, and love during this project as well as during my busy professional life keep me inspired and motivated! Thank you!

Loretta's mother, Juanita Shera, for always believing in me and her never-ending love and support as we revised this book.

Loretta's daughter, Erica Manning, for her continuing support and love as we were writing, rewriting, and editing over and over again to create a book that will make a difference in the lives of nursing students.

Jennifer Robinson, our administrative director, who was always willing to jump through a hoop to meet our deadlines. Her never-ending humor and love reminded us daily what was really important in life! A very special thank you for keeping our projects organized as well as our business running smoothly.

Michelle Briley, for your patience and eye for detail with all of those conversions. Thank you for your ongoing love and support with each of our projects! You are always an inspiration for us!

Kathy Gallun, for her attention to detail and her support with all of the final editing.

Linda Fisher, for her ongoing friendship, support, and patience while adding her final touches to the details throughout the book over her holiday vacation.

Teresa Davidson, our dear friend and artist, who was willing to create and work with us through the end with unexpected requests.

Sylvia McDonald, for her friendship, love, and support. Thank you for keeping life in perspective for me as we work on major projects and throughout our life.

Mary Jo Zazueta, our book designer, who formatted the text.

Thank you to Sylvia Rayfield & Associates who assist nursing graduates across the country to use this book and achieve successful outcomes on the NCLEX-RN®.

Thank you to all of you nursing students, graduates, and faculty who continue to read and study our books! Without each of you, we would not be writing any of these acknowledgments!

Our sincere appreciation to Dr. Phoebe K. Helm, who developed some of the test-taking strategies we have included in this book.

NCLEX-RN® 101: HOW TO PASS!
Ninth Edition

This ninth edition is current, updated and streamlined. The items are written succinctly to mimic the computer adaptive test. Our objective is to help you PASS by providing the latest information on the NCLEX-RN® exam. The exam, as reflected by the test plan published by the National Council of State Boards of Nursing, was updated in April 2016–2019. The chapter titles and items in this edition reflect these changes.

Due to the changes both in clinical practice and the NCLEX-RN®, we have revised the focus for this book to incorporate a focus on prioritization of nursing care. The strategies have been developed within the framework of the new NCLEX® Test Plan. Research demonstrates that the nursing graduate is making high-level clinical judgments due to the increase in client acuity, increase in the ages of the clients, multi-system involvement due to chronic illnesses, and polypharmacy.

As a result of this research, it is imperative to transform the traditional strategies used for answering exam items into new and current clinical decision-making strategies. We have included two new chapters to assist you in focusing and increasing your confidence when answering NCLEX®-style questions that evaluate clinical decision-making/clinical judgment.

Remember to keep this in perspective! The agenda for the NCLEX-RN® is to evaluate current and entry-level practice and be fair and comprehensive.

Your key to success is to FOCUS on questions evaluating the NCLEX-RN ® nursing activities! Let's get started in learning how to prepare for this BIG EXAM!

Loretta Manning and Sylvia Rayfield

Prelude

✔ What if you've just graduated from nursing school?

✔ What if you've just applied to take the NCLEX® or CGFNS™ exam?

✔ What if you have 50,000 pages of notes, tape recordings and nursing books and you don't have a clue as to where to start?

✔ What if you just need help?

Then ...

Read on ...

What if you knew—

✔ How to focus—not freak out

✔ Proven NCLEX® clinical decision-making (test-taking) strategies

✔ How the NCLEX® is organized

✔ How to determine your own study needs

✔ What the questions look like on the computer exam

✔ That test questions in this book are organized around the most current
   NCLEX-RN® Test Plan

The priority for the NCLEX® is always "SAFETY."
This acronym is organized around the priority
NCLEX-RN® activities.

S System-specific, focused assessment

A Accuracy of orders/assignments

F First—prioritize

E Evaluate outcomes (i.e., pharmacology, care, etc.)

T Teach and practice infection control

Y You must manage care to prevent "RISK" to the client

© National Council of State Boards of Nursing, Inc. (NCSBN) 2014. *RN Practice Analysis: Linking the NCLEX-RN® Examination to Practice U.S. and Canada* (Volume 62) January 2015

All of the gray boxes at the beginning of Chapters 1, 2 and 4–11 are interpreted from this Research Brief. Our appreciation to the NCSBN for their hard work in compiling this data.

Surround yourself with people who respect you and treat you well.

—Claudia Black

Supportive people give you strength. It's hard to think with people putting you down.

Remember...

If you think you can do it—you can!

Yes! You can do it!

Now let's get started on how you can be successful on the NCLEX-RN®!

Clinical Decision-Making/Test-Taking Strategies

Our passion is to assist you in being successful at passing this exam. We have conducted hundreds of NCLEX® reviews and pharmacology workshops and have more than fifty years total experience in helping new graduates obtain their licenses.

PASS THE NCLEX®!

Let's look at how this exam is organized. Here is the "bottom line."

➤ The National Council of State Boards of Nursing (NCSBN) (the organization that provides the exam to the local state board office), conducts periodic research on new graduates to determine what kinds of "nursing activities and roles" the new graduates perform most frequently in their work setting and which of these activities have the highest priority for client safety.

➤ After the research is completed, the "nursing activities" become the "backbone" of the NCLEX-RN® exam. These nursing activities are divided into four areas of client needs which are:

> ➤ Safe and Effective Care Environment
>   * Management of Care   17–23%
>   * Safety and Infection Control   9–15%
>
> ➤ Health Promotion and Maintenance   6–12%
>
> ➤ Psychosocial Integrity   6–12%
>
> ➤ Physiological Integrity
>   * Basic Care and Comfort   6–12%
>   * Pharmacological and Parenteral Therapies   12–18%
>   * Reduction of Risk Potential   9–15%
>   * Physiological Adaption   11–17%

YOU MAY RECOGNIZE THIS TERMINOLOGY—particularly if you have taken some sort of diagnostic pretest for NCLEX®. Many of the pretests use these words to indicate your strong and weak areas. The CGFNS™ certification exam is organized around the NCLEX-RN®.

The Nursing Process is also used as a way to approach the exam. If you are like most new grads, you know the nursing process because you have been trying to figure out which instructor wants which thing in which column of your care plans/concept maps for at least the last two years.

You will find a list of our interpretation of the nursing activities at the beginning of each chapter, except the Pretest, Posttest and Practice Exam. These nursing activities were interpreted from the National Council of State Boards of Nursing, Inc. (NCSBN) *2014 RN Practice Analysis: Linking the NCLEX-RN® Examination to Practice U.S. and Canada* (Volume 62) January 2015

First, let's look at techniques that will improve your pass rate!

Question Types:

The NCSBN has operationalized the use of "alternate item format" questions. These items will be in addition to the multiple choice format that has been used in the past. These questions may include:

* Fill in the blank (type numbers in a calculation item)
* Multiple-response items (select two or more responses)
* Hot spot items (identify one or more areas on a graphic or picture)
* Graphics (instead of text, the answer will be a graphic)
* Ordered response ("Drag and Drop" items to rank order)

* Charts or Exhibit Format
* Videos
* Audio

Any item formats, including standard multiple-choice items, could include multimedia, charts, tables, or graphic images.

The *NCLEX-RN® 101: How to Pass* includes some of these types of items for your practice.

PRACTICE ANSWERING TEST QUESTIONS

Step 1

Cover the Distracters.

> ➤ Did you know that in educational jargon, the question part of a multiple-choice question is called the stem and the options are called DISTRACTERS????

> ➤ Did you know that instructors stay up nights WRITING DISTRACTERS????

> ➤ We do not want you to be DISTRACTED—so cover the DISTRACTERS with your hand, a 5x7 card, a leftover Lotto ticket, your shirttail, or anything!!!

> ➤ YOU CAN'T BE DISTRACTED IF THEY ARE COVERED.

> ➤ Answer the question in your head. USE YOUR BRAIN. IT'S THE ONLY THING YOU CAN TRUST!!!

Step 2

Create a pool of answers.

*W*here were you on September 1, 2009?

Did you raise your palms to heaven and say, "How am I supposed to know that?"

That's exactly what some people do when they see an NCLEX-RN® question.

The brain thinks first in large clumps of material, then smaller clumps. Like this…

*T*hink—how old was I in 2009? Married, single, in school???

Most of you at least know where you were in September 2009.

First of school year? Near an anniversary, birthday, or holiday?

*D*on't worry about what you don't know. Think about what you do know!

Step 3

Uncover the distracters and make your decisions— one by one.

➢ After creating a pool of answers, uncover the first distracter.

Is it a yes or no?

MAKE A DECISION.

➢ Next, uncover the second distracter. *Is it a yes or no?* GET THE DRIFT?

➢ Uncover Distracter 3. *Yes or No?* BE SURE, and uncover Distracter 4. Even though you may have found a good answer in 1, 2, or 3, the last one might be the highest priority!

➢ Remember—these options are written to distract—so make a decision on **each** before continuing.

Step 4

Commit one hour per day to answering questions.

➤ Our experience has documented that the more questions practiced, the better success rate on NCLEX®!!!

➤ The people who wrote this book have over 50 years of collective successful experience in preparing graduates to PASS the state board exam. We have put together a team of experts in item writing and have given them specific guidelines that reflect the NCLEX-RN® Test Plan and the "nursing activities" that are the basis of the NCLEX-RN® exam.

➤ This book has been divided into sections of 60 items. WHY?

➤ We believe you should be able to answer approximately one (1) question per minute. Practicing at this pace will give you enough time to complete your exam in plenty of time. Besides, you'll probably want a break after an hour of practice!

Don't major in a minor activity.

Each question is worth one minute of your time.

➤ **DO NOT—repeat—DO NOT** look at the end of the chapter for the answers.

➤ Forget "instant gratification" until the entire hour is completed. Then determine which questions were missed and why.

➤ Looking at the answers after each question encourages memorization, and **WE DON'T WANT YOU TO MEMORIZE!** Why? Because we doubt if any question in this book or any other question/review book on the market will be exactly as it is on NCLEX®.

I thought we'd never take a break!

Take a break between Steps 4 and 5.

You deserve it!

All work and no play is no fun.

Step 5

Commit your second hour per day to studying what you don't know!

Our experience has taught us that new graduates like to study the material they are the most comfortable with. You want to forget the stuff you don't know because it gives you butterflies!

Here are some ways to use this book:

➢ Figure out which questions you got correct. FORGET THEM! Don't say, "Oh, that was just a lucky guess." You had some basis for choosing the correct answer. Let them go!

➢ Now, WHICH ONES DID YOU MISS? Were they on Safe Effective Care, Health Promotion, Psychosocial Integrity, Basic Care and Comfort, Physiological Adaptation, Pharmacology, Reduction of Risk Potential? Use the Test Worksheet, Content Analysis page, and Table of Contents to help.

➢ Once you have determined your study needs, use a good review book to refresh your memory on the facts. To help you with easy, fun ways to remember, we recommend *Nursing Made Insanely Easy, Seventh Edition* and *Pharmacology Made Insanely Easy, Fourth Edition* by Loretta Manning and Sylvia Rayfield, I CAN Publishing®, Inc. (1-866-428-5589). We also recommend *Illustrated Study Guide for the NCLEX-RN®, Eighth Edition* by JoAnn Zerwekh, Publisher Elsevier (www.elsevierhealth.com).

HOT TIPS to Decrease Stress and Improve Scores!

You can take the test in any state and practice in the state where you have applied for license. You will have choices of dates, times, and test centers. You will be **FINISHED WITHIN HOURS!** The NCSBN currently contracts with Pearson Vue for administration of the NCLEX®. Pearson Vue has over 200 testing sites that administer the NCLEX®.

How to use this computer

- ♥ You will get an authorization to test from your state board office. It's like American Express—"Don't leave home without it!"

- ♥ Don't leave home without your finger either because you will be fingerprinted and have your picture taken. You will need your signature and your picture identification for the testing center.

- ♥ You may be provided with lockers for your "stuff."

- ♥ You will be given a computer practice period with help on the equipment. There will be someone to help you get started on your computer—a warm-up time.

- ♥ The testing center will provide note boards and markers as you will not be allowed to take in any paper, books, food, drinks, purses, wallets, beepers, cell phones, guns, knives. *Security is very serious.*

♥There will be a drop-down calculator for math calculations and a mouse for your use.

❤ There are a minimum of 75 questions and a maximum of 265. About 60% of test takers complete the exam in about 75 questions. DO NOT PANIC if you hit question #76! It means you have more time to demonstrate your clinical decision-making skills.

❤ You will have six (6) hours to complete the NCLEX-RN® and five (5) hours to complete the NCLEX-PN®. This is from start to finish, including warm-up time.

❤ You will not be able to skip a question or go back and review questions once they have left the screen. This is an advantage since many "changed" answers are wrong.

❤ There is no time limit per question, BUT DO NOT SIT ON A QUESTION FOR MORE THAN TWO (2) MINUTES or you may not have enough time in the six-hour limitation to answer enough questions to pass.

❤ If you don't have a clue as to the answer, pick any one.

> *Which response represents the best guess?*
> 1. *Alright!*
> 2. *Boy Howdy!*
> 3. *Cool!*
> 4. *Delightful!*

❤ The questions in this book look similar to the ones you will see on the computer screen.

❤ The computer offers you break times. Take time for breaks!

YES!

Guideline "STANDARDS" for NCLEX® Success

S — "SAFETY" for the client is priority! Organize studying around the "SAFETY" Structure!

T — Therapeutic Communication, Teaching and Learning, Trends (Pay attention to assessment changes).

M A — Slow's (Maslow's) Hierarchy of Needs

N — Nursing Process

D — Determine relevant facts in both question and distracters

A — Alternate-Item Format Questions

R — Remember the 5 P's: Pathophysiology, Physical assessment, Prioritizing, Pharmacology, and Protect client from complication(s)

D — Delegation/Documentation

S — Study using Strategies for clinical decision-making! Stay CALM and believe in yourself! You can be SUCCESSFUL!

PRIORITIZATION: New Strategies for Success!

Due to the continuous changes in health care from the complexity of nursing care to multiple system involvement with both acute and chronic medical conditions, the aging population, the multiple medications clients use, and the list goes on, it has become imperative for the nursing student to learn how to be skillful in clinical decision making, clinical judgment, and prioritization of nursing care. Nursing students must learn how to prioritize all aspects of health care including (i.e., assessments, which client to see first due to either potential or actual complications, nursing interventions, medication administration, clients who are presenting with changes in the clinical presentation, and this list also goes on).

In the past, nursing students had to learn how to identify and recognize basic signs and symptoms of hemorrhaging, pain, fluid and electrolyte imbalance, etc. Today, it is of paramount importance for the nursing student to learn how to assess and recognize early versus late clinical findings for complications. The skill of prioritizing is developed by comparing, contrasting, and trending clinical assessment findings. Based on the analysis of the clinical findings, the student must learn how to prioritize the plan of care and determine what intervention should be implemented. This competency requires a new approach to learning, thinking, and processing clinical data. Today, the student needs to know more about the interpretations of the clinical assessment findings of bleeding such as if the client is presenting with early signs of shock versus late signs of shock than simply learning the signs and symptoms of bleeding.

Our focus for this chapter is to provide you with practice questions focusing on how to prioritize. We have included a new approach and structure to assist you in learning the process of prioritization. This new approach, as outlined in the mnemonic on the following page, requires you to expand the basic assessments to include the critical elements (i.e., client history, medications, equipment, etc.) that may impact these findings. Refer to the book *Nursing Made Insanely Easy* for further description. The outcome of these expanded assessments will facilitate prioritizing the plan of care. Prior to being able to initiate this process as an RN, we understand your initial goal is NCLEX® SUCCESS!!!!

Of course, you must have an excellent understanding of nursing in order to learn how to prioritize. Many of the traditional test-taking strategies do not work with the process of prioritizing, so we are going to assist you in learning new clinical-decision making strategies with this new approach to prioritization. The clinical-decision making strategies have been developed within the framework of the NCLEX® standards.

If you continue to feel overwhelmed with information from Medical Surgical Nursing, we recommend the book, *Medical Surgical Nursing Concepts Made Insanely Easy: A New Approach to PRIOTITIZING Nursing* by Manning & Zager. This book includes an additional chapter dedicated to learning how to prioritize. This can be purchased from I CAN Publishing, Inc. at www.icanpublishing.com. The Insanely Easy book package is also very popular and helpful as you continue to perfect this process. These other two books include, *Nursing Made Insanely Easy* and *Pharmacology Made Insanely Easy*, Manning & Rayfield.

Our hope for you is that after reviewing this chapter and book, you will progress from saying, *"How can I prioritize care when it seems that all of the clients are a priority to see"* to saying *"I understand how to prioritize nursing care based on the specific strategy for the clinical situation!"*

We wish you much success on your journey with learning prioritization! Remember, every journey begins with the first step. Of course, the first step is for you to believe in yourself, and know you CAN be SUCCESSFUL! Now, turn the page and let's get started!

Manning, L. and Zager, L. (2014). *Medical Surgical Nursing Concepts Made Insanely Easy! A New Approach to Prioritizing Nursing!* Duluth, GA: I CAN Publishing®, Inc., 2015

Clinical Decision-Making Strategies
for Prioritizing

P   Prioritize: Assess, the first step in the nursing process

R   Review if Maslow's Hierarchy of basic needs is the priority; review ABC's

I   Identify the client who is unstable or highest risk for developing complications

O   Organize priority nursing interventions based on the key concepts

R   Remember to think about what the desired outcome is from the care, med, etc. Evaluation is an ongoing process

I   Identify standard of practice (i.e., scope of practice, verify if order is wrong, drug interactions)

T   Trends, compare and contrast client's vital signs, clinical presentation, etc.

Y   You must manage care to prevent "RISK" to the client (*Refer to next page for description*)

Structure for Prioritizing Management and Safety Standards

R Recognize limitations of staff members; identify standard of practice (scope of practice, wrong orders, interactions, etc.). Scope of practice and standards of practice are often the focus of clinical nursing and/or test questions. The question may be asking if the standard of practice was implemented. It may be asking if the nurse needs to intervene due to the nurse not following the standard of practice. It may be asking what care is appropriate to delegate.

I Infection control is very important for the safety of clients and healthcare personnel. Clinical nursing and/or test questions may present the following: what are the necessary infection-control precautions for prevention and spread of the disease, to include how to avoid communicable diseases, or even activities such as room placement, handwashing, steps to donning.

S Safe medication administration is an important step in prioritizing. The book *Pharmacology Made Insanely Easy* by Manning & Rayfield will be the resource for these questions. Clinical nursing and/or test questions may review the protocol for accurate client identification or the need to question an order (i.e., a new prescription order for a nonselective beta blocker to a client with the diagnosis of asthma). Interactions are another component for safe medication administration.

Spiritual and cultural needs must be integrated as nursing care is prioritized.

K Keep client/environment safe (falls, equipment, etc.): ensure client safety. Reduction of hazards in the environment may include fall/accident prevention such as bed position, use of assistive devices, rugs, cords, etc., or may include a client who is at risk for suicide. Clinical and/or questions may ask about safety situations in both the home and the acute care setting.

Adapted from: National Council of State Boards of Nursing, Inc. (NCSBN) *2014 RN Practice Analysis: Linking the NCLEX-RN® Examination to Practice U.S. and Canada* (Volume 62) January 2015

Organized: Manning, L. and Zager, L. (2014). *Medical Surgical Nursing Concepts Made Insanely Easy! A New Approach to Prioritizing Nursing!* (p. 5), Duluth, GA: I CAN Publishing®, Inc.

Structure for Answering Pharmacology Questions Organized With the NCLEX® Pharmacology Standards

A Action of the medication, administration (based on "The 6 Rights of Medication Administration"), Assessment of client before and after receiving medication, Adverse effects, Accuracy/Appropriateness of medication order.

I Interactions (drug-drug, food-drug), Identify priority plan prior to and after giving med (i.e., vital signs, labs, allergies, etc.).

D Desired outcomes of the drug, Discharge teaching, Documentation.

E Evaluate client's response to medication.

S Safety (client identification, risk for falls, vital sign assessments, handle and maintain medication in a safe and controlled environment , etc.).

Reference: National Council of State Boards of Nursing, Inc. (NCSBN) *2014 RN Practice Analysis: Linking the NCLEX-RN® Examination to Practice U.S. and Canada* (Volume 62) January 2015

CHAPTER 1

*Be like a postage stamp—stick to
one thing until you get there.*
– Josh Billings

Prioritization

✔ Clarification of this test ...

This first chapter has been developed to assist you in reviewing strategies on how to PRIORITIZE. The clinical decision-making strategies for this chapter have been adapted from the NCLEX® standards. The NCLEX® requires high-level clinical decision-making and clinical judgment as outlined below in the minimal standards. Prioritize delivery of care, organize time, assess and respond to clinical changes, and recognize complications are a few of these standards requiring the skill in prioritization. These standards will also be organized within each chapter representing the category for the client needs.

☞ Prioritize the delivery of client care.

☞ Organize workload to manage time effectively.

☞ Assess and respond to changes in client vital signs.

☞ Recognize trends and changes in client condition and intervene as needed.

☞ Recognize signs and symptoms of complications and intervene appropriately when providing care.

☞ Apply principles of infection control (e.g., hand hygiene, surgical asepsis, isolation, technique, universal/standard precautions).

☞ Prepare and administer medications, using rights of medication administration.

☞ Provide care within the legal scope of practice.

☞ Recognize limitations of self and others and seek assistance.

☞ Assign and supervise care provided by others (e.g., LPN/VN, assistive personnel, other RNs).

☞ Recognize the need for referrals and obtain necessary orders.

☞ Collaborate with inter-professional team members when providing client care (e.g., healthcare professionals, language interpreter).

☞ Ensure proper identification of client when providing care.

☞ Prepare and administer medications, using rights of medication administration.

☞ Evaluate client response to medication (e.g., therapeutic effects, side effects, adverse reactions).

Continued ➡

- ☞ Evaluate appropriateness and accuracy of medication order for client.

- ☞ Educate client about medications.

- ☞ Review pertinent data prior to medication administration (e.g.,contraindications, lab results, allergies, potential interactions).

- ☞ Manage the care of a client with impaired ventilation/oxygenation.

- ☞ Manage the care of a client with alteration in hemodynamics, tissue perfusion and hemostasis (e.g., cerebral, cardiac, peripheral).

- ☞ Assess client need for pain management.

- ☞ Protect client from injury (e.g., falls, electrical hazards).

- ☞ Verify appropriateness and/or accuracy of a treatment order.

- ☞ Evaluate responses to procedures and treatments.

- ☞ Assist with invasive procedures (e.g., central line, thoracentesis, bronchoscopy).

- ☞ Use precautions to prevent injury and/or complications associated with a procedure or diagnosis.

- ☞ Monitor the results of diagnostic testing and intervene as needed.

- ☞ Assess the potential for violence and use safety precautions (e.g., suicide, homicide, self-destructive behavior).

- ☞ Use therapeutic communication techniques to provide client support.

- ☞ Assess psychosocial, spiritual and occupational factors affecting care, and plan interventions.

- ☞ Provide care and education for the newborn less than 1 month old through the infant or toddler client through 2 years.

- ☞ Provide care and education for the adult client ages 65 through 85 years and over.

- ☞ Provide care for a client experiencing visual, auditory or cognitive distortions.

- ☞ Provide post-op care.

1.1 What is the priority information to include in the teaching plan for a young female client who suffered a head injury, began having seizures, and is now being sent home on phenytoin?

① "If you stop taking the medication suddenly, an unpleasant, acute withdrawal syndrome is likely along with renal failure."

② "You may stop taking this drug when you have had no seizures for six months."

③ "Let's talk about what kind of contraception you plan to use while you are taking this medication."

④ "I know it's depressing to face this, but you absolutely must take this drug the rest of your life."

1.2 What is the priority of care for a client who becomes unresponsive and the blood pressure is 82/52 with pulse oximetry reading 88% on 50% face mask?

① Ask family to go to the waiting room.

② Initiate CPR.

③ Notify the Rapid Response Team.

④ Prepare to administer code drugs.

1.3 What is the priority intervention when admitting a client with a diagnosis of posttraumatic stress disorder (PTSD) to the mental health unit who becomes confused and disoriented during the process?

① Accept the client and help to make client feel safe.

② Orient the client to the unit and introduce to the staff.

③ Review the unit rules and provide a booklet outlining them.

④ Stabilize the client's physical needs.

1.4 Which client should the nurse assess initially after receiving reports on these pediatric clients?

① An 8-week-old client admitted 4 hours ago with substernal retractions and an oxygen saturation of 90%.

② An 11-month-old client admitted 8 hours ago with dehydration whose vital signs are as follows: T—99.7°F (37.6°C), HR—126, R—28.

③ A school-age child who had closed reduction of a fractured left tibia 2 hours earlier and has swelling of the left toes.

④ An adolescent client who had an appendectomy 10 hours ago and has a 2.0 cm (1-inch) circular area of serous drainage on the dressing.

1.5 Which of these clients should be assessed first following shift report?

① A client with COPD presenting with diminished breath sounds in bilateral lung fields with a pH—7.34, pCO_2—47 mm Hg.

② A client with burns on head, neck, chest, has an O_2 saturation of 90%, and is presenting with wheezes in bilateral lung fields.

③ A client with asthma presenting with a HR—90 bpm after receiving a treatment with albuterol.

④ A client with pneumonia who has a temperature of 102°F (38.9°C) and just received first dose of IV antibiotics 2 hours ago.

1.6 Which client should the nurse assess initially after receiving shift report on these obstetric clients?

① A primigravida client who is presenting in the last trimester with a small amount of painless, bright red blood and FHR—130 bpm with good variability.

② A primipara client, with an oxytocin infusion, who delivered an 8 lb. 4 oz. (3.74 kg) daughter 45 minutes ago.

③ A postpartum client who delivered 20 hours ago, is presenting with a temperature of 100°F (37.8°C) and in last 20 hours diuresed 2000 mL.

④ A multipara client, one hour after a precipitate delivery, presenting with a BP—98/62, HR—102 bpm, with pale and clammy skin. Fundus is firm and midline.

1.7 Which of these maternity clients should be assessed initially?

① A client who is 36 weeks gestation with a BP 150/88, periorbital edema, +3 protein in urinalysis.

② A client who is 36 weeks gestation with a BP 160/90, headache, blurred vision, and epigastric pain.

③ A client who is 36 weeks gestation presenting with painless bright red blood, FHR—140 bpm, and good variability.

④ A client who is 36 weeks gestation presenting with rectal pressure, loss of mucous plug, and 2 cm dilated.

1.8 Which of these infants in the newborn nursery should be assessed first following shift report?

① A 14-hour-old neonate with RR—45 breaths per minute and irregular.

② A 24-hour-old neonate who has a bulging anterior fontanel when crying.

③ A 48-hour-old neonate with a HR—180 beats per minute when quiet.

④ A 2-week-old neonate with seedy yellow stools after breastfeeding.

1.9 Which of these older adult clients should be assessed initially during AM rounds?

① An older client who is presenting with anorexia.

② An older client who presents with incontinence following the AM cup of coffee.

③ An older client who presents with confusion and a new symptom of incontinence.

④ An older client who complains of dizziness when getting up quickly after taking oxybutynin and dicyclomine, so remains sitting on bedside until nurse arrives.

1.10 Which client should the nurse assess immediately?

① The 58-year-old client who was admitted 2 days ago with heart failure, BP of 126/76, and has a respiratory rate of 21 breaths per minute.

② The 62-year-old client who was admitted one day ago with thrombophlebitis and is receiving IV heparin.

③ A 76-year-old client who was admitted 1 hour ago with new-onset atrial fibrillation and is receiving IV diltiazem.

④ The 88-year-old client with end-stage right-sided heart failure, BP of 78/50, and a DNR order.

1.11 Which of these clients is a priority to assess?

① A client with chronic renal failure who is preparing for hemodialysis in one hour and is presenting with HR—100 bpm and BP—160/92 with weight increase of 2 kg/48 hours.

② A newly diagnosed client with chronic renal failure who has begun hemodialysis and is presenting with nausea/vomiting, change in LOC, and agitation.

③ A client who is receiving an initial round of peritoneal dialysis is draining straw-colored dialysis return.

④ A client who is receiving peritoneal dialysis with an order to infuse in 500 mL of dialysate and only drains out 450 mL.

1.12 Which of these clients is a priority to assess?

① A client who is taking, dexamethasone and has a HR—118 bpm, presenting with an increase in abdominal distention, pain, and vomiting.

② A client presenting with some blood tinged sputum and a depressed gag reflex following a bronchoscopy.

③ A client presenting with rebound tenderness in the right lower abdominal quadrant, associated with decrease in the bowel sounds and vomiting.

④ A client who is third day post-op after a gastric resection and the nasogastric tube is draining bile-colored liquid containing coffee-ground material.

1.13 Which of these lab values is a priority to report to the provider of care prior to inserting a chest tube in a client with a spinal cord injury?

① Platelets—90,000/mm^3.

② Hgb—11 g/dL (110 g/L).

③ Hgb A$_1$C—7%.

④ Hct—37%.

1.14 What is the priority of care for a client with a pH—7.55, pCO$_2$—25 mm Hg, HCO$_3$—24 mEq/L (24 mmol/L)?

① Encourage turning, coughing, and deep breathing.
② Increase the frequency for using the incentive spirometer.
③ Monitor the client's weight daily as prescribed.
④ Encourage client to slow down the breathing and relax.

1.15 Which clinical assessment findings for a client with a decrease in cardiac output require priority intervention?

① Expiratory wheezing, substernal retracting, and SpO$_2$ 89% on 4 liters nasal cannula.
② BP—140/90, weight gain of 1.5 kg in 2 days, mild shortness of breath and dyspnea with activity.
③ Urine output 50 mL for last 2 hours, restless, and orthopnea.
④ BP—110/72, atrial flutter with HR—90, bibasilar crackles.

1.16 What is the priority psychosocial plan of care for a client who is dying?

① Administer pain medication, so the client will be comfortable.
② Encourage family to sit with client at bedside and touch and talk.
③ Recommend that only one family member should be in the room at a time.
④ Allow family members to only talk with client while nurse assists with food, hygiene, and physical comfort.

1.17 Which of these nursing actions is priority for a maternity client undergoing regional anesthesia (Epidural)?

① Explain the procedure, and after answering questions get the consent signed.
② Limit IV fluids prior to procedure to decrease risk of fluid overload.
③ If client experiences low blood pressure, position client in the semi-Fowler's position.
④ Hydrate client by giving increase isotonic fluids prior to, during and after procedure as long as client is not prone to heart failure.

1.18 Forty five minutes after a client with a C 4-5 vertical compression injury is admitted to the ED, the oxygen saturation drops to 86% and presents with rapid and shallow respirations. During the auscultation, the breath sounds are decreased in bilateral lung fields. What should the nurse implement next?

① Notify the provider of care immediately.
② Call the respiratory therapist for a non-rebreather mask.
③ Increase the oxygen flow to 6 L/minute.
④ Suction the client for oral and nasal secretions.

1.19 What is the priority plan of care for an elderly client on a medical unit who has minimal vision?

① Softly touch client to let client know the nurse is present.
② When guiding client while walking, walk behind client and place client's hand in the nurse's hand.
③ Assist with meal enjoyment by placing the meal in terms of the face of a clock (e.g., "meat at 6 o'clock").
④ When administering medications, provide client with a full glass of water and explain the number of medications.

1.20 What is the priority of care for a middle-aged client with severe epigastric pain due to acute pancreatitis?

① Assess client for tremors and diaphoresis.
② Discuss foods that are low in carbohydrates and high in protein.
③ Monitor client for CNS depression, decreasing muscle tone.
④ Position client with the head of the bed in semi-Fowler's position with knees flexed toward the chest.

1.21 Which of these interventions by the rehabilitation nurse is priority for a client who is a quadriplegic with a diagnosis of a C3-C4 fracture 4 months ago, has a tracheostomy, and is being maintained on a ventilator following a motor vehicle accident?

① Assist family in locating a support group and community resources following discharge.
② Maintain a regular bowel program to prevent impaction.
③ Offer fluids that promote alkaline urine.
④ Suction client when the low-pressure ventilator alarm sounds.

1.22 Which of these orders should the nurse initiate first for a post-operative client who has been in the recovery room for one hour and presents with the following vital signs: BP—100/70, HR—90 bpm, RR—22/min, and urine output is 45 mL/hour?

① Administer intravenous fluids to maintain a CVP of 5-8 mm Hg.
② Position child in the Trendelenburg position.
③ Place several blankets on the child to increase the temperature.
④ Administer nifedipine as ordered.

1.23 What is the priority of care for a client who is scheduled for a thoracentesis?

① Place the client in a sitting position with arms raised and resting on an over bed table.
② Encourage the client to cough during the needle insertion.
③ Ensure that no more than 100 mL of fluid is removed from the pleural cavity within the first 30 minutes.
④ Ensure that clean technique is used during needle insertion.

1.24 What is the priority outcome for a client with renal failure who is receiving epoetin?

① Calcium—8 mg/dL (2.0 mmol/L).
② Magnesium—3.2 mEq/L (1.6 mmol/L).
③ Hematocrit 48%.
④ RBC—2.2 10^6 µL.

1.25 What is the priority outcome for a client with cirrhosis of the liver that has progressed to portal-systemic encephalopathy and has a new order for lactulose?

① Decrease in the normal flora in the intestine.
② Increase in the number of stools.
③ Serum blood ammonia level—60 mcg/dL (35.2 µmol/L).
④ Serum pH—7.33.

1.26 Which of these clinical findings indicate the priority outcome for the treatment of syndrome of inappropriate antidiuretic hormone (SIADH)?

① Specific gravity—1.029.
② Serum sodium—149 mg/dL (149 mmol/L).
③ Serum osmolality—310 mOsm/kg of water.
④ Hemoglobin (Hgb) 13 g/dL (130 g/L), Hematocrit (Hct)—39%.

1.27 Which of these laboratory reports is the highest priority to evaluate and report to the healthcare provider for a client with Addison's disease?

① Serum calcium—7 mg/ dL (1.75 mmol/L).
② Serum potassium—3.1 Eq/L (3.1 mmol/L).
③ Serum glucose—50 mg/dL (2.78 mmol/L).
④ Serum sodium—148 mEq/L (148 mmol/L).

1.28 Which of these clinical findings indicate a desired outcome from terbutaline?

① Contractions absent with a fetal heart rate—130 bpm.
② Contractions occurring occasionally and lasting for 30 seconds.
③ Fetal heart rate—140 bpm with late decelerations.
④ Fetal heart rate—170 bpm with decrease in variability.

1.29 Which of these should the charge nurse intervene with immediately for a licensed practical nurse (LPN) who is administering medications?

① Lispro insulin to a client when the breakfast tray arrives.
② Metoprolol prior to surgery for a client with pheochromocytoma.
③ Propranolol for a client with hyperthyroidism.
④ Metformin HCL to a client with a creatinine of 3.8 mg/dL (336 µmol/L).

1.30 Which of these nursing actions by the unlicensed assistive personnel (UAP) for a client admitted to the cardiac unit with suspected heart failure require intervention by the charge nurse due to the standard of care not being followed?

① Reports to the RN the client who is taking digoxin is complaining of nausea.
② Positions client in the low-Fowler's position with legs elevated.
③ Assists client to the bathroom due to frequent urination after receiving furosemide.
④ Coordinates care with the RN to provide uninterrupted sleep.

1.31 Which of these nursing actions by the licensed practical nurse (LPN) should the charge nurse intervene with for a client who has an internal arteriovenous fistula on the right arm for hemodialysis?

① Palpates for a thrill over the site.
② Auscultates for a bruit over the site.
③ Takes blood pressure on the right arm.
④ Assesses the pulses distal to the access site.

1.32 Which of these clinical situations should the charge nurse intervene with due to not following the appropriate standard of practice?

① The licensed practical nurse (LPN) reinforces the instruction to a client that Hepatitis A can be transmitted through infected food handlers.
② The licensed practical nurse (LPN) puts on gloves to administer an injection with a client who has Hepatitis B.
③ The registered nurse (RN) discusses the need to avoid sexual activity for a client with Hepatitis A.
④ The unlicensed assistive personnel (UAP) puts on a gown and mask prior to giving a bath to a client with Hepatitis B.

1.33 Which of these nursing actions by the nurse require immediate intervention by the charge nurse due to lack of understanding regarding the standard of care?

① The RN accesses the vein in the antecubital area when initially starting the IV.
② The RN uses an 18-gauge needle when accessing the vein for a blood administration.
③ The RN flushes a heparin lock with heparin solution 100 units per 1 mL as prescribed based on the hospital policy.
④ The RN documents the time and date of insertion, the type of catheter and size and the status of fluid infusing.

1.34 Which nursing action by the licensed practical nurse (LPN) requires immediate intervention by the RN for a client who had a cardiac catheterization two hours ago?

① Compares the quality of the pulses on the right and left legs.
② Evaluates the vital signs every 2 hours.
③ Encourages early ambulation to the bathroom to prevent a deep vein thrombosis.
④ Encourages oral intake of fluids following the procedure.

1.35 What is the priority of care for a client with the diagnosis of tuberculosis and has an order to receive Isoniazid and Rifampin twice daily orally?

① Administer with lunch and dinner.
② Verify identity of client prior to giving meds.
③ Check and verify accuracy of order with provider of care.
④ Teach client that the urine and tears will turn orange.

1.36 Which of these orders should be questioned?

① Increase the pyridoxine (B_6) as prescribed for a client who takes Levodopa for Parkinson's Disease.
② Administer spironolactone for a client with a potassium level of 3.2 mEq/L (3.2 mmol/L).
③ Administer Lithium for a client who is manic.
④ Administer atenolol for a client with a BP—150/90; HR—90 bpm.

1.37 The healthcare provider's orders are: continue all previous medications which include digoxin 0.25 mg po each AM, and Propranolol 20 mg po tid; oxygen at 2L/minute via nasal cannula, establish an IV, and give furosemide 40 mg IV now, bathroom privileges, full liquid diet. Which part of the order is priority for the nurse to discuss with the healthcare provider for a client with a history of cardiac disease who is admitted to the hospital with a diagnosis of heart failure (HF) and COPD?

① Digoxin 0.25 ng/mL (0.3 nmol/L) PO in AM.
② Level of oxygen concentration.
③ Propranolol 20 mg tid.
④ The rate the IV should infuse.

1.38 An older adult-client with diabetes mellitus has an order for an intravenous pyelogram (IVP). What is the priority of care for this client?

① Assess for allergies to dyes.
② Educate client regarding the procedure.
③ Obtain a consent from the client.
④ Verify appropriateness for procedure with healthcare provider.

1.39 Which of these clinical findings is priority to report for a client who is experiencing cardiogenic shock?

① Cardiac output has gone from 4 L/min to 6 L/min in 2 hours.
② 8 AM: Breath sounds—clear in bilateral lung fields; 10 AM: Crackles in bilateral lung fields
③ 8 AM: central venous pressure (CVP)— 3 mm Hg; 10 AM: CVP—6 mm Hg
④ 8 AM: pulmonary artery wedge pressure (PAWP)—6 mm Hg; 10 AM: PAWP— 8 mm Hg

1.40 Which of these post-op clients should the nurse assess immediately after shift report?

① A client with a 8 AM: HR—84 bpm; urine output 60 mL/hr; 10 AM: HR 92 bpm; urine output 50 mL/hr and anxious.
② A client who at 8 AM: has a CVP of 8 mm Hg, BP—150/86; 10 AM: CVP 6 mm Hg, BP—142/78.
③ A client at 8 AM with a BP—120/78, restless and HR—92 bpm; 10 AM: BP—132/80, HR—88 bpm.
④ A client 8 AM with a HR—92 bpm, BP—120/82; 10 AM: HR 120 bpm; decrease in LOC, and BP—92/58.

1.41 Which of these clinical assignments is the highest priority to assign to the licensed practical nurse (LPN)?

① An older adult who needs new diabetic teaching.
② An elderly client who has terminal cancer and is being transferred home for hospice care.
③ An elderly client who needs assistance to the bathroom.
④ An elderly client in Bucks traction who is asking for pain medicine.

1.42 A nursing team consists of an RN, a licensed practical nurse (LPN), and an unlicensed assistive personnel (UAP). Which of the following clients should be assigned to the LPN?

① A young adult client who is a post-op appendectomy and is requesting the urinal.
② A middle aged adult client who is a new post-op CABG and is complaining of pain.
③ An older adult client who has diabetes and requires a dressing change for an ulcer.
④ An elderly adult client who had a CVA 1 month ago and needs assistance with AM care.

1.43 The team consists of a registered nurse (RN) and a licensed practical nurse (LPN). Which of these assignments is most appropriate to delegate to the LPN?

① A 3-year-old admitted to the Pediatric Oncology Unit for IV chemotherapy and needs evaluation of response to chemotherapy.

② A 5-year-old with asthma who has a new order for albuterol via metered-dose inhaler-2 inhalations q 4-6 hr that needs a plan of care developed.

③ A 27-year-old with cancer and needs a subcutaneous injection of filgrastim subcutaneously as prescribed.

④ A 37-year-old admitted for a blood transfusion of 1 unit of packed red blood cells over 4 hours.

1.44 Which of these nursing actions is priority to delegate to the unlicensed assistive personnel (UAP) to assist the RN in evaluating the progress for a 6-month old infant who is experiencing severe diarrhea?

① Weigh the infant daily.

② Record the Intake and Output.

③ Assess and record a sunken posterior fontanel.

④ Assess and record the skin turgor on the chest.

1.45 What task can be delegated to the unlicensed assistive personnel (UAP)?

① Obtain a dietary history from a client diagnosed with anorexia.

② Assist a client with diabetes who is learning how to perform a glucometer check.

③ Assess the judgment of a client admitted with a head injury secondary to a fall.

④ Obtain a stool specimen from a client with diarrhea secondary to Salmonella.

1.46 Which client should the charge nurse delegate to the new graduate RN who is orienting to the neurologic unit?

① An older adult client who had a CVA four days ago and has right-sided weakness.

② A young adult client newly admitted client with a spinal cord injury.

③ A middle aged adult client with Multiple Sclerosis who needs assistance with bathing.

④ An elderly adult client with dementia who is to be transferred to long-term care today.

1.47 Which assignment is most appropriate for the Labor and Delivery (L&D) nurse who will be working for one shift in the Intensive Care Unit?

① A 3-year-old with epiglottitis.

② A 30-year-old with malignant hypertension.

③ A 40-year-old with unstable angina.

④ A 50-year-old with heart failure.

1.48 Who is the most appropriate room-mate for a young adult client who is recovering from a renal transplant?

① A client with methicillin-resistant staph aureus (MRSA).

② A client admitted with diarrhea of unknown origin perhaps food poisoning.

③ A client admitted with systemic lupus erythematous.

④ A client recovering from herpes zoster.

1.49 When the nurse is educating a new graduate regarding the appropriate infection control measures for a client with tuberculosis, which of these statements are most important to include during the teaching?

① "The nurse should wear gown, gloves, and a surgical mask when in client's room."

② "The nurse should restrict visitors to immediate family only."

③ "The isolation precautions should be discontinued after one of the sputum smears is negative."

④ "The nurse should wear an N95 respirator when in client's room with monitored negative airflow."

1.50 Which staff nurse may need further instruction regarding wearing the appropriate personal protective equipment (PPE)?

① The RN wears a gown and gloves when entering the room for a client with Clostridium Difficile.

② The RN wears a N95 mask for a client in airborne precautions with TB.

③ The LPN wears sterile gloves when bathing an infant with Respiratory syncytial virus (RSV).

④ The LPN removes gloves and washes hands with soap and water after care for a client with Clostridium Difficile.

1.51 What is priority for the nurse to include in a teaching plan for a mother who has a child diagnosed with varicella?

① Instruct to keep fingernails short.
② Isolate child until all the vesicles have crusted.
③ Provide quiet activities to keep child occupied.
④ Recommend bathing the child in warm baths with a mild soap.

1.52 When making shift assignments, which of these clients is highest risk for suicidal precaution?

① An 89-year-old Caucasian male who lives alone following the death of his wife and has been giving away his favorite items.
② A 69-year-old African-American female who has been diagnosed with diabetes mellitus.
③ A 49-year-old Asian male who has been diagnosed with cancer.
④ A 29-year-old single Hispanic female who has recently had a mastectomy.

1.53 What is the priority nursing action for a client who has an order for clopidogrel and warfarin?

① Advise to take meds on an empty stomach.
② Continue to monitor AST / ALT.
③ Notify healthcare provider and verify appropriateness of this new drug order.
④ Review with client that a sore throat and chills are expected with these drugs.

1.54 Which information is priority for the nurse to include in the discharge teaching for a client being discharged on Amphojel and amlodipine?

① Discuss the importance of taking on an empty stomach.
② Review the possible side effect of a rapid heart rate and importance of reporting.
③ Discuss the importance of increasing dietary intake of fiber and fluid.
④ Review the possible side effect of diarrhea and the importance of drinking Gatorade.

1.55 Which statement from the client indicates an understanding of how to successfully take psyllium?

① "I will take this medication with 1 oz. of water."
② "I will take this medication in the dry form."
③ "I will mix this medication in 8-10 oz. (237–296 mL) of water."
④ "I will decrease the fiber in my diet."

1.56 What is most important to monitor for a client with a spinal cord injury who is taking naproxen and dexamethasone?

① Decrease in daily weight
② Hemoglobin and Hematocrit.
③ Muscle cramps in legs.
④ Presenting with cool and clammy skin.

1.57 Which of these plans indicates the priority additional information needed regarding how to safely provide home care for a client with Multiple Sclerosis?

① Advise client to conserve energy by using a cane to assist with ambulation.
② Encourage client to wear non-slip, flat, tie shoes.
③ Discuss the importance of only having a few throw rugs in the living and dining room.
④ Recommend client schedule major activities in the AM and rest in the afternoon.

1.58 What is priority of care for a client with a C4 spinal cord injury who begins complaining of a throbbing headache that suddenly started a short time ago? Assessment findings include: blood pressure—188/100, heart rate—48 bpm, diaphoresis, and flushing of the face and neck.

① Adjust room temperature.
② Administer the ordered acetaminophen.
③ Evaluate the Foley catheter for kinks or obstruction.
④ Initiate a complete neurological exam.

1.59 Which plan is priority to incorporate while educating the family members of an older Asian American client regarding the discharge teaching?

① Avoid making eye contact with authority figures since this is viewed as a sign of respect and trust.

② Touch client on the head to demonstrate respect.

③ Hug family after the teaching session is complete to demonstrate caring and acceptance.

④ Direct most of teaching-plan at the women in the family and the grandparents.

1.60 Which is priority to include in the teaching plan for a client who is being discharged with a new prescription for a walker?

① The client's wrists are even with the handgrips on the walker when arms are held straight downward.

② The client advances walker with the "affected" lower limb.

③ Wear no shoes when determining the right size for the walker.

④ The client advances the walker approximately 18 inches (46 cm).

Answers & Rationales

1.1 ③ Option #3 is the priority. Due to the drug interactions, birth control pills will not be as effective and may result in pregnancy. It is important for the client to be educated regarding the importance of using a barrier contraceptive when taking phenytoin and oral contraceptives together. Options #1 is not a true statement. Option #2 is not correct since this is not the standard of care for this medication. Option #4 is not the priority over Option #3.

I CAN HINT: Prioritizing Strategy: Assess, the first step in the Nursing Process.

If you did not know the information, you could get this correct by understanding that Option #3 is the only option that is focused on the client and is further assessing additional information regarding birth control. Note that when the developmental stage and the gender are in the stem and/or an option and the question evaluates a drug that goes through the first by-pass, there is a great possibility it is addressing a need for further information about contraceptives due to the risk for an interaction.

NCLEX® Standards: Review pertinent data prior to medication administration (e.g., potential interactions). Educate client about medications.

1.2 ③ Option #3 is correct. The Rapid Response Team should be notified immediately. The client needs evaluation and immediate treatment. Option #1 is incorrect. As long as the team can get to the client at the bedside, there is no reason to ask family to leave. In reality, it can be very comforting to the family to know all of the care that is possible is being provided for their loved one. Option #2 is incorrect. There is no indication that CPR should be implemented. Option #4 is incorrect.

Additional assessment and evaluation needs to be done prior to preparing meds for a code.

I CAN HINT: Prioritizing Strategy: Notify the Rapid Response Team.

The client is presenting with trends of rapid deterioration in clinical status. There is a blood pressure even though it is low and the client has become unresponsive both of which indicate ominous findings. The Rapid Response Team is crucial at this time. You can group Option #2 and Option #4 together, since these address a code which hasn't occurred yet, but is right around the corner. Option #1 is a psychosocial action and typically will be secondary to an intervention that is addressing the grave clinical findings.

NCLEX® Standards: Assess and respond to changes in client vital signs. Collaborate with inter-professional team members when providing client care (e.g., healthcare professionals, Rapid Response Team).

1.3 ① Option #1 is correct. The priority of care is all about making the client with posttraumatic stress disorder to feel safe. Options #2 and #3 are very similar in that they both address a general orientation to the unit versus focusing on the priority of care for the client. Option #4 is incorrect. Due to the diagnosis and the current clinical assessments the client is presenting with, safety is a priority over the physical needs.

I CAN HINT: Prioritizing Strategy: Maslow's Hierarchy of Needs.

The goal for client care is all about safety! If you knew nothing about this diagnosis, you could still get this correct by using the strategy of Maslow's Hierarchy of Needs.

NCLEX® Standards: Prioritize the delivery of client care. Protect client from injury (e.g., self-harm).

1.4　① Option #1 is correct due to the ABCs. Option #2 is not correct. The vital signs do not indicate a major complication with dehydration for the developmental stage. Option #3 is incorrect. This clinical finding would be an expected assessment 2 hours following a closed reduction of a fractured femur. Option #4 may be an expected finding following this surgical procedure. There are no additional assessments indicating a complication with hemorrhaging.

I CAN HINT: Prioritizing Strategy: ABCs

As you compare and contrast each of these options, you begin to observe that there is only one option focusing on airway. Refer to the book, *Nursing Made Insanely Easy* for review of clinical findings indicating hypoxia for an infant. The bottom line is that if the infant presents with "GRUNTS," there is a complication with hypoxia. This will be the priority client.

　Grunting, grimacing

　Retracting, restless

　Uninterested in feeding

　Nasal flaring

　Tachycardia, tachypnea

　Stridor

You may have selected Option #3 due to risk of compartmental syndrome. The swelling of the toes is a result of the procedure. Notice the time frame when this is included in the question or option. There is typically a reason. If there was a complication with compartmental syndrome, the time would not be as close to the procedure and there would have been several assessments such as change in pulse, pain, pallor, paresthesia, and/or paralysis.

NCLEX® Standards: Prioritize the delivery of client care. Recognize signs and symptoms of complications and intervene appropriately when providing client care.

1.5　② Option #2 is the priority due to the location of the burns may result in smoke inhalation. With the O$_2$ saturation and bilateral wheezing, this client is in acute distress mandating immediate intervention. Option #1 is not a priority due to the client experiencing a chronic medical condition with expected clinical findings. Option #3 is not a priority over #2 since the only assessment provided was an elevation in the HR and this can be an expected finding after albuterol. Option #4 is a concern, but is not the priority since the client just received IV antibiotics. The client will remain febrile until the medication becomes effective.

I CAN HINT: Prioritizing Strategy: ABCs

The key to answering this question successfully is to recognize that COPD is a chronic condition. Option #3 is an expected outcome from the medication, and the HR is not high enough to cause problems with perfusion. Option #4 is not presenting with any acute respiratory assessments. While the ABCs are your strategy, another strategy is to recognize ACUTE will typically be a priority over CHRONIC!

NCLEX® Standard: Prioritize the delivery of client care.

1.6　④ Option #4 is correct. This client is presenting with alterations in perfusion as indicated by the BP, HR, and skin color and temperature. Although the fundus is firm and midline, there are two other causes of hemorrhaging after a precipitate delivery. These include a retained placental fragment or cervical lacerations. Option #1 is a concern with placenta previa, but the bleeding is only small and the FHR is WDL and the variability indicates adequate oxygenation of the fetus. Option #2 is incorrect, since oxytocin can assist in minimizing bleeding by stimulating the uterus to contract. Option #3 is incorrect, since these are normal findings during the first 24 hours in the postpartum period.

I CAN HINT: Prioritizing Strategy: Identify

the client who is unstable or highest risk for developing complications.

Even if you did not know anything about maternity, you could get this question correct due to your understanding of the concept of perfusion. Bleeding is bleeding! No matter the location of the hemorrhaging, the hemodynamics will be the same. The difference that you will need to know for the NCLEX® is the system-specific assessment findings. For example, if the maternity client is hemorrhaging due to an abruptio placenta the abdomen will be firm, blood will be dark if it is visible, and client will experience pain. If the hemorrhaging is from a placenta previa, bleeding will be bright red and client will not experience any pain. If the pediatric client is bleeding from a tonsillectomy, the clinical findings will be frequent swallowing. If the client is bleeding post op, bleeding will most likely be at the area of the surgery. Whenever the client bleeds from any complication, the earliest signs include an increase in the HR and RR. Later signs of bleeding include a decrease in CVP, BP and urine output.

NCLEX® Standards: Prioritize the delivery of client care. Recognize trends and changes in client condition and intervene as needed.

1.7 ② Option #2 is correct since these symptoms represent late signs of preeclampsia. Mild preeclampsia is gestational hypertension with the addition of proteinuria of 1 to 2+ and a weight gain of more than 2 kg (4.4 lb.) per week in the second and third trimesters. Mild edema will also begin to appear in the upper extremities or face. Severe preeclampsia consists of blood pressure that is 160/100 mm Hg or greater, proteinuria 3 to 4+, oliguria, elevated serum creatinine greater than 1.2 mg/dL (106 μmol/L), cerebral or visual disturbances (headache and blurred vision), hyperreflexia with possible ankle clonus, pulmonary or cardiac involvement, extensive peripheral edema, hepatic dysfunction, epigastric and right upper-quadrant pain, and thrombocytopenia. Eclampsia is severe preeclampsia symptoms along with the onset of seizure activity or coma. Eclampsia is usually preceded by headache, severe epigastric pain, hyperreflexia, and hemoconcentrations, which are warning signs of probable convulsions.

Option #1 is incorrect since these would indicate moderate signs of preeclampsia, and is not a priority over option #2. Option #3 indicates the client may be presenting with placenta previa, but the FHR is WDL, and there is good oxygenation as indicated by the good variability which would not make this a priority over Option #2. Option #4 is not a priority. This is a normal sign that the body is preparing for labor, but there are no complications pending that would mandate immediate assessment following report.

I CAN HINT: Prioritizing Strategy: Identify the client who is unstable or highest risk for developing complications.

The key in answering this question appropriately is to organize the signs and symptoms for preeclampsia between what occurs early versus late. When taking the NCLEX®, recognize the expected findings for clients. These will NOT be the priority. This is an effective strategy for any question evaluating prioritizing. As you study, remember *"early assessments versus late assessments"* for perfusion, hypoxia, increased intracranial pressure, etc.

NCLEX® Standards: Prioritize the delivery of client care. Recognize signs and symptoms of complications and intervene appropriately when providing client care.

1.8 ③ Option #3 is correct. The normal neonatal heart rate is 120–160 beats per minute. A heart rate of 180 beats per minute at rest mandates assessment first, since other clinical findings need to be evaluated such as RR, neonate's color, O_2 saturation, any grunting, flaring, or retracting, etc. Option #1 is not a priority. The rate is WDL and the RR will still be irregular at 14 hours. Option #2 is an expected finding when crying. Option #4 is an expected finding for a breast fed neonate. The formula-fed newborn's stool is typically tan, brown, or green and about the consistency of peanut butter. The breast-fed newborn's stool is typically seedy yellow. The formula-fed newborn's stool is a bit firmer than the breast-fed newborn's stool.

I CAN HINT: Prioritizing Strategy: Identify the client who is unstable or highest risk for developing complications.

Remember *"the 4's for the neonate":* HR—120–160 with 140 in the middle; RR—30–50 with 40 in the middle. The key word in the option is when "quiet." Key words can be your best friend as you answer these questions! They will be there! Use them!

NCLEX® Standards: Prioritize the delivery of client care. Provide care for the newborn less than 1 month.

1.9 ③ Option #3 is a priority since these clinical findings indicate a complication from a urinary tract infection. Older clients do not respond to infections as younger clients. They do not present with dysuria, a fever, an elevation in the WBCs, etc. The first clinical finding is acute confusion with a new symptom of incontinence. Many professionals believe that this incontinence is a normal part of the aging process, so this may be ignored. Notice that for your clinical decision making strategy, the key word was "new" symptom. Option #1 is a concern, but the anorexia is not connected to any medication which would change the focus for this question, and would require Option #3 to be revised. The way it is currently written, however, the answer remains Option #3 due to the symptoms of infection. Option #2 is not a priority, since this may be an expected outcome from drinking the coffee. Option #4 may occur if client rises quickly. Anticholinergic side effects may occur with these medications. This still would not be a priority over option #3, since client is not attempting to get out of bed without the nurse.

I CAN HINT: Prioritizing Strategy: Identify the client who is unstable or highest risk for developing complications.

In addition to the prioritizing strategy, using the strategy of expected outcomes versus new symptom will assist you in answering the question correctly.

NCLEX® Standards: Prioritize the delivery of client care. Provide care and education for the adult client ages 65 through 85 years and over.

1.10 ③ Option #3 is correct. This client is presenting with a new onset of atrial fibrillation, and is receiving a calcium channel blocker that is not being effective in preventing the new onset of atrial fibrillation. The client must be evaluated prior to the other clients due to the new onset. Option #1 is in no acute distress in comparison to option #3. Option #2 has no indication of any undesirable effects from the treatment, so this is not a priority over the client with a new dysrhythmia. Option #4 is a DNR, so is not the priority in comparison to option #3.

I CAN HINT: Prioritizing Strategy: Identify the client who is unstable or highest risk for developing complications.

NCLEX® Standards: Prioritize the delivery of client care. Recognize changes in client condition and intervene as needed.

1.11 ② Option #2 is correct. This client is presenting with disequilibrium syndrome which may be caused by too rapid a decrease of BUN and circulating fluid volume. It may result in cerebral edema and increased intracranial pressure (ICP). Early recognition of disequilibrium syndrome is essential. Signs include nausea, vomiting, change in level of consciousness, seizures and agitation. Option #1 is incorrect. This is the reason the client is preparing for hemodialysis in one hour due to the renal failure and with an increase in fluid there would be an increase in the HR, BP and weight. Option #3 is an expected outcome. Option #4 does require some repositioning of the client in order to facilitate the drainage, but it is not a priority to Option #2 which is a complication.

I CAN HINT: Prioritizing Strategy: Identify the client who is unstable or highest risk for developing complications.

In addition to disequilibrium syndrome, other complications that may occur from dialysis and require prioritization may include sepsis and hepatitis B and C.

NCLEX® Standards: Prioritize the delivery of client care. Recognize trends and changes in client condition and intervene as needed.

1.12 ① Option #1 is correct. This client is taking corticosteroids which can lead to a bleeding ulcer. The HR is elevated and the other assessments in this option indicate an intestinal perforation requiring immediate nursing action. Option #2 is an expected outcome following this procedure, so this would not be a priority client to assess. Option #3 is incorrect; this client is presenting with appendicitis. Rebound pain is elicited by pressing firmly over the area known as the McBurney's point; pain occurs when pressure is released. The rebound pain, decreased bowel sounds, fever, and tender abdomen are all characteristic of the clinical findings of appendicitis. This is important to assess, but not a priority over the clinical findings of a perforated intestine. Option #4 is not a priority. Coffee-ground material is old blood. This is normal on the third postoperative day and should be assessed and correlated with the vital signs. The tube must be in the correct position since it is draining gastric secretions. There is no indication that the tube is obstructed or needs to be irrigated.

I CAN HINT: Prioritizing Strategy: Identify the client who is unstable or highest risk for developing complications.

NCLEX® Standards: Prioritize the delivery of client care. Recognize trends and changes in client condition and intervene as needed.

1.13 ① Option #1 is the priority due to the risk for bleeding. The normal platelet count is between 150,000–400,000/mm³ (150–400 x 10⁹/L). This count in Option #1 is very low which increases the risk for bleeding. Option #2 is only slightly low. Range is from 12.0–16.0 g/dL (120–160 g/L). The Hct is within the normal range: 37%–47% (0.370–0.470). Option #3 should be 6% or less, but it is evaluating the management of diabetes mellitus and is not a priority for evaluating prior to chest tube insertion. The priority concern with this procedure is the risk for bleeding.

I CAN HINT: Prioritizing Strategy: Organize priority nursing plan/interventions based on the key concepts.

If you were uncertain of the answer, focus on the fact that the procedure will require a tube being inserted which could result in bleeding. This can apply to biopsies, any centesis, or any procedure that may result in bleeding. Note that the other options have a focus on anemia or diabetes mellitus. Option #1 is the only option that has a focus on the concept of risk of alteration in perfusion due to hemorrhage. See you CAN do this by incorporating your nursing knowledge. Refer to *Nursing Made Insanely Easy* for a review of all of the procedures that involve a "centesis".

NCLEX® Standards: Use precautions to prevent injury and/or complications associated with a procedure. Prioritize delivery of care.

1.14 ④ Option #4 is correct. The labs in the stem of the question indicate a complication with respiratory alkalosis. Options #1 and #2 would require implementation for a client presenting with respiratory acidosis. Option #3 is incorrect. This would be appropriate for a client who was either vomiting or had diarrhea which would be reflective of a client with a metabolic problem versus a respiratory complication.

I CAN HINT: Prioritizing Strategy: Organize priority nursing plan/interventions based on the key concepts.

In this question, the pH is high and the $PaCO_2$ is low; which means the client is breathing off too much CO_2. Remember the strategy "ROME." Refer to the book *Nursing Made Insanely Easy*, for more review of this strategy. The goal is to "SLOW" down the breathing and assist with rebreathing in order to hold on to more CO_2.

NCLEX® Standards: Prioritize delivery of care. Manage the care of a client with impaired ventilation/oxygenation. Monitor the results of the diagnostic test (labs) and intervene as needed.

1.15 ③ Option #3 is correct. A low urine output *(UO of 50 mL for 2 hours is < 30 mL/hr)*, restless, and orthopnea are signs of decreased cardiac output. These would be the priority since these clinical findings are linked to the problem with decreased cardiac output, and with the oliguria there is a need for immediate intervention. Keep in mind the importance of linking the pathophysiology with the clinical findings and nursing assessment. Option #1 is incorrect. These assessments would be for a client who had asthma. Option #2 is incorrect. While these do need to be monitored, the key is the client in the stem of the question has a decreased cardiac output, and these do not represent a decrease in cardiac output. These exemplify fluid overload. Option #4 is incorrect. Atrial flutter can result in a decrease in the atrial output, but the blood pressure and heart rate are stable and not irregular. No additional signs of decreased cardiac output.

I CAN HINT: Priority Strategy: Organize priority nursing plan/interventions based on the key concepts.

The key here is to connect the clinical assessment findings with the complication of decreased cardiac output. Remember, the entire option must be correct for the option to be the correct answer.

NCLEX® Standards: Prioritize the delivery of client care. Manage the care of a client with alteration in hemodynamics, tissue perfusion and hemostasis (e.g., cerebral, cardiac, peripheral).

1.16 ② Option #2 is the best answer. It is important for the family to be with client and support during the end-of-life care. Option #1 is incorrect. There is no indication that client is in pain. Option #3 is incorrect, since family should be there to support. Option #4 is incorrect, since family should be allowed to assist and participate in care.

I CAN HINT: Priority Strategy: Organize priority nursing plan/interventions based on the key concepts. "SPIRIT" will assist you in organizing your facts regarding "end of life."

Support for clients who are dying "Hospice or palliative care."

Promote spiritual comfort—encourage/assist client to contact spiritual advisors.

Isolation feelings by client—prevent by responding quickly to call lights, check on client often.

Recommend client's family to be at bedside to talk, sit and touch client and help with basic care.

Incorporate cultural needs by providing personal preferences and cultural implications regarding death.

Treatment decisions—assist client and family to make decisions such as in preparing advance directives

NCLEX® Standards: Prioritize the delivery of client care. Assess psychosocial, spiritual and occupational factors affecting care, and plan interventions. Providing end-of-life care to clients and families. Assisting client and family to cope with end-of-life interventions

1.17 ④ Option #4 is correct. The client needs to be well hydrated to prevent complications with hypotension. BP less than 100 mm Hg systolic or any significant decrease must be reported to provider of care. Position client flat and administer oxygen if hypotension does occur. Option #1 is incorrect since it is not within the scope of practice for the nurse to explain the procedure. Option #2 is incorrect since the client needs fluids. Option #3 is incorrect since this will result in a lowered blood pressure. Client needs to be positioned in the supine position.

I CAN HINT: Priority Strategy: Organize priority nursing plan/interventions based on the key concepts.

NCLEX® Standard: Use precautions to prevent injury and/or complications associated with a procedure.

1.18 ① Option #1 is the correct answer. The greatest risk to the client with a spinal cord injury (SCI) at the level of C 4–5 is respiratory compromise secondary to involvement of the phrenic nerve. Maintenance of an airway and provision of ventilator support would be the priority interventions both of which would need medical intervention. Option #2 is incorrect since the mask will have no effect on the phrenic nerve. Option #3 is incorrect due to the same rationale as option #2. Option #4 is incorrect since this level of the spinal cord injury is about the phrenic nerve and is not about secretions.

I CAN HINT: Priority Strategy: Organize priority nursing plan/interventions based on the key concepts.

Notice that Options #2 and #3 are both about oxygen devices and Option #4 is about suctioning. The key words in the stem of the question include the type of spinal cord injury, the clinical presentation of the oxygen saturation dropping to 86%, and client presenting with rapid and shallow respirations.

NCLEX® Standard: Recognize signs and symptoms of complications and intervene appropriately when providing client care.

1.19 ③ Option #3 is correct. Organizing the meal in a consistent placement will facilitate the client enjoying the foods by knowing where each type of food is located on the plate. A few additional plans that may be helpful for this client with minimal vision may include: identifying self upon entering the room, always raising side rails for newly sightless persons (e.g., clients wearing postoperative eye patches), walking client around the room and acquainting client with all objects: bed, TV, telephone, etc. Option # 1 is incorrect. The nurse should never touch a client unless client knows nurse is present. Option #2 is incorrect. When guiding client while walking, walk ahead of client and place client's hand in the bend of the nurse's elbow. Option #4 is incorrect. When administering medications, inform client of number of pills; however, what makes

this option incorrect is that only a half glass of water should be given in order to avoid spills.

I CAN HINT: Priority Strategy: Organize priority nursing plan/interventions based on the key concepts.

Remember for the option to be correct, the entire information must be correct. If part of the option is wrong, the entire option cannot be used as an answer. SAFETY is a big key to success!

NCLEX® Standards: Prioritize delivery of care. Provide care for a client experiencing visual, auditory or cognitive distortions.

1.20 ④ Option #4 is correct. The client is more comfortable sitting up with knees flexed toward the chest or in side lying position with knees drawn up to the chest. Option #1 is incorrect since the potential complication with acute pancreatitis may my hyperglycemia versus hypoglycemia. These assessments represent hypoglycemia. Refer to I CAN HINT for more ways to recall this information.
Option #2 is incorrect since the client should be NPO during an acute episode. Typically the client will not take in any food until they are pain free. Diet should be bland, low fat, high carbohydrate, protein recommendations vary when not in an acute exacerbation. Option #3 is incorrect. These are signs of hypercalcemia and the client with acute pancreatitis may experience signs and symptoms of hypocalcemia. Including the following: tetany, Chvostek's sign, Trousseau's sign, neuromuscular irritability, numbness and tingling in extremities or around mouth, seizures.

I CAN HINT: Priority Strategy: Organize priority nursing plan/interventions based on the key concepts.

NCLEX® Standards: Prioritize delivery of client care. Implement measures to promote circulation (e.g., active or passive range of motion, positioning and mobilization).

1.21 ② Option #2 is correct. A priority for this client is to prevent autonomic dysreflexia which can result from bladder distention and/or bowel impaction. Out of these options, maintaining a regular bowel program to prevent impaction is a priority of care to prevent complications with bowel impaction. Other plans that may decrease additional complications for this client include the following: administer chest physiotherapy; provide kinetic bed to promote blood flow to extremities; apply antiembolic stockings or SCDs; facilitate ROM exercises; turn frequently; keep skin clean and dry; observe for impending skin breakdown; bowel and bladder retraining, etc. Option #1 is an important part of the care, but is not the priority over Option #2 which can result in an emergency situation with a significant increase in the blood pressure, a decrease in the HR and RR, and a pounding headache. Option #3 is incorrect. Bacteria grow best in alkaline media, so keeping urine dilute and acidic is prophylactic against infection. A common cause of death after spinal cord injury is a urinary tract infection. Fluids the client should drink in order to promote acidic urine include: cranberry juice, prune juice, bouillon, tomato juice, and water. Option #4 is incorrect. When the low-pressure ventilator alarms this is indicative of an air leak. The high-pressure alarm indicates the need for suctioning.

I CAN HINT: Priority Strategy: Organize priority nursing plan/interventions based on the key concepts.

Following a spinal cord injury of T6 or higher, it is important to monitor the "3 F's": Funny feeling with the skin, Fecal impaction, and/or Full bladder to prevent complications with autonomic dysreflexia.

NCLEX® Standards: Prioritize delivery of care. Assess and manage client with an alteration in elimination (e.g., bowel, urinary).

1.22 ① Option #1 is correct. The key to answering this is to review the time frame and the vital signs. The time out of the operating room is one hour. There are no other vital signs to compare, so you have to make a clinical decision based on the information you are given. BP may be normal or may be low (no comparison); HR may be elevated but no comparison, RR is ok; however, urine output is only 45 mL/hr. Is this a trend? No, this is one hour post-op. Is this a complication? No. The client needs to maintain hydration with IV fluids to maintain a CVP of 5–10 mm Hg to help with renal perfusion. (This is normal range for CVP reading.) Option #2 is incorrect. There can be complications involved with this intervention, but in reality there is no need to place this client in this position. The client is not in shock. Option #3 is incorrect. There is no indication the client is hypothermic. Options #4 is incorrect. This is a calcium channel blocker and would result in the BP being decreased. This is not our goal! We want to keep the client perfused. BP needs to be maintained or increased, but definitely not decreased!

I CAN HINT: Priority Strategy: Organize priority nursing plan/interventions based on the key concepts.

NCLEX® Standards: Prioritize delivery of care. Provide post-op care.

1.23 ① Option # 1 is correct. This is the position that aids in spreading out the spaces between the ribs for needle insertion. Option # 2 is incorrect as the client should not cough while the needle is inserted in order to avoid puncturing the lung. Option #3 is incorrect as no more than 1000–1500 mL should be removed in the first 30 minutes. Approximately 100 mL of pleural fluid is used for diagnostic studies. Option #4 is incorrect as a thoracentesis requires a sterile technique.

I CAN HINT: Priority Strategy: Organize priority nursing plan/interventions based on the key concepts.

Refer to the book *Nursing Made Insanely Easy* for a review of the priority care for diagnostic procedures such as thoracentesis, bronchoscopy, any test ending in "gram," etc.

NCLEX® Standards: Use precautions to prevent injury and/or complications as associated with a procedure or diagnosis. Prioritize delivery of care. Assist with invasive procedures (e.g., central line, thoracentesis, bronchoscopy).

1.24 ③ Option #3 is correct. Epoetin (Epogen) stimulates the production of red blood cells. The desired outcome would be the hematocrit is within the defined range. Options #1 and #2 are incorrect for this medication. Option #4 is still too low and does not indicate a desired outcome from this medication.

I CAN HINT: Priority strategy: Remember to think about the desired outcome.

It is important to also know the normal ranges for the values in each of the options: Calcium—9.0–10.5 mg/dL (2.25–2.62 mmol/L); Magnesium—1.3–2.1 mEq/L (0.7–1.1 mmol/L); Hematocrit—37–47%; RBC–4.2-5.4 10^6 μL.

NCLEX® Standard: Evaluate response to medications.

1.25 ③ Option #3 is the correct answer. Lactulose is used to reduce the amount of ammonia in the blood of clients with liver disease by drawing out the ammonia from the flood that is in the colon where it is removed from the body. Lactulose may also be used to treat constipation since it pulls water into the colon to facilitate movement of waste through the GI system. Option #1 is incorrect. Neomycin decreases the normal flora in the intestines to reduce bacterial activity on protein. This is the action of the drug versus the outcome. Option #2 does occur as a result of the action of the drug, but the question is asking about the desired outcome from the medication. Option #4 is not correct. A potential complication from this medication may be metabolic acidosis if too much bicarbonate is lost in the stools. If anything, this pH would indicate an undesirable effect versus a desired outcome.

I CAN HINT: Priority Strategy: Remember to think about the desired outcome.

"POO," from the book *Pharmacology Made Insanely Easy*, will help you remember the major concepts for lactulose.

> PSE (portal system {hepatic} encephalopathy) and constipation are indications
>
> Orientation (LOC) should be monitored
>
> Output (stools) and electrolytes should be monitored; outcome: Serum ammonia WDL (or at least decreasing)

NCLEX® Standard: Evaluate response to medications.

1.26 ④ Option 4 is correct. The desired outcome is that the client is no longer demonstrating symptoms of fluid overload due to the inappropriate antidiuretic hormone. The hematocrit should be 3x the hemoblobin and it is. The value would be dilutional if SIADH treatment was not effective. Option #1 is incorrect since the specific gravity remains elevated. Remember the range is from approximately 1.003 to 1.030. The low values indicate the urine is dilute and the high values indicate concentrated urine. The range in the middle, 1.012–1.017 indicates appropriate hydration. Option #3 is incorrect; this value is elevated. If this occurred following treatment, then the client lost too much fluid.

I CAN HINT: Priority Strategy: Remember to think about the desired outcome.

Refer to the book *Nursing Made Insanely Easy* for a review. The key to answering this correctly is to link the labs with fluid volume overload and cluster the labs together. Note that with fluid overload, the BUN, serum sodium, serum osmolality, and Hct values will be decreased. The urine specific gravity will be elevated since the client has an inappropriate amount of inappropriate antidiuretic hormone.

NCLEX® Standard: Evaluate response to medications/treatment.

1.27 ③ Option #3 is correct. Decreased hepatic gluconeogenesis and increased tissue glucose uptake may result in hypoglycemia in clients with Addison's disease. Option #1 is incorrect. There may actually be an elevation in the calcium. The normal calcium level is 9–10.5 mg/dL (2.25–2.62 mmol/L). Option #2 is incorrect. Serum potassium actually may be increased with Addison's disease, and Option #4 is incorrect, since the sodium is typically decreased. The normal serum potassium is 3.5–5.0 mEq/L (3.5–5.0 mmol/L); normal serum sodium is 135–145 mEq/L (135–145 mmol/L); and the serum glucose is 70–110 mg/dL (3.9–6.1 mmol/L).

I CAN HINT: Priority Strategy: Remember to think about the desired outcome.

Addison's disease is caused by a decrease in secretion of the adrenal cortex hormones. There is a decrease physiologic response to stress, vascular insufficiency, and hypoglycemia. There is a decrease in the aldosterone secretions (mineral corticoids), which normally promote concentration of sodium and water and excretion of potassium. As a result of this, the sodium may be low and potassium elevated.

NCLEX® Standard: Evaluate response to medications/treatment.

1.28 ① Option #1 is correct. Terbutaline is a tocolytic agent which decreases contractions from occurring in preterm labor. It activates beta 2 receptors resulting in smooth muscle relaxation in the uterus. The objective is to prevent labor until fetus is ready for extra-uterine life. Option #2 is incorrect. Oxytocin would stimulate contractions, but not terbutaline. Options #3 and #4 are incorrect. Option #3 would not be a desired outcome since late decelerations indicate utero-placenta insufficiency. Option #4 is incorrect since a decrease in variability indicates a decrease in oxygenation.

I CAN HINT: Priority Strategy: Remember to think about the desired outcome.

Refer to the book *Pharmacology Made Insanely Easy* to further review terbutaline and the priority information necessary to remember. If you were unable to remember this, just think about the other reason a client may be prescribed terbutaline. Does asthma ring a bell? If not, let's ring it for you! Now, think about this for a minute … if this drug is used for clients with asthma to relax the alveoli, then it would make sense that it would relax the uterus since they both have beta 2 receptors. See you can do this! Focus on what you know!

NCLEX® Standard: Evaluate response to medications.

1.29 ④ Option #4 is correct. Metformin HCL (Glucophage) may cause lactic acidosis. Since the creatinine is 3.8 mg/dL (336 μmol/L) *(normal: 0.5–1.5 mg/dL)*, metformin (Glucophage) should not be administered due to the risk of renal complications developing from lactic acidosis. The nurse needs to intervene since the LPN should hold this medication and notify the healthcare provider (HCP). The medication should not be administered if the serum creatinine is > 1.5 mg/dL (133 μmol/L). Options #1, #2, and #3 are all correct for the identified clients, so there would be no need for the charge nurse to intervene with the LPN regarding the care. Option #1 is a rapid acting insulin and should only be administered in the AM when food is available. Option #2 is necessary due to the hypertension these clients can develop. This is a result of this rare disorder of the adrenal medulla characterized by a tumor that secretes an excess of epinephrine and norepinephrine. An increase in these catecholamines produces vasoconstriction, with a precipitant increase in blood pressure, glycogenolysis, and cardiac workload. Option #3 would be necessary from the risk of tachycardia as a result of the increase in the thyroid hormones that may occur in hyperthyroidism.

I CAN HINT: Prioritizing Strategy: Organize the priority nursing interventions based on the key concepts. *(Recognize limitations of staff members.)*

NCLEX® Standard: Recognize limitations of self and others and seek assistance.

1.30 ② Option #2 is correct. This nursing action is incorrect for this client. The client should be almost upright in bed with the feet and legs on the mattress in order to decrease venous return to the heart, which will result in a decrease cardiac workload. The elevation of the legs will increase the venous return causing an increase in the preload. This could be unsafe for this client due to the suspicion of heart failure. Options #1, #3, and #4 are all within the standards of care for a client with heart failure.

I CAN HINT: Prioritizing Strategy: Organize the priority nursing interventions based on the key concepts. *(Recognize limitations of staff members.)*

NCLEX® Standards: Recognize limitations of self and others and seek assistance. Implement measures to promote circulation (e.g., active or passive range of motion, positioning and mobilization).

1.31 ③ Option #3 is correct. There is a need for further intervention and teaching about the standard of care for this client with an AV fistula. Blood pressure, blood samples, or infusing fluids or medications in the access site of the extremity that has a vascular access site should NOT be performed. Options #1, #2, and #4 are appropriate standards of care for this client.

I CAN HINT: Prioritizing Strategy: Organize the priority nursing interventions based on the key concepts. *(Recognize limitations of staff members.)*

"PATENT" will help you remember the care of the AV fistula:

Patency is evaluated by *"hearing a bruit or feeling a thrill."*

Assess the pulses distal to the access site.

The blood pressure or blood samples should NOT be taken on this extremity.

Evaluate weight, blood pressure, peripheral edema, lung and heart sounds, and vascular access site before and after dialysis.

Note: most common side effects from dialysis include hypotension, headache, muscle cramps, and bleeding from site.

The COMPLICATIONS that may occur include: dialysis disequilibrium syndrome (cerebral edema and neurologic complications, including headache, nausea, vomiting, seizures). Others include: sepsis, Hepatitis B and C.

NCLEX® Standards: Provide care for a client with a vascular access site before and after hemodialysis. Recognize limitations of self and others and seek assistance.

1.32 ④ Option #4 is the answer. Standard precautions are the appropriate type of infection control for all clients with hepatitis. Droplet precautions are not necessary for these clients. There is no need for a mask due to how Hepatitis B is transmitted which is by blood and blood products. The nurse would need to put on gloves while giving a bath as outlined in the infection control protocol for Standard precautions from the CDC. The UAP needs to put on gloves and review the appropriate infection control standards for this infection. Options #1, #2, and #3 do not require further intervention, since they are following the appropriate standards of care.

I CAN HINT: Prioritizing Strategy: Organize the priority nursing interventions based on the key concepts. *(Recognize limitations of staff members.)*

The key to answering this question correctly is to understand that hepatitis requires the infection control guidelines of standard precautions that include blood and body fluids. Refer to *Nursing Made Insanely Easy* for an overview of the different kinds of infection control procedures.

NCLEX® Standards: Apply principles of infection control. Recognize limitations of self and others and seek assistance.

1.33 ① Option #1 is correct. Areas of flexion, especially the antecubital area should be avoided on the initial attempt. Other IV sites to avoid would include the veins that were previously injured by infiltration or phlebitis; veins of an affected extremity: mastectomy, dialysis access; veins of an extremity affected by a stroke or neurologic trauma; veins in the lower extremities and sclerosed or irritated veins; and/or areas of previous venipuncture sites, areas of inflammation or bruising. This nurse needs additional information regarding the standard of care for IV access with a focus on IV sites to avoid. Option #2 is acceptable practice and does not require additional intervention. 18- or 20-gauge needle or catheters are recommended for blood or rapid administration of fluids. Remember the larger the gauge of needle or cannula, the smaller the needle or cannula. A 22-gauge needle or catheter is the most common size for typical IV fluids. Option #3 is correct practice. There is no need for further teaching with the RN. A note to remember, however, is that it can be easy to mistake the heparin 1–10,000 units as a flush solution. Be alert and CAREFUL! Option #4 is correct practice. This information should all be documented clearly in the nursing notes.

I CAN HINT: Prioritizing Strategy: Organize the priority nursing interventions based on the key concepts. *(Recognize limitations of staff members.)*

Note that ANTecubital is NOT the first place to start an IV because the client CAN'T bend arm or be as mobile with this location. ANT = CAN'T

NCLEX® Standards: Insert, maintain or remove a peripheral intravenous line. Recognize limitations of self and others and seek assistance.

1.34 ③ Option #3 is correct. The client should maintain bed rest; avoid flexion; keep extremity straight for 3 to 6 hours following the procedure. The LPN needs direction from the RN regarding the standard of care for the client. This is dangerous to have the client up to the bathroom. Options #1, #2, and #4 are within the standard of care for this procedure. There is no need to immediately intervene with these nursing actions.

I CAN HINT: Prioritizing Strategy: Organize the priority nursing interventions based on the key concepts. *(Recognize limitations of staff members.)*

NCLEX® Standards: Use precautions to prevent injury and/or complications associated with a procedure or diagnosis. Recognize limitations of self and others and seek assistance.

1.35 ③ Option #3 is the correct answer. These medications should only be administered one time a day. The current order reads twice daily, so the order needs to be verified with the provider of care. Option #1 is incorrect since these should be administered on an empty stomach. Option #2 is incorrect since the medication order is incorrect, and needs to be rewritten prior to even getting to the bedside to administer the medication. Option #4 is incorrect. Once again, the priority is the incorrect order that is written in the stem of the question. While the client does need to know that orange colored tears and urine are expected outcomes, the question is inquiring about the "priority of care".

I CAN HINT: Priority Strategy: Verify if order is appropriate and accurate.

The book *Pharmacology Made Insanely Easy*, by Manning, Loretta and Rayfield, Sylvia outlines an easy way to remember both of these drugs. *Nursing Made Insanely Easy* has a quick approach to the "Rights to Medication Administration." The key to answering the question is to know the frequency the medication is being administered in the stem of the question is incorrect.

NCLEX® Standards: Evaluate appropriateness and accuracy of medication order for client. Prepare and administer medications, using rights of medication administration.

1.36 ① Option #1 is correct. It does need to be questioned. The order for pyridoxine (B_6) should be decreased instead of increased. Pyridoxine decreases the effect of Levodopa and can result in toxic effects. This also means that foods high in pyridoxine (B_6) should also be decreased. These foods include avocado, bananas, bran, eggs, hazelnuts, legumes, organ meats, shrimp, tuna, and wheat germ. Option #2 does not need to be questioned. Spironolactone is a potassium sparing diuretic and will assist in holding on to potassium that will assist with this low level. (Potassium-Normal—3.5–5.0 mEq/L or 3.5–5.0 mmol/L) Options #3 and #4 are correct for these clients.

I CAN HINT: Priority Strategy: Verify if order is appropriate and accurate.

An easy way to remember when to increase or decrease pyridoxine can be found in the book *Pharmacology Made Insanely Easy*, by Manning and Rayfield. Just remember there is an "L" in Levodopa to assist you in remembering the need to Lower the pyridoxine and an "I" in Isoniazid to assist you in remembering the need to increase the pyridoxine. See how EASY that is! You CAN do it!

NCLEX® Standards: Evaluate appropriateness and accuracy of medication order for client. Review pertinent data prior to medication administration (e.g., contraindications, lab results, allergies, potential interactions).

1.37 ③ Option #3 is the correct answer. Propranolol (Inderal) is contraindicated in clients with HF and COPD. It is possible the healthcare provider overlooked this in reordering all of the client's previous medications. The oxygen, and digoxin are appropriate. There is no specific order regarding the rate of infusion or any fluids to be infused. Since the client is on po fluids, this is probably a heparin/saline lock. This order should be clarified. However, option #3 is a priority due to the risk involved with a nonselective beta blocker for a client with COPD and with HF. The nonselective beta part is a risk for the COPD. Any type of beta blocker can slow the heart rate down, and should not be administered if a client has HF. Option #2 does not need to be discussed, since the client has COPD. These clients typically do not receive large amounts of oxygen.

I CAN HINT: Priority Strategy: Verify if order is appropriate and accurate.

The key to successfully answering this question is to focus on the diseases and the medications. Beta blockers decrease the contractility, renin release, and sympathetic output. Beta 1 affects one heart. Beta 2 affects 2 lungs. The book *Pharmacology Made Insanely Easy* will assist you with the names of these. For now, however, keep in mind that propranolol (Inderal) is a nonselective beta blocker, which means it affects both beta 1 and beta 2. If a client has COPD, do we want the drug to block the beta receptors in the lungs? Of course not, you are so correct! The client would get into further respiratory problems. Remember the *"Road Block to Beta Blockers."* If the client has a slow heart rate, we would not administer the med. Low blood pressure may need to hold. Asthma—not if nonselective. Diabetics—masks low blood sugar. Safety is the issue!

NCLEX® Standards: Evaluate appropriateness and accuracy of medication order for client. Review pertinent data prior to medication administration (e.g., contraindications, lab results, allergies, potential interactions).

1.38 ④ Option #4 is correct. Due to the age of the client, the medical diagnosis, and the procedure, there may be a risk for this test. There is a risk for a decrease in renal perfusion and the IVP requires a dye which requires the client to have effective renal function to excrete the dye. Since the renal function is unknown, the order needs to be verified due to the possible risk to the client. Option #1 is incorrect since the order may not even be appropriate for this client. Options #2 and #3 are incorrect since the order may not be implemented due to the risks involved. Remember, as clients age the renal function decreases, diabetes mellitus may also result in alteration in renal perfusion, and the dyes used in the procedure require renal excretion of the dye.

I CAN HINT: Priority Strategy: Verify if order is appropriate and accurate .

Refer to the book *Nursing Made Insanely Easy* for a review of the priority of care for the diagnostic procedures requiring dyes, such as grams, CAT Scan with contrast, and cardiac catheterizations.

NCLEX® Standards: Verify appropriateness and/or accuracy of a treatment order. Use precautions to prevent injury and/or complications associated with a procedure or diagnosis. Provide care and education for the adult client ages 65 through 85 years and over.

1.39 ② Option #2 is correct. Cardiogenic shock occurs secondary from heart/pump failure. This may be the result of heart failure, cardio-myopathy, valvular rupture, valvular stenosis, or dysrhythmias. The hemodynamic changes include crackles in the lungs, elevation in the central venous pressure reading (CVP) and the pulmonary artery wedge pressure (PAWP). Crackles must be reported due to the need for further intervention. This is indicative of fluid overload. Options #1, #3, and #4 are incorrect since the readings are still within the desired limits. The range for the cardiac output is 4–6 L/min and the range for the CVP is 1–8 mm Hg. The PAWP range is from 4–12 mm Hg.

I CAN HINT: Priority Strategy: Identify trends and changes.

Nursing Made Insanely Easy, by Manning and Rayfield, will assist you in remembering these values.

NCLEX® Standards: Recognize trends and changes in client condition and intervene as needed. Manage the care of a client with alteration in hemodynamics, tissue perfusion and hemostasis (e.g., cardiac, peripheral).

1.40 ④ Option #4 is correct due to the trending of the vital signs. The HR increased and the BP dropped in addition to a decrease in the LOC. Option #1 is incorrect because the HR and urine output do not present with a significant change. Option #2 is incorrect because the

CVP remains in the normal range and the BP has decreased. Option #3 is incorrect since the HR decreased; BP not increased significantly.

I CAN HINT: Priority Strategy: Identify trends and changes.

NCLEX® Standards: Recognize trends and changes in client condition and intervene as needed. Prioritize the delivery of client care.

1.41 ④ Option #4 would be a great option for the LPN since it is requiring medication administration, and LPNs do this routinely. Option #1 is incorrect since initial teaching is not part of the scope of practice for the LPN as outlined in the Nurse Practice Act. Option #2 is incorrect since this will mandate teaching and coordinating the plan of care. Option #3 can be delegated to the unlicensed assistive personnel (UAP).

I CAN HINT: Priority Strategy: Recognize scope of practice. (Delegation)

Nursing Made Insanely Easy, by Manning and Rayfield, will assist you in organizing this information. The LPN does not do "PART" of the Care. The LPN will NOT do the following: Push IV meds, Plan in isolation of the RN; will not Analyze care, Assessments (initial); Review (Evaluate) in isolation of the RN; Teach—initial, Tasks that require advance clinical judgment and have unexpected outcomes. It is so much easier to remember what care the LPN does NOT do versus all of the care they do. The acronym "BART" will assist you in remembering the UAP's scope of practice.

Bathe a routine client

Ambulate if stable

Routine tasks

Tasks that do NOT require critical thinking

NCLEX® Standards: Assign and supervise care provided by others (e.g., LPN/VN, assistive personnel, other RNs). Provide care within the legal scope of practice.

1.42 ③ Option #3 is correct. The key to answering this question appropriately is to have an understanding of the scope of practice for the UAP, LPN, and RN. Options #1 and #4 could be delegated to the UAP. Option #2 should be delegated to the RN due to client being a new post-op CABG and requiring further assessment.

I CAN HINT: Priority Strategy: Recognize scope of practice. (Delegation)

Nursing Made Insanely Easy, by Manning and Rayfield, will assist you in organizing this information. **Refer to question #41 for the I CAN HINT.**

The LPN's scope of practice is to complete dressing changes. Option #1 is incorrect. The UAP should be assisting with the urinal due to the scope of practice. Option #2 is incorrect since this is a new client with a post-op CABG, so the RN should be providing the care. This client is going to need initial assessments which is not in the scope of practice for the LPN and UAP. Option #4 would be appropriate for the UAP due to the length of time the client had the CVA and the type of care that is being required.

NCLEX® Standard: Assign and supervise care provided by others (e.g., LPN/VN, assistive personnel, other RNs). Provide care within the legal scope of practice.

1.43 ③ Option #3 is the correct answer. Subcutaneous injection is within the scope of practice for the LPN. Option #1 is incorrect since there are many undesirable effects with chemotherapy, and the LPN does not evaluate in isolation of the RN. This would be done collaboratively with the RN. Option #2 is not correct due to the fact that it is a new order with risks of undesirable effects, and there is a need to make new assessments and evaluations regarding the effectiveness of the medication. The LPN does not plan the care in isolation of the RN. This is done through collaboration with the RN. Option #4 would not be appropriate due to the unexpected outcomes that may occur

with the transfusion. The LPN would need to make initial assessments regarding potential complications with hemolytic, allergic, and/or febrile interactions.

I CAN HINT: Priority Strategy: Recognize scope of practice. (Delegation)

Nursing Made Insanely Easy will assist you in organizing this information. **Refer to question #41 for the I CAN HINT.**

NCLEX® Standards: Assign and supervise care provided by others (e.g., LPN/VN, assistive personnel, other RNs). Provide care within the legal scope of practice.

1.44 ① Option #1 is correct. The daily weight is the best indicator of the hydration status since the higher proportion of an infant's body weight is water, compared to the adult. Option #2 is important to document, but is not a priority over the weight, since this is a measurable assessment of the infant's progress. I & O measures what went in and what came out, but does not provide the nurse with the infant's physiological response to the hydration, like the daily weight. Option #3 is incorrect since the posterior fontanel would be closed as this age. It closes between 2–3 months of age. This also is an assessment and is not included in the scope of practice of the UAP. Option #4 is incorrect. While monitoring the skin turgor is an important assessment for fluid volume status, the abdomen is commonly used to assess skin turgor in an infant due to the large surface area, and it is easily accessed. Assessment is not included in the scope of practice for the UAP.

I CAN HINT: Priority Strategy: Recognize scope of practice. (Delegation)

Nursing Made Insanely Easy will assist you in organizing this information. **Refer to question #41 for the I CAN HINT.**

NCLEX® Standards: Provide care and education for the newborn less than 1 month old through the infant or toddler client through 2 years. Assign and supervise care provided by others (e.g., LPN/VN, assistive personnel, other RNs). Provide care within the legal scope of practice.

1.45 ④ Option #4 is correct. The key to answering this question correctly is to understand the scope of practice for the UAP. The UAP is able to perform tasks that are routine and are similar in the steps each time the task is implemented. Refer to I CAN HINT for an easy way to remember the scope of practice for the UAP. Option #1 is incorrect since the UAP would need to assess this from the client and need to use specific communication principles in order to facilitate the dietary history. Initiating a history on the client is not within the scope of practice for the UAP. Option #2 is incorrect since the client is learning how to perform the task. If the client was not learning and this was a routine task then this would be acceptable for the UAP as an assignment. Option #3 is incorrect since the client requires an assessment and a clinical decision requiring clinical judgment are definitely not within the scope of practice for the UAP.

I CAN HINT: Priority Strategy: Recognize scope of practice. (Delegation)

Nursing Made Insanely Easy, by Manning and Rayfield, will assist you in organizing this information. **Refer to question #41 for the I CAN HINT.**

NCLEX® Standard: Assign and supervise care provided by others (e.g., LPN/VN, assistive personnel, other RNs). Provide care within the legal scope of practice.

1.46 ① Option #1 is the correct answer due to the nursing care required. Option #2 would be incorrect for the new graduate since this is a newly admitted client and the nursing care is very complex. Option #3 is incorrect since the unlicensed assistive personnel (UAP) can do this care. Option #4 is incorrect since this will require coordination of numerous services and meetings that will not be appropriate for a new graduate RN who is orienting.

I CAN HINT: Priority Strategy: Recognize scope of practice. (Delegation)

"GRAD" will assist you in remembering what can be delegated to the new graduate.

Give assignment client who has expected outcomes and is stable

Ready with necessary skills and knowledge

Admission and assessments that are not new or initial

Do not have to coordinate many disciplines, services, agencies, etc.

NCLEX® Standard: Assign and supervise care provided by others (e.g., LPN/VN, assistive personnel, other RNs). Provide care within the legal scope of practice.

1.47 ② Option #2 is the correct answer. Labor and Delivery nurses provide care to maternity clients with pre-eclampsia. When delegating, it is always important to focus on the nurse's skills and expertise. Option #1 is incorrect. The 3-year-old with epiglottitis requires very specialized care due to the risk of airway obstruction. The nurse would need to understand the importance of never doing an oral airway assessment. The L & D nurse does not provide this type of pediatric care, so in contrast to Option #2 it is incorrect. Options #3 and #4 are both about cardiac clients. These could be clustered together since the L& D nurse does not provide care to cardiac clients routinely.

I CAN HINT: Priority Strategy: Recognize scope of practice. (Delegation)

The key to successful clinical decision making in this question is to consider the care the L&D nurse practices and also cluster together medical conditions to assist with the elimination process.

NCLEX® Standard: Assign and supervise care provided by others (e.g., LPN/VN, assistive personnel, other RNs). Provide care within the legal scope of practice.

1.48 ③ Option #3 is correct. This client is immunocompromised which puts client at a high risk for infection. Systemic lupus erythematous is a multisystem inflammatory autoimmune disorder. While it affects multiple organs and causes diffuse production of autoantibodies that attack and cause damage to body organs and tissue, the client is not septic and presents no complication to the client who is recovering from a renal transplant. Option #1 would definitely not be an appropriate roommate due to the risk for infection. MRSA is highly contagious. Option #2 is incorrect because it reads *"unknown origin perhaps food poisoning."* The client could have gastroenteritis from a bacteria. Option #4 is also very contagious.

I CAN HINT: Priority Strategy: Infection Control. (Room assignment)

NCLEX® Standard: Apply principles of infection control (e.g., hand hygiene, surgical asepsis, room assignment).

1.49 ④ Option #4 is correct. Due to the infectious agents being smaller than 5 mcg, this client will be placed in Standard/Airborne precautions. The private room will have monitored negative airflow (air exchange and air discharge through HEPA filter). If the client is transported outside of negative-airflow room, then the client will wear a surgical mask. Option #1 is incorrect. The gown is not necessary, and the mask is not the appropriate mask. The mask should be the N95 respirator. Option #2 is not necessary. The visitors will just need to be educated about the appropriate infection control precautions in order to adhere to the standards. Option #3 is incorrect. The Standard of Care is three negative sputum smears.

I CAN HINT: Priority Strategy: Infection Control.

NCLEX® Standard: Apply principles of infection control (e.g., hand hygiene, surgical asepsis).

1.50 ③ Option #3 is the correct answer. The staff nurse does need further discussion regarding the appropriate PPE to wear since an infant with RSV does not require the nurse to wear sterile gloves. This infant is not immunocompromised. If the nurse is bathing the infant then gloves would be appropriate for following the Standard Precaution Guidelines for Infection Control; however, there is not a need for sterile gloves. Options #1, #2 and #4 are correct statements and do not require further instruction.

I CAN HINT: Priority Strategy: Infection Control.

The key to successfully answering this question is to recognize the standards of care for infection control. This is a frequently tested concept on the NCLEX® because it is frequent part of providing safe nursing care. Remember SAFETY is the key to quality care.

NCLEX® Standards: Apply principles of infection control (e.g., hand hygiene, surgical asepsis). Recognize limitations of self and others and seek assistance.

1.51 ② Option #2 is the correct answer. The key to answering this question is to understand the diagnosis of varicella (chickenpox) and the communicability. These are transmitted via contact and airborne. The incubation period is 14 to 16 days. Varicella is highly contagious, usually occurring in children under 15 years of age and presenting with maculopapular rash with vesicular scabs in multiple stages of healing. The communicability is 1 day prior to the lesions appearing to the time when all lesions have formed crusts. The child should be isolated, and family members, healthcare providers, etc. need to follow the appropriate infection control precautions in order to prevent others from being exposed to the infection. Option #1, while it is important to keep the fingernails short to prevent scratching, is not a priority over option #2 due to the risk for others being exposed and possibly resulting in an infection. Option #3 is also important, but not a priority over option #2. Option #4 is incorrect; the water would be cool-tepid and no soap would be used.

I CAN HINT: Priority Strategy: Infection Control.

NCLEX® Standard: Apply principles of infection control (e.g., hand hygiene, surgical asepsis).

1.52 ① Option #1 is correct. The high-risk factors for suicide include Caucasian males, advanced age, hopeless, living alone, family history of suicide, psychosis, substance abuse. Males 65 and older are high risk, especially males 85 and older. Diagnoses (psychiatric) are some of the most reliable factors for suicide such as substance disorders, schizophrenia, and depression. This client who is alone following the death of his wife is a high risk for suicide. Options #2, #3, and #4 are not within this category. They will be concerned, but typically do not consider suicide.

I CAN HINT: Priority Strategy: Environmental Safety. *(Keep client/environment safe (suicide, falls, equipment, etc.)*

It would be important for you to be able to compare and contrast who is highest risk for suicide. "SUICIDE" will assist you in organizing who these clients may be. Refer to *Nursing Made Insanely Easy.*

NCLEX® Standard: Assessing the potential for violence and use safety precautions (e.g., suicide, homicide, self-destructive behavior).

1.53 ③ Option #3 is correct. Clopidogrel (Plavix) is a platelet aggregation inhibitor and works by inhibiting the first and second phases of ADP-induced effects in platelet aggregation. Warfarin (Coumadin) interferes with the hepatic synthesis of vitamin K-clotting factors (II, VII, IX, and X). When these drugs are taken together, the risk is bleeding. Consequently, these drugs should not be administered together due to the drug-drug interaction resulting in bleeding. Option #1 is incorrect because they should be taken with food to minimize GI discomfort, but please note that even if this was stated appropriately for the client to take with food this still would not the PRIORITY. The drugs should NOT be administered together due to risk for bleeding. Remember, this is all about CLINICAL DECISION MAKING. Option #2 is important to monitor if the client is taking clopidogrel (Plavix), but in this situation the PRIORITY still remains that the healthcare provider should be notified due to the risk involved with taking these drugs together. Option #4 would be a concern for clopidogrel (Plavix), but once again this is not the PRIORITY, since it would be unsafe to administer these drugs together.

I CAN HINT: Prioritizing Strategy: Safe Medication Administration.

While you are in school, you learn to focus on facts and connect these facts to nursing concepts or drugs. Now that you are preparing for the NCLEX® and clinical practice that is all about clinical decision making, it is important to wire your brain for the importance of "comparing and contrasting" the options. Several of the options will actually be close to being correct; however, the stem of the question will drive you to the right answer! Now that you reflect back on the question, you may be able to see that the key is there are two drugs that should NEVER be administered together. This is where we begin!

NCLEX® Standards: Medication Administration. Review pertinent data prior to medication administration (e.g., contraindications, lab results, allergies, potential interactions). Evaluate appropriateness and accuracy of medication order for client.

1.54 ③ Option #3 is correct. Amphojel is an aluminum based antacid and can cause a complication with constipation. Amlodipine (Norvasc) is a calcium channel blocker with the action of inhibiting calcium ion influx across the cardiac and smooth-muscle cells. It can reduce myocardial contractility and oxygen demand. This drug can also result in an undesirable effect with constipation. The last effect we want for a client taking amlodipine (Norvasc) for the heart is a problem with constipation. This would result in stress to the heart. Option #1 is incorrect since amlodipine (Norvasc) can be taken with meals. Yes, you are correct that Amphojel can be and should be taken on an empty stomach, but the question reads that they are being discharged on both drugs. As a result of this statement, the option must be correct for both drugs. Option #2 is incorrect. Due to the action of this drug *(as outlined in the correct rationale)*, the possible side effect would be bradycardia versus tachycardia. Option #4 is incorrect since the possible side effect is constipation versus diarrhea. The extra sodium in Gatorade would also not be great for a client with cardiac involvement requiring the amlodipine (Norvasc).

I CAN HINT: Prioritizing Strategy: Safe Medication Administration.

When two drugs are referred to in the stem of the question, pay attention to these since the options must address both drugs. If part of the option is incorrect, the entire option is wrong. This is a great clinical decision making strategy.

NCLEX® Standards: Medication Administration. Educate client about medications.

1.55 ③ Option #3 is correct. Psyllium (Metamucil) is a bulk-forming laxative. This is used for chronic constipation. This must be mixed with a full glass of water to prevent problems with irritation and impaction. Option #1 is incorrect since this may result in an intestinal obstruction if not taken with adequate water. Option #2 may cause irritation; this should never be taken in the dry form. Option #4 is incorrect since the client should increase fiber in diet as first-line treatment for constipation.

I CAN HINT: Prioritizing Strategy: Safe Medication Administration.

NCLEX® Standard: Medication Administration.

1.56 ② Option #2 is correct. Both of these drugs can cause GI irritation which can result in peptic ulcers that can cause bleeding. Monitoring the hemoglobin and hematocrit will assist the nurse in determining if the client is developing any complications from bleeding. Option #1 is incorrect; although the dexamethasone (Decadron) may result in fluid retention, naproxen (Aleve) would not contribute to this

clinical finding. The focus of the question is for both of these drugs. Option #3 could be an issue with dexamethasone (Decadron) alone, but not with naproxen (Aleve). Option #4 is incorrect since the concern would be more with hyperglycemia, but still not an issue for naproxen (Aleve).

I CAN HINT: Prioritizing Strategy: Safe Medication Administration.

The key to answering this question appropriately is to remember the common undesirable effects both medications have in common. The book, *Pharmacology Made Insanely Easy*, by Manning, L. and Rayfield, S. has great images to help this information stick in the long-term memory. One look at *"Cushy Carl"* and you will remember forever the major undesirable effects from dexamethasone (Decadron).

NCLEX® Standards: Medication Administration. Evaluate client response to medication (e.g., therapeutic effects, side effects, adverse reactions).

1.57 ③ Option #3 is correct. Multiple sclerosis (MS) is an autoimmune disorder characterized by development of plaque in the white matter of the central nervous system (CNS). This plaque damages the myelin sheath and blocks impulse transmission between the CNS system and the body. As a result of this medical condition, there is an impairment of the physical mobility. The nurse's responsibility is to promote and maintain a safe home and hospital environment to reduce the risk of injury. Even a few throw rugs in the living room can be a safety hazard to this client. Option #3 should read "have no rugs due to the risk for falling" for this option to be correct. Options #1, #2, and #4 are correct plans for this client.

I CAN HINT: Prioritizing Strategy: Environmental Safety. *(Keep client/ environment safe (falls, equipment, etc.)*

There is no "CURE" for the disease. The goals are to prevent complications and provide support for client/family.

Communication is effective due to complication with (dysarthria) i.e., use a communication board or a speech language therapist; Cognitive changes – maintain function (reorient, place routine objects in routine places).

Urinary tract infections—decrease risk of UTI by encouraging fluid intake, assist with bladder elimination (intermittent self-catheterization, bladder pacemaker, Crede).

Resources and respite services for the client and family as the disease progresses.

Eye patches should be alternated to treat diplopia. Teach scanning techniques. Environment—safety precautions.

NCLEX® Standard: Protect client from injury (e.g., falls, electrical hazards).

1.58 ③ Option #3 is correct. This client is experiencing autonomic dysreflexia which can occur in clients with spinal cord injuries at T6 or higher. A noxious stimulus below the level of injury triggers the sympathetic nervous system, which causes a release of catecholamines (epinephrine, norepinephrine). Most common stimuli causing the response are a full bladder or bowel, UTI, pressure ulcers, and/or skin stimulation. Severe hypertension, nausea, pounding headache, bradycardia, restlessness, flushing piloerection, and blurred vision are the most common body responses. Option #3 needs evaluated since a catheter kink or obstruction could result in this complication. Options #1, #2, and #4 are incorrect for this clinical presentation of autonomic dysreflexia. The key to answering this question is to understand the complication that can occur from the spinal cord injury. Option #4 is incorrect. Due to the clinical assessment findings, there is not time to complete a neurological exam. The exam needs to be a focused or a system specific assessment.

I CAN HINT: Prioritizing Strategy: Environmental Safety. *(Keep client/environment safe (falls, equipment, etc.)*

The key to answering this question correctly is to link the assessment findings in the stem of the question with the cause which is most likely the obstructed Foley. The key assessments were bradycardia, hypertension, diaphoresis, and flushing.

Nursing Made Insanely Easy, by Manning and Rayfield, will further assist you in organizing the priority care for autonomic reflexia.

NCLEX® Standard: Protect client from injury (e.g., falls, electrical hazards).

1.59 ① Option #1 is a sign of respect for the Asian Americans. Option #2 may be considered disrespectful since the head may be considered to be sacred. Option #3 is not typical with the Asian American culture. Client and family members may be very modest and public display of affection are not typical. The African American, on the other hand, shows affection by touching, hugging, and being close. Option #4 is incorrect since this group is more patriarchal. In contrast to the Asian American, women typically head the household in the African American culture.

I CAN HINT: Prioritizing Strategy: Cultural needs.

The key to answering this question is to have an understanding of the cultural needs of Asian Americans.

NCLEX® Standard: Incorporate client cultural practice and beliefs when planning and providing care.

1.60 ② Option #2 is within with standard of practice for a client using a walker. The standard is to advance the walker with the "affected" leg. Option #1 is incorrect. The client's wrists should be even with the handgrips on the walker when arms are dangling downward. Option #3 is incorrect. Shoes should be worn when determining the right size for the walker. Option #4 is incorrect. The walker should be advanced approximately 12 inches (31 cm). Eighteen inches (46 cm) is too much and may result in a fall.

I CAN HINT: Prioritizing Strategy: Assist client with the use of assistive devices.

Wear shoes when determining the correct size for the walker. Wrists of client are even with the handgrips on the walker when arms are dangling downward.

Advance the walker approximately 12 inches (31 cm).

Lower limb that is affected should be advanced with walker.

Keep unaffected limb back, and then after affected limbs has moved forward then move unaffected limb forward.

NCLEX® Standards: Assist client to compensate for a physical or sensory impairment (e.g., assistive devices, positioning, compensatory techniques). Protect client from injury (e.g., falls, electrical hazards). Educate client on safety issues.

CHAPTER 2

There is an art to clearing away the clutter and focusing on what matters most. It is simple and it is transferable. It just requires courage to take a different approach.
— GEORGE ANDERS

Alternate-Item Format Questions

✔ Clarification of this test ...

The minimal standards evaluated with these alternate-item format questions are included below. Examples include: infection control, system-specific assessment, medication administration, management and prevention of complications with diagnostic procedures, safe use of equipment, education, and health promotion. Alternate-item format questions will also be integrated throughout the book. The minimal standards outlined below will also be organized within the specific client need category throughout the book.

- ☞ Apply principles of infection control (e.g., hand hygiene, surgical asepsis, isolation, sterile technique, universal/standard precautions).

- ☞ Ensure proper identification of client when providing care.

- ☞ Prepare and administer medications, using rights of medication administration.

- ☞ Educate client about medications.

- ☞ Recognize signs and symptoms of complications; intervene appropriately when providing care.

- ☞ Prioritize the delivery of client care.

- ☞ Perform focused assessment/system-specific assessment.

- ☞ Use precautions to prevent injury and/or complications associated with a procedure or diagnosis.

- ☞ Obtain/Monitor/Intervene/Evaluate response to diagnostic tests (i.e., O_2 sat, glucose monitoring, etc.).

- ☞ Assign and supervise care provided by others (e.g., LPN/VN, assistive personnel, other RNs).

- ☞ Use ergonomic principles when providing care (e.g., safe patient handling, proper lifting).

- ☞ Provide client nutrition through continuous or intermittent tube feedings.

- ☞ Assess client's need for sleep/rest and intervene as needed.

- ☞ Assess and manage client with an alteration in elimination (e.g., bowel, urinary).

- ☞ Assess client for abuse or neglect and intervene as appropriate.

CONTINUED

☞ Collaborate with inter-professional team members when providing care.

☞ Evaluate client response to medication (e.g., therapeutic effects, side effects, adverse reactions).

☞ Administer blood products and evaluate client response.

☞ Monitor IV infusion and maintain site (central, PICC, epidural, and venous access).

☞ Perform calculations needed for medication administration.

☞ Insert, maintain, and remove a peripheral IV line.

☞ Facilitate appropriate and safe use of equipment.

☞ Educate client about treatment.

☞ Assess need for pain management/intervene with nonpharmacological care.

☞ Act as client advocate/verify client comprehends consents/informed consent.

☞ Provide post-operative care.

☞ Assist client to compensate for a physical or sensory impairment (e.g., assistive devices, positioning, compensatory techniques).

☞ Perform skin assessment and implement measures to maintain skin integrity (e.g., turning, respositioning).

☞ Provide pulmonary hygiene (e.g., chest physiotherapy, incentive spirometry).

☞ Verify that client comprehends and consents to care and procedures.

☞ Manage the care of the client with a fluid and electrolyte imbalance.

☞ Provide care and education for the newborn less than 1 month.

☞ Provide care and education that meets special needs of older adult client.

☞ Perform hemodialysis or continuous renal replacement therapy.

☞ Participate in maintaining institution's security plan (i.e., fire emergency).

2.1 Which of these clinical assessment findings are most important to monitor and report for a client admitted to the medical surgical unit one-hour post abdominal surgery? **Select all that apply.**

① BP—150/90
② CVP—7 mm Hg
③ HR—120 bpm (weak)
④ Pulses bounding
⑤ RR—40/min

2.2 What are the appropriate plans of care for a client admitted with the diagnosis of Hepatitis C (HCV)? **Select all that apply.**

① Admit client to a private room with monitored negative-airflow.
② Apply gown, mask, and gloves whenever nurse is in contact with the client.
③ Apply a mask when in direct contact with client.
④ Place in a semi-private room with a client with HIV; wear gloves when in contact with blood/body secretions.
⑤ Discard all needles and sharps in the appropriate containers; do not recap.

2.3 Put in chronological order the steps for transferring an older client from the bed to chair? Use all of the options.

① Lower the bed to the lowest setting.
② Instruct client how to assist when possible.
③ Assist the client to stand, and then pivot.
④ Position the bed or chair, so that the client is moving toward the strong side.
⑤ Assess if client understands the steps of getting up from bed to chair.

2.4 What are the most important nursing actions to prevent back injury to the nurse when assisting a client out of bed to the standing position with no weight bearing to the left leg? **Select all that apply.**

① Apply an immobilizer to the left leg as prescribed and position client on side of bed.
② Position nurse's feet close together to assist with stability.
③ Instruct client to position arms around the waist of the nurse.
④ Instruct client to lean slightly forward and bear weight on the right foot as the left foot and leg are held forward.
⑤ Apply a transfer belt around the waist of the client.

2.5 An older client who is being seen on the medical unit by the healthcare provider complains of having difficulty sleeping at night. Which interventions are appropriate to include in the plan of care for this client? **Select all that apply.**

① Advise client to have a cup of warm tea 1 hour prior to going to bed.
② Avoid all caffeinated beverages.
③ Advise to drink a glass of water 20 minutes prior to going to bed.
④ Limit naps throughout the day.
⑤ Recommend the routine bath that is taken at home in the evening.

2.6 Point and click on the image where the nurse would initiate a gastrostomy feeding for an elderly client in the long-term facility.

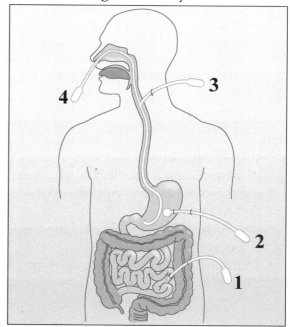

2.7   Following report, the nurse needs to assess each of these clients. Place in chronological order of care delivery how the nurse would assess this group of clients. (1 = highest priority)

| ① Client with a Theophylline level of 22 micrograms/ml. |
| ② Client with Pheochromocytoma and heart rate = 155 beats per min. |
| ③ Client with carbamazepine level of 10 micrograms/ml. |
| ④ Client with Addison's disease and peaked T-waves on the ECG. |

| |
| |
| |
| |

2.8   What clinical observation findings indicate safety standards have been met for an elderly client one-day after experiencing a cerebrovascular accident (CVA) presenting with complete right-sided hemiplegia? **Select all that apply.**

①   Bed exit alarm set for client.
②   Restraint mitts in place after client attempted to pull out nasogastric tube.
③   Client left on bedside commode for privacy.
④   Client instructed to ambulate often, including toileting to assist with independence.
⑤   Nurses apply gloves prior to having any contact with the client.

2.9   What nursing plans are most appropriate for a client with chronic renal failure receiving dialysis and is presenting with constipation? **Select all that apply.**

①   Discuss the importance of eating fruits such as oranges and bananas.
②   Encourage the use of the laxative magnesium citrate.
③   Encourage a diet high in fiber.

④   Encourage exercise in plan of care working within the dialysis management protocol.
⑤   Discuss the importance of increasing fluids in the diet such as orange juice.

2.10   Following a comprehensive assessment of an older adult, what documentations indicate the nurse understands the normal physiological sensory function changes that occur in the older client? **Select all that apply.**

①   Increased sensitivity to glare
②   Decreased number of taste buds
③   Decreased ability in discriminating consonants
④   Decreased sensitivity to pain
⑤   Increased temperature sensation
⑥   Increased sensitivity to high pitched sounds

2.11   During the admission process for a toddler, what clinical findings will cause the nurse to suspect the parents are abusing the child? **Select all that apply.**

①   The child cries when the parents leave.
②   The child has a bruise on the right knee.
③   The parents blame the child for being so active and not sitting down when told.
④   The parents demand the child give the parents the stuffed animal the child is clinging to or child will get a whipping.
⑤   The child has some scars on abdomen that are small circular; parents had no idea they were present.

2.12   Which of the laboratory reports should the nurse notify the provider of care for a client in labor who is now 6 centimeters dilated and is requesting an epidural for relief of pain?

Serum Laboratory Test	Client's Value
RBC	4, 800 mm³
WBC	9,000 cells mm³
PLATELETS (PLT)	49,000/mm³
Hemoglobin (Hgb)	11.5 g/dL
Hematocrit (Hct)	34.5%

①   Red blood cells (RBC)
②   White blood cells (WBC)
③   Platelets (PLT)
④   Hemoglobin (HGB)

2.13 Which of these clinical findings for a client following a thoracentesis should be reported to the provider of care? **Select all that apply.**

① A small amount of drainage on the dressing
② Discomfort around the incision site
③ BP change from 130/80 to 100/68
④ SaO_2 86%
⑤ Hemoglobin 8 g/dL

2.14 Which of the clinical findings indicate the client is experiencing a therapeutic effect from a Dopamine hydrochloride drip? **Select all that apply.**

① Peripheral pulses difficult to palpate
② Urine output from 38 mL/hr to 62 mL/hr
③ 8 AM: BP—148/98, 10 AM: BP—96/66
④ 8 AM: BP—96/66, 10 AM: BP—130/88
⑤ Glasgow Coma Scale at 8 AM: 8, 10 AM: 14

2.15 What dose is the client receiving of lidocaine hydrochloride if it is infusing at 20 mL/hr and the dilution is 1,000 mg/250 mL?

_____ mg/min.

2.16 Which of these recommendations should be included in a health promotion session for women experiencing stress incontinence? **Select all that apply.**

① Reduce fluid intake to 400–600 mL/day.
② Carry and wear incontinence pads when at home and away from home.
③ Discuss that incontinence is always secondary to an infection.
④ Review how to perform Kegel exercises.
⑤ Reduce the intake of tea, coke, and alcoholic beverages.

2.17 There is an order to administer 1000 mL of D5.45NS over 12 hours. The tubing calibration factor is 15 gtt/mL. The infusion should be set to_____ drops/min.

2.18 Place in chronological order the sequence of events for the nurse to implement in a Code Red (fire alarm). **Use all the options.**

① Contain the fire.
② Aim the extinguisher to the base of the fire.
③ Activate the alarm.
④ Pull the pin on the extinguisher.
⑤ Extinguish the fire from side to side.
⑥ Remove any clients from the fire.

2.19 Which of the clinical findings should a nurse document in the chart, report to healthcare provider, and include in the plan of care for client with Addison's disease? **Select all that apply.**

① Melanosis of skin
② Temperature: 97.8°F (36.6°C)
③ Spiked T waves on ECG monitor
④ BP—98/64
⑤ Weight gain of 2 lbs. (0.9 kg) over last two days

2.20 Which nursing actions should a nurse implement for a client with tuberculosis? **Select all that apply.**

① Restrict visitors to immediate family only.
② Apply on a gown.
③ Wear N95 respirator mask.
④ Place in a negative airflow room.
⑤ Wear gloves when in contact with the client's secretions.

2.21 Point and click to the clinical findings that would require the RN to seek physician consultation for an older adult client. **Select all that apply.**

①

②

③

④

⑤

2.22 Which nursing actions are important to include in the plan of care for an older adult client who is on bed rest and the goal is to decrease the risk of developing pressure ulcers? **Select all that apply.**

① Reposition client every 3–4 hours to prevent pressure.
② When the client is lying on side, use the 30-degree lateral inclined position.
③ Massage bony prominences.
④ Use donut-type devices to minimize pressure.
⑤ Maintain the head of the bed at or below 30 degrees.

2.23 The client with a diagnosis of ulcerative colitis is scheduled for an ileostomy. Which area of the stomach would the nurse assess the stoma?

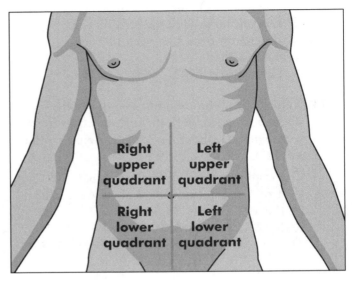

① Right lower quadrant
② Left lower quadrant
③ Transverse colon
④ Right upper quadrant

2.24 Which of these actions indicate the client understands the appropriate and safe use of the cane? **Select all that apply.**

① The cane and the unaffected leg move together.
② The cane is used on the side opposite of the affected leg.
③ The cane is placed approximately 3 feet in front.
④ The cane and the affected leg move together.
⑤ The cane is placed on the affected side and moved with the affected leg.

2.25 Which assessment findings for a client post-abdominal surgery indicate a positive outcome from the hourly use of an incentive spirometer? **Select all that apply.**

① The absence of fever.
② The absence of atelectasis on x-ray.
③ A decrease in pain on inspiration.
④ The absence of crackles upon auscultation.
⑤ A decrease in forced vital capacity.
⑥ A decrease in respiratory rate.

2.26 What actions are appropriate for the client with meningitis who has just been admitted to the unit? **Select all that apply.**

① Institute droplet precautions.
② Maintain head of bed at 30 degrees.
③ Place the client near the nurses' station.
④ Encourage visitors.
⑤ Monitor neurological signs every 8 hours.

2.27 In what order should the nurse prioritize the client assessments following the evening shift report. Use **all options.**

① A client with a decubitus on the sacral area with a temperature of 101°F (38.3°C).
② A client with type 1 diabetes mellitus and Bells Palsy scheduled for discharge in AM.
③ A client with a tracheostomy tube and was just admitted to the Med Surg unit from ICU.
④ A client receiving D5.2 NS at 80 mL/hour with 90 mL remaining in the bag.

2.28 What plans should be included for a client diagnosed with AIDS and has developed *Pneumocystis jirovecii* pneumonia (PCP)? **Select all that apply.**

① Apply an N95 mask when entering the client's room.
② Wear a gown when assisting the client with personal hygiene.
③ Wear a mask when assisting the client with personal hygiene.
④ Explain to client the reason he cannot have any visitors.
⑤ Wear gloves when assisting with personal hygiene.

2.29 Using the options below, place the steps in the order the nurse should follow to administer the unit of packed red blood cells (PRBCs) for a client who is diagnosed with anemia. **Use all the options.**

① Flush the intravenous tubing and line with normal saline solution.
② Verify the identifiers on the blood bag, ABO group, and compatibility against the client identifiers with another RN.
③ Remain with the client and watch for signs of a transfusion reaction during the start of transfusion.
④ Record the client's vital signs.
⑤ Check the PRBC's for abnormal color, clumping, gas bubbles and expiration date.

2.30 Which of these nursing actions should be implemented by the nurse to prevent an air embolus from occurring during the removal of the central venous catheter (CVC)? **Select all that apply.**

① Instruct client to bear down while removing the catheter.
② Position client in the recumbent position.
③ Position client in the semi-Fowler's position with head turned away from the insertion site.
④ Advise client to breathe in when CVC tube is being removed.
⑤ Encourage frequent coughing during the procedure.

2.31 Prior to administering the prescribed exenatide subcutaneous, which observations are most important? **Select all that apply.**

① Bed number
② Medical record number
③ Name band
④ Name of healthcare provider
⑤ Room number

2.32 Which nursing actions are appropriate for an obstetric client in labor and delivery who is receiving an I.V. infusion of oxytocin by an infusion pump? **Select all that apply.**

① Check the pump prior to starting the infusion to make certain it is working appropriately.
② Check the alarm settings when the client is repositioned in the bed.
③ Check the alarm settings after the client receives an epidural.
④ Check the alarm settings when infusion is started.
⑤ Check the alarm settings at the beginning of each shift.

2.33 What information is most important to include in the teaching plan for a client with bipolar disorder who is being discharged to go home with a new prescription for Lithium? **Select all that apply.**

① Restrict oral fluids to under 1 liter per day.
② Adjust dosage according to how client feels.
③ Use effective contraceptive measures if sexually active.
④ Contact the healthcare provider if diarrhea or fever develops.
⑤ Schedule appointment in one week to have Lithium levels drawn.

2.34 During a teaching session, which of these foods should the nurse include when discussing foods that are good sources of iron? **Select all that apply.**

① Beans
② Dried fruit
③ Spinach
④ Tuna fish
⑤ Yogurt

2.35 Which interventions are appropriate for an older client to decrease complications with incontinence and also has a diagnosis of glaucoma? **Select all that apply.**

① Teach client how to perform Kegel exercises daily.
② Review the importance of taking the newly prescribed dicyclomine as ordered.
③ Review the importance of avoiding or decreasing the intake of caffeine.
④ Discuss the importance of increasing the use of a daily vitamin.
⑤ Review the rationale for avoiding alcohol consumption.

2.36 Which of these clinical observations should the unlicensed assistive personnel (UAP) report to the nurse for a client with a brain tumor who is taking dexamethasone? **Select all that apply.**

① Weight gain of 3 lbs (1.4 kg) since yesterday.
② Tremors and diaphoretic skin.
③ Blood pressure change from 150/90 to 120/78.
④ Complains of a sore throat.
⑤ Moist cough.

2.37 The healthcare provider (HCP) prescribes phenytoin IV. The child weights 120 lbs. (55 kg). The order is to administer 20 mg/kg in three divided doses in 2-hour intervals. How many milligrams (mg) should the nurse administer per dose?

_____ mg (Record as a whole number.)

2.38 Which additional clinical findings should the nurse assess and document in the chart for a client presenting with a S_3 during the cardiac assessment? **Select all that apply.**

① Weight gain.
② Enlarged abdominal girth.
③ Photosensitivity.
④ Headache.
⑤ Swollen ankles.

2.39 What are the appropriate nursing actions for a client with undiagnosed abdominal pain? **Select all that apply.**

① Give client sips of water.
② Apply heat on the abdomen.
③ Maintain client on bed rest.
④ Administer morphine for acute pain.
⑤ Assess intake and output.

2.40 Which nursing actions should the nurse delegate to the unlicensed assistive personnel (UAP) for a client with renal failure who has Fluid Volume Excess related to compromised regulatory mechanisms? **Select all that apply.**

① Monitor and record vital signs every 4 hours.
② Weigh client every morning using standing scale.
③ Listen to breath sounds every 4 hours.
④ Teach client the importance of eating oranges and bananas.
⑤ Remind client to save all urine for intake and output record.

2.41 The client with a spinal cord injury has been diagnosed with Clostridium Difficile. Which of these nursing actions indicate the nurse understands how to safely provide care for this client? **Select all that apply.**

① Place a client in a room with another client who has MRSA.
② Wash hands with hand sanitizer outside the client's room.
③ Put on a gown when in contact with the client.
④ Put on gloves when in contact with the client.
⑤ Refuses to share blood pressure cuff with the licensed practical nurse (LPN) who needs one for another client.

2.42 The staff nurse is leading an in-service orientation program regarding informed consents. Which of these statements indicates the nurse understands the manner for obtaining these consents? **Select all that apply.**

① "The nurse will assess knowledge level of surgical procedure and answer any questions client may have."
② "The client indicates a voluntary consent with this signature."
③ "The client's spouse must be present during the process of signing the informed consent."
④ "The information discussed with client prior to the signature will be adequately disclosed."
⑤ "The client was informed clearly of the risks involved with the procedure, surgery, etc., and verbalized this understanding prior to signing the consent."

2.43 Put in chronological order the nursing actions for a female client in labor and after membranes ruptured the umbilical cord prolapsed and was visible from the vagina. **Use all options.** (1 is the first step and 4 the last step.)

① Notify the healthcare provider.
② Put sterile saline soaks loosely around the exposed cord.
③ Assist client in the knee-chest position and administer oxygen.
④ Increase the current IV flow rate.

2.44 Based on the nurse's documentation, what is the priority of care for a client who is 6 hours postpartum?
Progress Notes: 9/16/15
Client's VS: HR—88 bpm
RR—22/min
BP—10 AM 128/80

Fundus palpated left of the umbilicus. Small amount of serosanguinous drainage on the perineal pad. ---------L.Shera, RN

① Notify the healthcare provider.
② Elevate the head of the bed.
③ Encourage client to empty bladder.
④ Prepare to insert a catheter to assist with voiding.

2.45 Which of these clinical assessment findings require immediate intervention by the nurse for a maternity client who is receiving oxytocin? **Select all that apply.**

① A maternal heart rate of 72 bpm.
② A maternal blood pressure of 168/90.
③ Fetal heart monitor displaying late decelerations.
④ Fetal heart monitor displaying a decrease in variability.
⑤ Crackles in client's bilateral lung fields.

2.46 Which of these clinical findings require further evaluation for the maternity client in labor? **Select all that apply.**

① FHR—140 bpm and increase in variability.
② Early decelerations noted on the external fetal monitor.
③ Complaints of pain throughout the contraction.
④ Amniotic fluid is meconium stained.
⑤ Variable decelerations noted on the external fetal monitor following the rupture of the membranes.

2.47 Which information should be included in the discharge teaching for the parents of a newborn? **Select all that apply.**

① The newborn can be bathed in a tub while the circumcision heals.
② Notify the healthcare provider for apnea lasting 5-10 seconds.
③ The diaper should be placed under the cord.
④ Antibiotic ointment should be applied to the cord three times a day.
⑤ Use alcohol to clean the length of the cord several times a day.

2.48 Which of these positive clinical symptoms for schizophrenia should be reported to the healthcare provider? **Select all that apply.**

① Alogia
② Anergia
③ Anhedonia
④ Delusions
⑤ Hallucinations

2.49 Place in chronological order the steps for starting an IV. **All options must be used.**

① Release tourniquet.
② Cleanse site thoroughly; re-cleanse if area is palpated prior to insertion.
③ Insert needle with bevel up at 15-degree to 30-degree angle.
④ Apply gloves.
⑤ Apply the tourniquet 4 to 6 inches above the site.
⑥ Cover the insertion site with a transparent dressing .

2.50 A client in diabetic ketoacidosis has an order to start an insulin drip with 40 units of insulin in 100 mL of Normal Saline, and the infusion pump is set at 10 mL/hr. How many units of insulin per hour is the client receiving?

_____ units/hour

2.51 Place in chronological order the steps the nurse would take when caring for a client and assisting a physician who is going to perform a liver biopsy for a client. **Use all the options.**

① Review blood coagulation study results and make certain on the chart.
② Position client on bed rest for 12 to 14 hours and on right side for 2 hours.
③ Assess for right upper abdominal pain or referred should pain; observe for tachycardia, hypotension.
④ Verify the client has signed the informed consent.
⑤ Instruct client to take a deep breath, exhale completely, and hold breath.

2.52 Which order should the nurse teach the client to use when taking albuterol with a metered-dose inhaler (MDI)? Place in chronological order. **Use all of the options.**

① Breathe out through the nose.
② Activate the MDI when inhaling.
③ Wash hands.
④ Hold breath for 5 to 10 seconds and then exhale.
⑤ Shake the inhaler.

.

2.53 The nurse has an assignment of four clients. Prioritize in order from highest to lowest priority how the nurse would assess the clients following report?

① A middle-aged client who is presenting with COPD and is sleeping up in a chair at night.
② A young adult client with asthma who has a scheduled dose of a steroid inhaler to be administered.
③ A middle-aged client with pneumonia who has been on antibiotics for 24 hours and needs pain medicine to assist with coughing and deep breathing.
④ An older adult client who is presenting with a new onset of incontinence and does not seem to be as oriented as yesterday.

2.54 Which clinical findings are most important to report to the healthcare provider during the immediate postoperative period for a client who is the recipient of a kidney transplant? **Select all that apply.**

① Pink and bloody urine
② BP—122/78 at 8 AM;
BP—118/68 at 10 AM
③ T—99.1°F (37.3°C) at 8 AM;
T—101°F (38.3°C) at 12 Noon
④ Day 1: Weight—120 lbs (54.4 kg) at 8 AM;
Day 2: Weight—123 lbs (55.8 kg) at 8 AM
⑤ Serum postassium—4.8 mEq/L (4.8 mmol/L)

2.55 Which clinical findings should be documented in the progress notes for an older adult admitted with delirium? **Select all that apply.**

① The client is experiencing a progressive loss of judgment.
② The client has a recent history of a respiratory infection.
③ The change in behavior has been acute.
④ The client's family report a progressive loss of memory.
⑤ The client is becoming more disoriented over the last year.

2.56 What information is most important to include in the teaching plan for a client receiving Insulin glargine? **Select all that apply.**

① This insulin should be administered three times/day.
② This insulin can be mixed with other insulin.
③ This insulin will peak in 15 minutes.
④ Use only insulin syringes to draw up dose.
⑤ Rotate injection sites.

2.57 What information should be included in the discharge teaching for a client with a new prescription for levothyroxine? **Select all that apply.**

① Instruct to take a single dose before breakfast.
② Review the importance of not changing brands.
③ Advise to expect the normal change of a rapid weight loss.
④ Review how to take heart rate and to hold med if above 88 bpm.
⑤ Review the importance of notifying HCP if experiences tremors.

2.58 Which of these clinical findings for a client diagnosed with schizophrenia and is taking risperidone would require further evaluation by the healthcare provider? **Select all that apply.**

① Dry mouth
② Sore throat
③ Temperature—101°F (38.3°C)
④ Reddish brown urine
⑤ Complaints of dizziness when rising quickly

2.59 What information should be included in the discharge teaching plan for a client who is taking prednisone? **Select all that apply.**

① Monitor the BP three times a week and keep a log to share with HCP.
② Avoid potatoes, bananas, and cantaloupe.
③ Use salt instead of salt substitutes.
④ Report to healthcare provider any feelings of being hot, dry, and flushed.
⑤ Identify potential hazards for falls, after completing a home assessment.

2.60 Which of these actions by the client who is using a metered-dose inhaler (MDI) for taking albuterol indicates an appropriate understanding for the use of this MDI? **Select all that apply.**

① When two puffs are needed, client allows for 1minute elapse between the two.
② The activation of the MDI is coordinated with expiration.
③ Special care is taken to not shake the inhaler prior to using.
④ When using the MDI, the client inspires slowly.
⑤ Client understands that albuterol is used on a continuous basis in the absence of symptoms.

Answers & Rationales

2.1 ③ Options #3 and #5 are correct. The key
    ⑤ words in the stem of the question are *"clinical assessment findings"* and *"one hour post abdominal surgery."* Option #3, HR—120 bpm (weak) is correct, since it is compensating from loss of blood. Option #5, RR—40/min is correct, since tachypnea indicates shock is progressing.

I CAN HINT: The strategy is to organize the system specific assessment findings around the types of shock. Note, BP and CVP are not low as would be the case if there was a decrease in volume. The CVP is within the defined limits. There is no need to report. The CVP would be decreased in a complication with bleeding or hypovolemia. Refer to the book *Nursing Made Insanely Easy* by Manning & Rayfield, for an easy way to remember the values. The pulse may be bounding in distributive shock. After you have an understanding of the concept, then when answering questions evaluating *"Select all that apply,"* each of the options can be treated like a *"true or false"* question. Remember, one step at a time. Stay focused on what you do know!

2.2 ④ Options #4 and #5 are correct. Standard
    ⑤ precautions in addition to appropriate needle disposal are required precautions. Option #4 has a client that would require the same infection control standards. Hepatitis C is transmitted through blood and body fluids. Twenty percent of HCV cases result from high-risk sexual behavior. Option #1 is incorrect based on CDC standards. There is not a need for a private room based on the type of organism/infection control guidelines necessary for the care of HCV. The negative airflow room would be a part of care for a client in airborne precautions. Option #2 is incorrect due to how Hepatitis C is transmitted. These PPE in this option are not included in standard of care when just "in contact" with client. If blood and / or body secretions are going to be splashed, then this will need to be stated in

the option to assist you in making the correct decision. Option #3 is not necessary for this client.

I CAN HINT: Refer to *Nursing Made Insanely Easy* for an easy approach to remembering Infection Control Precautions.

2.3

⑤ Option #5 is the initial step. Assess if client understands the steps of getting up from bed to chair. *Assessment is a great place to begin! Helps the nurse know what information to include when teaching.*
② Option #2 is the second step. Instruct client how to assist when possible. *Remember, nurses must educate prior to interventions.*
① Option #1 is the third step. Lower the bed to the lowest setting. *Remember client safety is always important prior to moving ahead with intervention!*
④ Option #4 is the fourth step. Position the bed or chair, so that the client is moving toward the strong side. *Now focus on the equipment or chair, and the side it must be on (strong side leads).*
③ Option #3 is the last step. Assist the client to stand, and then pivot. *This is the last step to the goal!*

2.4 ① Options #1, #4, and #5 are correct. Option #1:
    ④ The nurse should make certain the
    ⑤ immobilizer is applied as prescribed and the client is positioned to the side of the bed to assist with the transfer. If the client has been in the supine position for an extended period of time, this will also facilitate decreasing the risk of orthostatic hypotension. Option # 4 is correct. To assist with the client's center of gravity, have the client lean slightly forward from the hips. This will assist in positioning the trunk and head in the same direction as the transfer. The nurse should remain in front of the client positioning one foot forward and one

back while flexing the hips, knees, and ankles. The nurse should use the leg muscles to assist the client to the standing position. Option #5: To assist with holding onto the client, the transfer belt will provide this security by providing a way for the nurse to control the movements. Option #2 is incorrect since the nurse should be positioned in a broad stance. The narrow stance will only provide the nurse with a narrow base of support. Option #3 may result in the nurse losing balance.

2.5 ④ Options #4 and #5 are correct. Clients may be
⑤ instructed in developing a bedtime routine. In addition to limiting naps throughout the day and continuing with routines from home, such as an evening bath, older clients can be encouraged to exercise regularly at least 2 hours prior to bedtime. Organize the sleep environment for comfort. Caffeine, alcohol, and nicotine should be limited at least 4 hours prior to bedtime. Fluids should be limited to 2 to 4 hours prior to bedtime. If client is anxious or stressed, engage in muscle relaxation. If someone is available for a back rub 15 min. prior to going to bed, this can also be very therapeutic. Warm milk and crackers can be soothing prior to going to bed. Options #1, #2, and #3 are incorrect for assisting with sleep.

I CAN HINT: Refer to *Nursing Made Insanely Easy* for an easy approach to remembering priority nursing care for geriatrics.

2.6 Line 2 is the correct option. The gastrostomy tube (Line 2) is surgically placed through an abdominal incision into the stomach. The distal end of the gastrostomy tube is secured to the anterior gastric wall, a tunnel is created, and a permanent stoma is formed by the proximal end of the tube being brought through the abdomen. Line 1 is a jejunostomy tube that

is similarly placed as the gastrostomy tube; however, the distal end of the jejunostomy tube extends pass the pylorus into the jejunum. Line 3 is an esophagostomy tube. Line 4 is a nasogastric tube. This tube ends in the stomach.

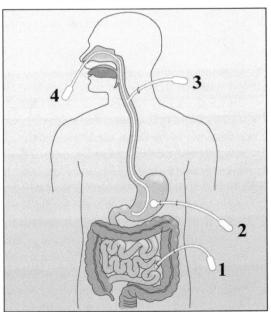

2.7

④	Client with Addison's and peaked T-waves on the ECG. *(Risk for dysrhythmias)*
②	Client with Pheochromocytoma with heart rate of 155 beats per minute. *(tachycardia)*
①	Client with Theophylline level of 22 micrograms/ml. *(slightly elevated; normal 10–20 micrograms/mL.)*
③	Client with Carbamazepine (Tegretol) level of 10 micrograms/mL. *(normal range)*

2.8 ①
② Options #1 and #2 are correct. Option #1: Bed exit alarm for client following a CVA is a safety need. Option #2: Restraint mitts are less restrictive and may be very effective to alleviate client pulling tubes and decreasing safety risks related to treatments and care. Option #3 is incorrect: Leaving client on bedside commode alone following a CVA can pose a safety risk due to the new paralysis from the CVA. Option #4 is incorrect. Client ambulation and toileting unassisted following a CVA can pose a safety risk as #3 above. Option #5 is incorrect. Applying gloves prior to any contact with the client is not necessary and is not included in the guidelines for infection control. If the nurse is going to handle blood or come in contact with body secretions, then yes, gloves would be imperative.

I CAN HINT: Note that the two correct options include doing something for the client to assist with safety. Options #3 and #4 both focus on client performing an aspect of care alone. Option #5 requires an understanding of Standard / Universal precautions.

2.9 ③
④ Options #3 and #4 are correct. Increasing fiber will increase bulk and result in a decrease in constipation. Exercise will facilitate motility. Option #1 is incorrect. These two fruits are high in potassium and should not be given to clients in chronic renal failure due to risk with hyperkalemia which may lead to cardiac dysrhythmias. Option #2 is incorrect. Magnesium laxatives should not be given to clients in renal failure because this can lead to hypermagnesemia. Option #5 is incorrect since the client is in renal failure. If the option would have read "Take fluids within the client's fluid restriction", then this could have been an answer if orange juice was not included. It is unsafe to increase fluids without a limit due to the renal failure as well as including fluids high in potassium, such as orange juice.

I CAN HINT: Refer to *Nursing Made Insanely Easy* for an easy approach to remembering priority nursing care for chronic renal failure and dialysis.

2.10 ①
② Options #1, #2, #3, and #4 are correct. These
③ are all sensory function changes that occur in
④ the older adult. Options #5 and #6 are both decreased. They are cooler even when it is warm outside. The older client has a challenge hearing high-pitched sounds. The voices of women and children are difficult for older client to hear.

I CAN HINT: A quick and easy way to remember the physiological changes that occur in the older adult is that everything is decreased with the exception of "fat and sensitivity to glare". This is not fair, but this is just how the aging process goes!

2.11 ③
④ Options #3, #4, and #5 are correct. Option #3
⑤ indicates parents do not have an appropriate understanding of growth and development for the 3 year old, and may have unrealistic expectations for this developmental stage. Option #4 also indicates a lack of understanding of how the child is feeling and not understanding that a decrease in the child's sense of security is the reason the child is clinging to the familiar object. Option #5 is correct. Parents should have an idea the reason for the scars that are on their young child; at least the parents should have known these scars were present. Option #1 does not cause any suspicion of abuse since this is normal behavior for a toddler experiencing separation anxiety. Option #2 can occur with any active child.

I CAN HINT: Refer to *Nursing Made Insanely Easy* for an easy approach to remembering the clinical findings for a child who is suspected of being abused.

2.12 ③ Option #3 is correct. Platelets less than 100,000/mm³ are considered abnormal. Due to the risk for hemorrhaging, regional anesthesia would be contraindicated with a platelet count below 50,000/mm³. Options #1, #2, #4 may be slightly abnormal in pregnancy and labor, but these would not be a contraindication for the provider administering the regional anesthesia.

I CAN HINT: "Plate" in platelet has 5 letters and if these are < 50,000/mm³, then the epidural should not be administered due to risk for bleeding.

Refer to *Nursing Made Insanely Easy* for an easy approach to remembering these lab values.

2.13 ③ Options #3, #4, #5 are correct. Options #3
④ and #5 should be reported due to the
⑤ significant drop which could be a result from a complication with bleeding. Option #4 should be reported due to the low value. This could indicate a complication from a pneumothroax due to the injury to the lung during the procedure. In addition to the SaO_2—86%, the nurse should monitor the vital signs, respiratory rate and rhythm, breath sounds hourly for the first several hours after the thoracentesis. Options #1 and #2 are expected findings following the thoracentesis, and should not be reported.

I CAN HINT: Refer to *Nursing Made Insanely Easy* for an easy approach to remembering the priority care for a client who had a "CENTESIS".

2.14 ② Options #2, #4 and #5 are correct. The
④ therapeutic effects of dopamine hydrochloride
⑤ are due to its positive inotropic effect on the myocardium, increasing cardiac output and improving circulation to the renal vascular bed. Therefore, the nurse would observe for an increase in hourly urine output, increased blood pressure and an increased state of alertness from the client. Options #1 and #3 indicate that the effect has not proven therapeutic or that the client is experiencing an adverse effect of the medication. These clinical findings indicate hypovolemia.

2.15 **1.3** mg/min.

STEP ONE: Calculate the concentration of mg/mL:

$$\frac{\overset{4}{\cancel{1,000\ mg}}}{\underset{1}{\cancel{250\ mL}}} = 4\ mg/mL$$

STEP TWO: Multiply the number of milligrams per milliliter by the pump setting in milliliters per hour:

$$\frac{4\ mg \times 20\ \cancel{mL}}{1\ \cancel{mL}\quad 1\ hr} = 80\ mg/hour$$

STEP THREE: Divide the milligrams per hour by 60 to obtain milligrams per minute: 80 mg/hour divided 60 minutes = **1.3** mg/minute.

2.16 ④ Options #4 and #5 are correct. Option #4
⑤ will assist in strengthening the sphincter and structural supports of the bladder. Option #5 should be included because dietary irritants and natural diuretics, such as caffeine and alcoholic beverages, may increase stress incontinence. Option #1 is incorrect. If clients are non-restricted to the fluid intake, they should have a fluid intake of at least 2 to 3 L/day. Clients with stress incontinence may reduce their fluid intake to avoid incontinence at the risk of developing dehydration and urinary tract infection. This needs to be discouraged! Option #2 is incorrect. It would be more effective for a client to establish a voiding schedule that is regular than to carry incontinent pads. Option #3 is an incorrect statement. While a NEW symptom of incontinence may definitely occur in older clients if they have a UTI, the option reads "always" which does not take into account the numerous reasons for incontinence.

2.17 The answer is <u>21</u> drops/min.

STEP ONE: What is the volume to be infused? 1000 mL

STEP TWO: What is the duration of time for the infusion? 12 hours

STEP THREE: What is the drop factor? 15 gtt/mL

STEP FOUR:
Equation

$$\frac{\text{Volume (mL)} \times \text{Drop factor (gtt/mL)} \times 1\ \text{hour}}{\text{Time (hr)} \qquad\qquad 60\ \text{min}}$$

IV flow rate (gtt/min) =

$$\frac{1000\ \cancel{mL}}{12\ \cancel{hr}} \times \frac{15\text{gtt}}{\cancel{mL}}\ \frac{1\ \cancel{hr}}{60\ \text{min}}$$

Cancel out identical units. Multiply the numerator. Multiply the denominator. Divide the numerator by the denominator.

Answer = 20.8333 = <u>21</u> gtt/min

I CAN HINT: Always reevaluate to determine if the calculated number makes sense!!! You do NOT want to provide unsafe care. Always THINK and make great decisions.

2.18

| ⑥ Remove any clients from the fire. |
| ③ Activate the alarm. |
| ① Contain the fire. |
| ④ Pull the pin on the extinguisher. |
| ② Aim the extinguisher to the base of the fire. |
| ⑤ Extinguish the fire from side to side. |

I CAN HINT: The strategies for answering this question is to use the acronym **"RACE"** to assist you in remembering the emergency fire response. Fire extinguisher safety can be recalled by another acronym: **"PASS"**

RACE: Rescue, Activate, Contain, Extinguish

PASS: Pull the pin, Aim at the base of the fire, Squeeze the trigger, and Sweep from side to side

2.19 ①
③ Options #1, #3, and #4 are correct. Addison's
④ disease is caused by a decrease in secretion of the adrenal cortex hormones. There is a decrease physiologic response to stress, vascular insufficiency, and hypoglycemia. The decrease in the aldosterone secretions (mineral corticoids) normally promotes concentration of sodium and water and excretion of potassium. As a result of this, the sodium may be low and potassium elevated. The clinical outcome is the client development of Addison's disease. The clinical findings have a very slow onset, and skin hyperpigmentation (melanosis) is a classic sign. This bronze coloring of the skin is seen primarily in those areas exposed to the sun, pressure points, joints, and in skin creases (especially on the palms). Option #3 is correct due to the elevated potassium level. Option #4 is correct due to the decrease in aldosterone. Option #2 is not a true statement. Option #5 should read "weight loss versus gain" in order for this option to be correct.

I CAN HINT: The key to answering this question successfully is to understand the pathophysiology for Addison's disease, and connect the clinical assessment findings and interventions to the medical condition. Refer to *Nursing Made Insanely Easy* for an easy approach to remember this concept with the image *"Anemic Adam"*!

2.20 ③
④ Options #3, #4, and #5 are correct. Airborne
⑤ precautions are used in addition to standard precautions for clients who are known or suspected to be infected or colonized with infectious organisms. Diseases known to be transmitted by air for infectious agents smaller than 5 micrometers (measles, varicella, pulmonary or laryngeal tuberculosis) must follow these precautions as outlined by CDC. Personal protective equipment (PPE) should include gloves due to being in contact with secretions, mask (N95 respirator) for known or suspected TB. In addition to standard precautions, the client should be in a monitored negative airflow (air exchange and air discharge through HEP filter). Doors of the room should be kept closed. If client

leaves the room for a medical necessity, a small particulate mask should be applied to the client. Options #1 and #2 are not essential in airborne precautions.

2.21 ① Options #1 and #3 are correct. These would
③ definitely need physician consultation.

Option #1 is pitting edema, which can be a sign of fluid overload from medications, cardiac, renal, endocrine, or other medical conditions.

Option #2 may occur with clients who have osteoarthritis, but does not require a consultation. Heberden's nodes are palpable protuberances that are often associated with flexion and lateral deviation of the distal phalanx. These nodes may become tender, red, and swollen, often beginning in one finger and spreading to others. Usually, there is no significant loss of function, but clients are often distressed by the resulting disfigurement.

Option #3 is a melanoma which is malignant.

Option #4 is a seborrheic keratosis which is a commonly occurring normal skin lesion in older people. This lesion can be macular-papular lesion seen on neck, chest, back, and at hair line; can be warty, scaly or greasy in appearance. There is no need for consultation for this finding.

Option #5 is a senile lentigine. It is an irregular gray-brown macular lesion found on sun-exposed areas of the face, arms, and hands. This is also a commonly occurring normal skin lesion in the older adult which does not require further consultation.

I CAN HINT: It is useful to understand the normal changes that occur with the aging process to assist in answering questions requiring further consultation.

2.22 ② Options #2 and #5 are correct for preventing
⑤ pressure ulcers. Both of these positions will assist in decreasing pressure ulcers. Option #1 is incorrect. It should have read "every 1 to 2 hours" for this to be correct. Option #3 is incorrect; Bony prominences should not be massaged. Option #4 is incorrect; these donut-type devices should not be used due to the risk for ulcers.

I CAN HINT: The key to answering this question accurately is to understand and remember the care necessary for preventing or relieving pressure. **"PRESSURE"** will assist you in organizing this care.

Position change every 1–2 hours.

Remember, nutrition is important; increase carbohydrates, protein, vitamin C, and zinc.

Eggcrate—style or other foam mattress to allow circulation under the body and keep area dry.

Special bed with mattresses that provides for a continuous change in pressure across the mattress.

Silicone gel pads placed under the buttocks of clients in wheelchairs; sheepskin pads to protect skin.

Use active and passive exercises to promote circulation.

Remositurize after bathing with lotion or protective moisturizer; remember to maintain head of the bed at/or below 30 ° or at the lowest degree of elevation.

Eliminate rubbing excessively and hot water with skin care.

"AVOID" will assist you in reviewing what nursing care should NOT be done when preventing pressure.

Avoid massaging bony prominences.

Very important to teach chair-bound clients, who are able, to shift weight every 15 minutes.

Omit using donut-type devices.

If lying on side is used in bed, avoid positioning client directly on the trochanter; use 30° lateral inclined position.

Do not rub excessively, and do not use hot water with skin.

2.23 ① Option #1 is correct. Ulcerative colitis usually affects only the innermost lining of your large intestine (colon) and rectum. To perform surgery for ulcerative colitis usually means removing your entire colon and rectum (proctocolectomy) which would result in the stoma being created in the right lower quadrant.

I CAN HINT: Refer to quadrants to assist you in organizing your physical assessment.

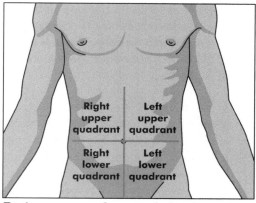

Right upper quadrant includes these anatomic structures: liver and gallbladder, pylorus, duodenum, head of pancreas, right adrenal gland, portion of right kidney, hepatic flexure of colon, portions of ascending and transverse colon.

Left upper quadrant includes these anatomic structures: left lobe of liver, spleen, stomach, body of pancreas, left adrenal gland, portion of left kidney, splenic flexure of colon, portions of transverse and descending colon.

Right lower quadrant includes these anatomic structures: lower pole of right kidney, cecum and appendix, portion of ascending colon, bladder (if distended), ovary and salpinx, uterus (if enlarged), right spermatic cord, right ureter.

Left lower quadrant includes these anatomic structures: lower pole of left kidney, sigmoid colon, portion of descending colon, bladder (if distended), ovary and salpinx, uterus (if enlarged), left spermatic cord, left ureter.

2.24 ② ④ Options #2 and #4 are correct. The cane is used on the side opposite of the affected leg for safety reasons. It provides more balance. Option #4 is correct; the cane and affected leg should be moved together. This will provide the necessary support for the balance due to one leg being weaker or not able to provide much support and will assist in the prevention of falls. Option #1 is incorrect based on the rationale above. Option #3 is too far in front. This distance may result in a fall. Option #5 is incorrect; correct rationale in previous options.

I CAN HINT: Cane is used on the side opposite the affected leg. The affected leg and cane move together. Note, that the cane should be advanced simultaneously with the opposite affected lower limb. Evaluating for correct size … Measure from the wrist to the floor. *Nursing Made Insanely Easy* will provide you with an EASY approach to remember the use of "CANES."

2.25 ① ② ④ ⑥ Options #1, # 2, #4 and # 6 are correct. A goal of incentive spirometer use is to reverse lung atelectasis, as noted by a decrease or absence of crackles upon lung auscultation, and to decrease the body temperature of a post-operative client with a fever. When atelectasis improves, so does gas exchange. As such, the client's respiratory rate decreases. Option #3 is incorrect as deep breathing may increase pain in the post-op client. Therefore, pre-medication of the client using an incentive spirometer should be considered. Option #5 is incorrect as forced vital capacity reflects the maximum amount of air that can be inhaled or exhaled from the lung, and should increase with the continued use of an incentive spirometer.

I CAN HINT: "BREATHE" will assist you in organizing the desired outcomes from the incentive spirometer.

Breath sounds improve

Respiratory rate decreased

Evaluate absence of atelectasis on x-ray

Absence of crackles upon auscultation

Temperature decreased

Heart rate within normal range

Evaluation of the oxygen saturation needs to be ongoing

2.26 ① ② Options #1 and #2 are correct. Clients with meningitis need to be in droplet precautions until antibiotics have been administered. The head of the bed should be elevated 30 degrees to assist with the cerebral brain flow. Option #3 is incorrect. A quiet environment is important for these clients, and the nurses' station has too much stimulation. Option #4 should be decreased due to need to minimize stimulation. Option #5 is incorrect. Neurological

assessment should be done more frequently than 8 hours; these should be done per hospital protocol or as prescribed for this diagnosis.

I CAN HINT: Refer to *Nursing Made Insanely Easy* for an EASY way to remember the priority care.

2.27

③ Option #3 is first priority. *Due to the major risk for complications with the tracheostomy from obstruction or extubation which could be life-threatening.*
① Option #1 is the second, since the client has a temperature with the decubitus. *There is a need for further assessment to determine if the temperature is from an infection in the decubitus or a pulmonary infection. If the decubitus is draining, there can be additional complications with the temperature from the insensible fluid loss. The vital signs need to be evaluated in addition to the hydration status.*
④ Option #4 would be the third client to assess since there is a need to evaluate status of appropriate fluid replacement. *The assessment would include IV site for no signs of infiltration or phlebitis, characteristics of the lips and mucous membranes, skin turgor, urine output and specific gravity.*
② Option #2 would be the last to assess. *The client has no assessments to indicate client is unstable. Discharge is in the AM which indicates this client would be the last client to assess immediately following evening shift report.*

2.28 ② ⑤ Options #2 and #5 are correct. Pneumocystis jirovecii pneumponia (PCP) is not easily transmitted from an infected client to a healthy person. This pathogen is frequently dormant in the body and is reactivated when the client's immune system is significantly depressed. Standard precautions must be adhered to with the client. It is not necessary to follow droplet or airborne precautions. Therefore, options #1, #3, and #4 are not appropriate for this client.

2.29　　Rationale: To administer a blood transfusion the nurse should follow the steps as listed to ensure safe identification, administration and observation of adverse reactions.

④ Record the client's vital signs.
⑤ Check the PRBC's for abnormal color, clumping, gas bubbles and expiration date.
② Verify the identifiers on the blood bag, ABO group, and compatibility against the client identifiers with another RN.
① Flush the intravenous tubing and line with normal saline solution.
③ Remain with the client and watch for signs of a transfusion reaction during the start of transfusion.

2.30　①②　Options #1 and #2 are correct. Insertion or removal of a central line provides an opportunity for air to enter the client's circulation. A recumbent position and the Valsalva's maneuver increases intrathoracic pressure and pressure in the central veins. Option #3 and #4 are incorrect. While in option #3 turning head away from the insertion site would make it easier to remove the catheter and decrease the risk of infection, it has no effect on preventing air embolism. Option #4 could result in an air emboli. Option #5 is incorrect. Coughing is not encouraged. Bearing down would be more appropriate for preventing an air embolus.

2.31　②③　Options #2 and #3 are correct. A National Patient Safety Goal of The Joint Commission is to improve the safety and accuracy of patient identification. In order to achieve the goal, nurses must use at least two client identifiers when providing care, administering meds, procedure, treatment or any services. Two appropriate identifiers include the client's name and the medical record number. Options #1 and #5 are incorrect since the client can change rooms and beds; these have not been identified as acceptable identifiers. Option #4 is incorrect. This also has not been adapted as criteria for client identification.

I CAN HINT: Notice that options #1, #4, and #5 all focus away from the client, but options #2 and #3 focus on the client by reviewing a medical no. and name band. Refer to *Nursing Made Insanely Easy* for a review of the standard.

2.32　①④⑤　Options #1, #4, and #5 are correct. All equipment should be checked to make certain it is working appropriately prior to applying to a client. Options #4 and #5 are correct. The alarm settings should be checked for appropriate functioning when the infusion is started, at the start of each shift, and when client is moved from one unit to another. Option #2 is incorrect. The client being repositioned in the bed does not mandate checking the alarm settings. If the alarm is triggered, however, with repositioning client in bed, then the settings should be verified at that time. Option #3 is incorrect since there is no need after the procedure. This should have been done prior to any procedure versus following the procedure.

2.33　③④⑤　Options #3, #4, and #5 are correct answers. Lithium behaves like a salt in the body, therefore, it is imperative that the client stay hydrated and take in at least 1-3 liters per day of fluids and avoid becoming dehydrated. A fluid restriction would not be necessary, therefore Option #1 is incorrect. Dosages should always be adjusted by the healthcare provider, not the client; therefore, option #2 is incorrect. Option #3, Lithium is a Pregnancy Category D medication, therefore it can cause harm to the fetus. Pregnancy should be avoided while on this medication in order to avoid teratogenic effects to the fetus. Option #4, diarrhea and fever can cause dehydration and elevate the level of lithium in the blood, thereby causing toxicity. Option #5, the drug should never be stopped abruptly. Lithium levels must be drawn after one week of therapy and every few weeks thereafter to avoid toxicity.

I CAN HINT: Refer to *Nursing Made Insanely Easy* or *Pharmacology Made Insanely Easy* for an EASY way to remember the strategies for answering questions regarding Lithium.

2.34 ① Options #1, #2, #3 and #4 are correct. These
② are high in iron. Option #5 is not high in iron.
③
④

2.35 ① Options #1, #3, and #5 are correct options.
③ Urinary incontinence is a significant
⑤ contributing factor to falls, fractures,
depression, and altered skin integrity, especially
in older adult clients. There are six major
types of urinary incontinence. These include:
stress, urge, overflow, reflex, functional, and
total incontinence. Part of the collaborative
care for these clients include: teaching how
to perform Kegel exercises daily, reviewing
the importance of avoiding or decreasing the
intake of caffeine, and reviewing the rationale
for avoiding alcohol consumption. Specific
medications may result in the stimulation of
voiding. Vaginal cone therapy may be used
to strengthen pelvic muscles for clients with
stress incontinence. Option #2 is incorrect.
While dicyclomine (Bentyl) may be used to
decrease urgency for a client with a neurogenic
or overactive bladder, if the client has a
diagnosis of glaucoma this medication can
increase intraocular pressure. The order should
be verified due to inappropriateness of this
order for a client with glaucoma. Option #4
is incorrect. The vitamin is not prescribed to
decrease incontinence.

I CAN HINT: The key to this question is
that the client has glaucoma along with the
incontinence. Anticholinergic medications are
contraindicated for these clients. The intake
of alcohol or caffeine that results in relaxation
can cause an increase in the urination. Notice
in the stem of the question, if there is a
medication, disease, lab value, age, clinical
assessment finding, etc., there is a reason, so
pay attention! This will most likely be your clue
to assist in selecting the correct answer(s).

2.36 ① Options # 1, #4, and #5 are correct.
④ Dexamethasone (Decadron) is a corticosteroid.
⑤ It is an anti-inflammatory and can result in
an increase in fluid retention as indicated
by option #1, weight gain and may result in
option #5, the moist cough. Option #4 is

correct since the medication may cause the
client to be immunosuppressed. The client
may present with an infection such as the sore
throat as many of the other signs of infection
may be masked. Option #2 is incorrect. These
symptoms indicate a complication with
hypoglycemia and the actual undesirable effect
of this medication would be hyperglycemia.
Remember that *"if the skin is hot and dry the
blood sugar is high, but cool and clammy means
they need some candy."* Option #3 is incorrect
since the BP has decreased. The undesirable
effect from this medication would be an
elevation in the blood pressure.

2.37 Answer = <u>367</u> mg

Step 1: Convert pounds to kilograms.
1 kilogram equals 2.2 pounds (120/2.2 = 55kg).

Step 2: Determine total dose
(20 mg x 55 kg = 1,100mg)

Step 3: Determine amount for each dose
(1,100/3= 367mg)

2.38 ① Options #1, #2 and #5 are correct. This cardiac
② sound is indicative of heart failure. These
⑤ are clinical findings for a client with right-
sided heart failure. Options #3 and #4 are
not associated with S_3. S_4 would indicate a
complication with hypertension, diplopia, etc.

I CAN HINT: An easy way to remember
this is that there are 3 syllables in "heart failure" and there is a S_3 with this complication.
Left sided heart failure presents with lung
involvement and there is an "L" in left and in
lungs to help you remember. Right sided heart
failure is the "Rest of the body" which includes
peripheral edema, ascites, and jugular vein
distention. There are 4 syllables in "Hy-per-
ten-sion" and this is assessed by a S_4. Signs and
symptoms of hypertension may be headache,
diplopia, etc. See how EASY this can be!
Clinical decision-making is all about using the
information we already have in our head. The
key is to move information from short term to
long-term memory, so it can be retrieved and
used!!

2.39 ③ Options #3 and #5 are correct. The key in
⑤ the stem of the question is "undiagnosed abdominal pain." The Do's for this diagnosis include: maintain on bed rest, place in a position of comfort, assess hydration, assess intake and output, assess abdominal status: distention, bowel sounds, passage of stool or flatus, generalized or local pain, keep client NPO until notified otherwise. Option #1 is incorrect since the client should get nothing by mouth. Option #2 is incorrect. Do not apply heat to the abdomen. Cold applications may provide some relief or comfort. Option #4 is incorrect. Do not give narcotics for pain control before a diagnosis of appendicitis is confirmed, because this could mask signs if the appendix ruptures. The Do Not's for this diagnosis include giving nothing by mouth, do not put heat on the abdomen, no enemas, no strong narcotics, and no laxatives.

2.40 ① Options #1, #2, and #5 are correct. These are
② within the scope of practice for the UAP and
⑤ are also appropriate for this concept of fluid excess. Option #3 is not within the scope of practice for the UAP. Option #4 would be incorrect for this client. These foods are high in potassium and could lead to a cardiac dysrhythmia if client took a diet high in these foods. Even if these foods were appropriate for the client, it is not within the scope of practice for the UAP to teach the client.

I CAN HINT: There are two concepts that are necessary for success with this question. The first is to understand the signs of fluid excess which are outlined on the right upper side of this page. Just remember these are all elevated just like the fluid volume is increased. The second concept is to understand the scope of practice for the UAP which includes basic care that does not require assessment, teaching,

analysis, clinical decision making, or providing care for a client with unexpected outcomes.

↑ pulse

↑ temperature

↑ blood pressure

↑ in edema

↑ in ascites

↑ in crackles in lungs

↑ swelling neck (jugular vein distention)

↑ in confusion, headache and seizures

2.41 ③ Options #3, #4, and #5 are correct. This
④ diagnosis requires standard/contact
⑤ precautions. Hand hygiene; personal protective equipment (gloves and gown) if in contact with client. Disposal of infectious dressing material into nonporous bag. Dedicated equipment for the client or disinfect after each use. Option #5 is correct since the equipment should not be shared with clients if one is in contact precautions. Option #1 is incorrect. These clients should not be placed with a client with Clostridium Difficile. Option #2 is incorrect since this is not a sporicidal. Hands should be washed with soap and water.

2.42 ② Option #2, #4, and #5 are correct regarding
④ informed consents. Option #2 does indicate a
⑤ voluntary consent with the signature. Option #4 is correct. This indicates client will be provided with appropriate information prior to signature. Option #5 is correct. Client should have an understanding of the risks involved prior to signing consent. Option #1 is not within the scope of practice of the nurse. Option #3 is not standard.

2.43

> ③ Assist client in the knee-chest position and administer oxygen. *The priority nursing action is immediately relieve the pressure on the umbilical cord and increase the oxygenation that is being delivered to the fetus. In order to relieve the pressure, the mother should be positioned in the knee-chest, Trendelenburg, or modified Sim's. Another action that may need to be implemented is to insert sterile, gloved fingers into the vagina on either side of the cord and apply gentle manual pressure to relieve the pressure of the presenting part of the cord.*
>
> ① Notify the healthcare provider. *The second step would be to notify the healthcare provider of the emergency.*
>
> ④ Increase the current IV flow rate. *It is important to hydrate client in case there is a need for an emergency cesarean delivery or vaginal delivery.*
>
> ② Put sterile saline soaks loosely around the exposed cord. *The exposed cord should be kept moist, but the other options are a priority in order to reduce risk to the fetus.*

2.44 ③ Option #3 is correct. A full bladder may alter the location of the fundus of the uterus to the right or left of the abdomen. Option #1 is incorrect, since nursing interventions should be implemented prior to reaching out to the healthcare provider. Option #2 is incorrect. This will not alter the position of the uterus. Option #4 is incorrect, since the client should be able to void without any invasive procedures.

2.45 ② Options #2, #3, #4, and #5 are correct.
③ Undesirable effects of oxytocin in the mother
④ include hypertension, tachycardia, and fluid
⑤ excess. Undesirable effects of oxytocin with the fetus include late decelerations, decrease in variability, and changes in the fetal heart rate. Option #1 is incorrect, since this is within the defined limits for the mother's heart rate.

2.46 ④ Options #4 and #5 are correct. Option #4
⑤ is indicative the fetus has passed meconium while still in utero and may result in fetal distress. Option #5 may indicate a prolapsed cord requiring further evaluation and/or intervention such as position changes and/or an emergency delivery. Option #1 does not require further evaluation, since the FHR is within desired limits and increase in variability indicates oxygenation. Option #2 does not require further evaluation, since these decelerations indicate head compression and do not indicate a complication. Option #3 is an expected finding.

2.47 ③ Options #3 and #5 are correct. The diaper
⑤ should be placed under the cord to prevent from getting contaminated with urine and allow the cord to air-dry. Option #5 is correct, since the cord should be cleaned several times a day using a cotton swab with alcohol. Option #1 is incorrect. The newborn should be bathed with a sponge bath to prevent infection. Tub baths are not recommended until the circumcision is healed. Option #2 is incorrect because this is a normal assessment for a newborn. Option #4 is not the standard of care for cord care. Antibiotic ointments are typically only used if there are signs of an infection.

2.48 ④ Options #4 and #5 are correct. Positive
⑤ symptoms for schizophrenia include alterations in speech, delusions, and hallucinations. Options #1, #2, and #3 are negative symptoms. Affect, alogia, avolition, anhedonia, and anergia represent the negative symptoms of schizophrenia.

2.49 Place in chronological order the steps for starting an IV.

② Cleanse site thoroughly; re-cleanse if area is palpated prior to insertion.

⑤ Apply the tourniquet 4 to 6 inches above the site.

④ Apply gloves. *(Standard Precautions)*

③ Insert needle with bevel up at 15-degree to 30-degree angle. *(After there is a good blood return, release the tourniquet.)*

① Release tourniquet.

⑥ Cover the insertion site with a transparent dressing. *(Do not place tape directly over the insertion site. A sterile gauze may be applied if not using the transparent dressing. Then always label the site with time, date, catheter/needle size and initials of the nurse. Label the infusion container with time it was hung; rate of infusion; any medications added. Do not encircle the arm with tape; this can restrict circulation to the extremity.)*

2.50 The answer is <u>4</u> units/hour.

Step 1: Determine the number of units in each milliliter of fluid.

$$\frac{40 \text{ units}}{100 \text{ mL}} = 0.4 \text{ unit/mL}$$

Step 2: Multiply the units per milliliter by the rate of milliliters per hour.

0.4 unit x 10 mL/hour = <u>4</u> units

2.51

④ Verify the client has signed the informed consent.

① Review blood coagulation study results and make certain on the chart. *(Physician needs to make certain client will not have any complications with the procedure bleeding due to altered studies. Liver is a very vascular organ.)*

⑤ Instruct client to take a deep breath, exhale completely, and hold breath. *(This should be done immediately before needle insertion. This will immobilize the chest wall and decrease the risk for penetration of the diaphragm with the needle.)*

② Position client on bed rest for 12 to 14 hours and on right side for 2 hours. *(This will apply pressure and decrease risk for bleeding.)*

③ Assess for right upper abdominal pain or referred should pain; observe for tachycardia, hypotension. *(These are assessments for complications following the procedure. Other complications may include pneumothorax; development of bile peritonitis.)*

2.52

③ Wash hands.

⑤ Shake the inhaler.

④ Hold breath for 5 to 10 seconds and then exhale.

② Activate the MDI when inhaling.

① Breathe out through the nose.

2.53

④ An older adult client who is presenting with a new onset of incontinence and does not seem to be as oriented as yesterday. *(The older client with a new onset of incontinence and acute confusion is the most acutely ill client out of these four and need immediate attention.)*

③ A middle-aged client with pneumonia who has been on antibiotics for 24 hours and needs pain medicine to assist with coughing and deep breathing. *(Assessment needs to be made to determine how client is progressing with coughing and deep breathing and to assess characteristics of the pain.)*

② A young adult client with asthma who has a scheduled dose of a steroid inhaler to be administered. *(Next priority due to the need to administer the scheduled dose of steroid inhaler as close to the schedule as possible.)*

① A middle-aged client who is presenting with COPD and is sleeping up in a chair at night. *(Last priority due to this is an expected behavior due to the chronic condition of COPD.)*

2.54 ③ Options #3 and #4 are correct. During the
④ post-procedure period following a kidney transplant, it is important to assess vital signs for fluid overload such as weight increase, hypertension, tachycardia; signs of infection such as fever, dyspnea, incisional drainage and redness. Option #1 is incorrect. This is an expected finding for the first few days. Option #2 is incorrect. If there was an immediate complication, it would be hypertension. Option #5 is incorrect since a complication would result in hyperkalemia.

I CAN HINT: The focus of care is on the recipient of a kidney transplant. "RIPE" will assist you in organizing the clinical findings for recipient clients during the postoperative care for a kidney transplant.

Rejection—can occur within days; 3 months is most common time, but can be as last as 2 years; ↑ WBCs, ↑ fever; ↑ serum creatinine and BUN levels, ↑ BP; tenderness over graft site—early sign along with malaise.

Infection—shaking, chills, fever, tachycardia, leukocytosis, and tachypnea.

Psychological needs—Fear of rejection.

Electrolytes and fluid status.

Evaluate to analyze renal graft function.

2.55 ② Options #2 and #3 are correct. Delirium is
③ an acute that is typically secondary to another physiologic process. Options #1, #4, and #5 are indicative of dementia which is more progressive.

I CAN HINT: The bottom line is that "Delirium" is acute and reversible. "Dementia" slowly progresses and is irreversible.

2.56 ④ Options #4 and #5 are correct. Option #1 is
⑤ incorrect; Insulin glargine (Lantus) is a long-acting insulin with a constant concentration over 24 hours and with no pronounced peak. Option #2 is incorrect; Insulin glargine (Lantus) should not be mixed with any insulin and do not administer IV. Option #3 is incorrect, since there are no pronounced peak times.

2.57 ① Options #1, #2, and #5 are correct. Option #1
② is correct. Levothyroxine should be taken on
⑤ an empty stomach before breakfast. Option #2 is correct. Do not change brands since they are not bioequivalent. Option #5 is important to report since this may indicate they are receiving too much of the medication. Option #3 is incorrect since this may indicate too much of the medication. This rapid weight loss is not an expected outcome. Option #4 is incorrect due to the HR identified in the option. The medication should be held if HR is > 100 bpm. The client does need to learn how to take the HR, but the second part of the statement is incorrect. The entire option must be correct for the answer to be right.

2.58 ② Options #2 and #3 are correct. A sore throat
③ and fever may be signs of agranulocytosis,
an undesirable effect from this medication.
Option #1 is an expected finding due to the
anticholinergic effects with this medication,
but does not need further evaluation. Option
#4 may also be an expected finding and does
not need further evaluation. Option #5 is a
result of the orthostatic hypotension that may
occur with this medication. This is a concern,
but due to rising quickly does not mandate
further evaluation by the healthcare provider.
*This can happen to us with no medication if we
rise too quickly.*

2.59 ① Options #1, #4, and #5 are correct. Option #1
④ is important due to the risk for hypertension
⑤ with the corticosteroid. Option #4 is
important due to the risk for developing
hyperglycemia. Option #5 is important due to
the risk of hypocalcemia resulting in fractures
if client was to fall. Option #2 is incorrect
because the client should eat these foods due to
the risk of developing hypokalemia. Option #3
is incorrect because with the risk of the sodium
being elevated, the client should not use salt.

2.60 ① Options #1 and #4 are correct. Option #2
④ is incorrect since this is coordinated with
inspiration. Option #3 is incorrect, since the
inhaler should be shaken up prior to use to
provide an adequate amount of inhalation
medication. Option #5 is incorrect. Albuterol
(Proventil) is used for short-term relief of acute
reversible airway problems. This is not used on
a continuous basis in absence of symptoms.

Notes

There are no secrets to success. It is the result of preparation, hard work, and learning from failure.
– Colin Powell

The Pretest

✔ About this test …

This 60-item test will help you begin to pinpoint your study needs.

FOR BEST RESULTS:

☞ Complete the entire Pretest. Do NOT look in the back of the book for the answers until you have completed the exam.

☞ Spend a few minutes analyzing the questions you have missed. Use the test worksheet and Category Analysis to help determine your study needs. Once you determine your weak area(s), spend the next hour studying this content using a good review book as a guide.

REMEMBER THAT MISTAKES ARE A WAY OF GROWING— BE GENTLE WITH YOURSELF!

"The reason that angels can fly is that they take themselves so lightly."
—G. K. Chesterson

These activities are taken from the National Council of State Boards of Nursing, Inc. 2014. *2015 RN Practice Analysis: Linking the NCLEX-RN® Examination to Practice.*

TOMORROW—

☞ Skip to the chapter in this book that evaluates questions in the area(s) of your biggest identified weaknesses—we like to think of these as areas for growth!

☞ Take the test from this chapter and note the questions that you missed. Spend the next hour studying this content. ETC! ETC! ETC!

As NIKE says, "Just do it!"
You are the only one who can pinpoint your own study needs.
This is an excellent way to begin.

3.1 What is the priority of care for an elderly client who has an order for metformin?

① Discuss the importance of taking metformin with digoxin.
② Evaluate the HbA1c prior to administering the order.
③ Monitor AST and ALT while taking metformin.
④ Notify the provider of care and question the appropriateness of this order.

3.2 Which one of these clinical findings indicates a potential complication of pneumonia for an elderly client in a long-term care facility?

① Difficulty breathing and complaints of a headache.
② Difficulty with anorexia along with new behavioral problems.
③ Fever and muscle aches.
④ Nonproductive cough and chest pain.

3.3 Which statement made by the client indicates an understanding of how to use a metered-dose inhaler?

① "I will exhale immediately after inhaling the medication."
② "I will take my respiratory rate for 60 seconds after the medication."
③ "I will wait 2 minutes before taking the second dose of medication."
④ "I will pull the top of the medication canister while I take a deep breath."

3.4 What is the priority plan of care for an elderly client admitted to the medical unit with poor capillary refill, lethargy, and urinary incontinence?

① Document characteristics of lips, mucous membranes, and skin turgor.
② Evaluate client for skin breakdown.
③ Initiate active range of motion per hospital protocol.
④ Monitor intake and output.

3.5 Which one of these nursing instructions from the licensed practical nurse (LPN) requires further intervention for a client with an arterial ulcer of the left lower extremity from peripheral arterial disease (PAD)?

① Instruct client to keep legs elevated as much as possible.
② Discuss the importance of not crossing legs.
③ Review the importance of quitting smoking.
④ Teach the importance of stopping activity when pain in the calf occurs and start again when pain has subsided.

3.6 What is the priority of care for an older client who has chronic atrial fibrillation and has been on bed rest for 3 days in the ICU and presents with a RR—36/min; HR—120 bpm; diaphoresis; SaO_2—82%, crackles in bilateral lower lung fields, chest pain, and congestive cough?

① Position in high-Fowler's.
② Position with head of bed flat with legs elevated.
③ Position on the left Sims' position with knees flexed.
④ Position in the supine position.

3.7 What is the priority of care for a young child who is admitted to the Pediatric Unit with numerous bruises, fractured left humerus and several lacerations of unexplained origin?

① Report the findings to the Child Protection Agency.
② Share this information only with other healthcare professionals.
③ Document this information in the chart only.
④ Share the information with the Pediatric Social Worker.

3.8 What is the priority plan for two staff members who are in an argument regarding the interpretation of a standard of care?

① Report the incident to the manager due to unprofessional behavior.
② Send both staff members to an educational program to clarify the standard of care.
③ Review appropriate communication strategies with each staff member.
④ Assess the understanding of the issue of conflict; maintaining positive regard for each person.

3.9 Which statement made by the nurse indicates an understanding of cost effectiveness for a postpartum client requesting peripads, diapers, tucks, and Americaine spray prior to discharge?

① "I will be glad to get these supplies for you."
② "It would be much better if you would just stop and pick them up on your way home."
③ "I will be happy to get them for you and pull some extras for you to take home."
④ "What items do you need until you leave to go home?"

3.10 In a seven-month-old infant, which is the best way to detect fluid retention?

① Weigh the child daily.
② Test the urine for hematuria.
③ Measure abdominal girth weekly.
④ Count the number of wet diapers.

3.11 Which nursing approach would be most appropriate for obtaining a specimen from a retention catheter?

① Disconnect the drain at the bottom of the draining bag and drain urine into a sterile container.
② Disconnect the tubing between the catheter and the drainage bag and drain urine into sterile container.
③ Clamp the drainage tube. When fresh urine collects, open the tubing and drain into a sterile container.
④ Use a sterile syringe and needle to obtain urine from the porthole.

3.12 Which one of these documentations indicates the nurse has an understanding of the priority of care for a young child admitted with the diagnosis of Kawasaki disease?

① Positioned on the right side with the head of the bed elevated.
② Applied lotion to decrease skin discomfort.
③ Monitored intake and output hourly.
④ Instructed UAP to encourage child to drink Gatorade q 2–3 hours to replace electrolytes.

3.13 What statement indicates the client understands the collection of urine specimen for culture and sensitivity?

① "I will call the lab before I collect my urine."
② "I will drink several glasses of water before the urine is collected."
③ "I will call the nurse to help me with aseptic technique."
④ "I will discard my first voiding in the morning."

3.14 Which nursing observation would most likely indicate an early side effect of the elderly client taking digoxin?

① Confusion
② Bradycardia
③ Constipation
④ Hyperkalemia

3.15 Which assessment of the lungs by auscultation would the nurse expect to evaluate if a client has a left lower lobe consolidation?

① Absent breath sounds
② Bronchophony
③ Vesicular breath sounds
④ Wheezes

3.16 Which of these undesirable effects should the nurse teach a client who is being discharged on diphenhydramine for allergic rhinitis? **Select all that apply.**

① Diarrhea
② Dry mouth
③ Nonproductive cough
④ Rash
⑤ Urinary retention

3.17 Which neonatal assessment finding should the nurse report to the healthcare provider 1 hour after delivery?

① A caput succedaneum that crosses the suture lines.
② A resting heart rate of 140 and a respiratory rate of 40.
③ Head circumference—34 cm.
  Chest circumference—30 cm.
④ The umbilical cord has 2 arteries and 1 vein.

3.18 Which assessment indicates a neonate with an infection is not fully recovered?

① Heart rate of 150.
② Axillary temperature of 98.6°F (37°C).
③ Weight increase of 4 oz. (0.11 kg).
④ Resting respiratory rate of 65.

3.19 Which of these documentations regarding restraints made by the LPN would need immediate intervention by the charge nurse?

① Restraints applied from an order that was written 48 hours ago.
② Restraints removed 1 hour ago and client allowed to exercise one hand at a time.
③ Bilateral radial pulses strong with sensation and movement in both hands.
④ Client cooperating with procedure and asking about the length of time for wearing restraints.

3.20 A client with a pneumothorax has a chest tube connected to a water-seal chest tube drainage system in place. Identify the chamber by placing an X where continuous bubbling should occur.

3.21 A client has had profuse vomiting for 6 hours. Arterial blood gases note a pH—7.50; $PaCO_2$—40 mm Hg; and HCO_3—40mEq/L (40 mmol/L). Which additional physical assessment finding would be most important for the nurse to report?

① Muscular twitching
② Kussmaul's respirations
③ Anuria
④ Irregular pulse

3.22 A client has a history of oliguria, hypertension, and peripheral edema. Current lab values include BUN—25 mg/dL (1.4 mmol/L); K—5.0 mEq/L (5.0 mmol/L). Which nutrients should be restricted in this client's diet?

① Protein
② Fats
③ Carbohydrates
④ Magnesium

3.23 An older client with diabetes is being managed with insulin in the AM and PM. Which observation is the best for indicating the overall therapeutic response to the management?

① Glycosylated hemoglobin (HgbAlc) is 6%
② Fasting blood sugar 128 mg/dL (7.1 mmol/L)
③ Blood pressure is maintained at 130/82
④ Serum amylase is normal

3.24 Which assessment finding would indicate an increase in the intracranial pressure in a four-month-old infant?

① A positive Babinski
② High-pitched cry
③ Bulging posterior fontanel
④ Pinpoint pupils

3.25 Which action demonstrates an understanding of how to manage confidential information?

① Discuss this information with all of the nurse's colleagues.
② Document the information only on the client's flow sheet.
③ Review the information with those staff involved in the plan of care.
④ Share the information with nobody.

3.26 Which client should be assessed first after shift report?

① A client who had a lobectomy 24 hours ago with a chest tube inserted.

② A postoperative larnygectomy client.

③ A client with headaches of unknown origin.

④ A client who is in Buck's traction.

3.27 Which clinical finding would require the next dose of procainamide to be held?

① Premature ventricular contractions.

② Occurrence of severe hypotension.

③ Recurring paroxysmal atrial tachycardia.

④ A sedimentation rate of 10.

3.28 Which of these clients would be the highest risk for acquiring pneumonia during hospitalization?

① A postoperative client who is ambulating.

② An infant in Bryant's traction who is frequently crying and screaming.

③ A school-age child with diabetes mellitus.

④ An immobile client with a spinal cord injury.

3.29 A hospitalized client has been vomiting for three days with a low-grade temperature, and feels lethargic. Which nursing action is most appropriate in evaluating for fluid volume deficit?

① Obtain a urinalysis for casts and specific gravity.

② Determine client's weight and assess gain or loss.

③ Ask client to provide a 24-hour intake and output record.

④ Determine the quality of the skin turgor.

3.30 A client is placed on bed rest with an order to immobilize the right leg due to tenderness, increased warmth, and diffuse swelling. Which nursing action is most appropriate to maintain skin integrity?

① Apply a trapeze to client's bed.

② Assess bony prominence every 12 hours.

③ Apply granular spray to the bony prominence.

④ Turn client every 2 hours.

3.31 During the first 24 hours after a below-the-knee amputation, which nursing action would be most important?

① Notify the healthcare provider for a small amount of serosanguineous drainage.

② Elevate the stump on a pillow to decrease edema.

③ Maintain the stump flat on the bed by placing the client in the prone position.

④ Do passive range of motion TID to the unaffected leg.

3.32 Which measure should the nurse take in reducing the discomfort of gas pains in a one-day post-op client?

① Encourage a diet high in fiber.

② Assist with early ambulation.

③ Teach how to splint the abdomen with activity.

④ Position on right side.

3.33 What is the priority teaching for the mother of a school-age child with a piece of glass imbedded in the eye?

① "Put a loose eye patch over both eyes and have the child taken to an emergency room immediately."

② "Place pressure dressing to the injured eye and have the child taken to an emergency room."

③ "Remove the broken glass immediately from the eye to reduce the possibility of further trauma and apply Vaseline on the eyelid."

④ "Irrigate the injured eye with warm normal saline and apply a dressing to the eye."

3.34 What information would be priority for the LPN to report to the RN regarding a client who is 1 day postoperative for an appendectomy and is receiving hydromorphone?

① Client is requesting the pillow to assist with splinting when coughing.

② Client is slow to get out of bed due to being dizzy with quick movements.

③ Client's urine output was 270 mLs for an 8 hour shift from 400 mL's from previous 8 hour shift.

④ Client has hypoactive bowel sounds.

3.35 In which position would a nurse place a client who is in respiratory distress, extremely anxious, edematous, and cyanotic?

① Lithotomy position

② Low-Fowler's position

③ Sim's position

④ High-Fowler's position

3.36 A client has just been intubated in preparation for mechanical ventilation. What would be the first action to evaluate the effectiveness of the intervention?

① Assess lung sounds.
② Call for a stat chest x-ray.
③ Call for stat arterial blood gasses.
④ Suction the endotracheal tube.

3.37 A client has been complaining of sharp pain in the epigastric area and has an order for an antacid. Which statement made by the client indicates a correct understanding of when to take the antacid?

① "It is important to only take my medicine prior to bedtime."
② "By taking the medication before meals, I will decrease the side effects."
③ "I will take the medication one hour after meals."
④ "As I start to feel uncomfortable, I will take the medication."

3.38 The client needs an infusion of IV fluid at 40mL/hr. If the tubing set is calibrated at 15 gtt/mL, what is the drip rate?

Answer: _____ gtts/min

3.39 Which selection indicates compliance for a client with cardiac disease?

① Baked chicken, green vegetables, and fresh fruit
② Hot dog, cup of canned soup, and lettuce salad
③ Baked fish, baked apples, and avocado salad
④ Baked ham, rice, and fruit cup

3.40 An RN assigns the care of a new post-operative mastectomy client to an LPN. At the time of the assignment, the RN reminds the LPN not to take the blood pressure on the operative side. Later in the shift, the RN discovers the blood pressure cuff deflated, but still on the arm of the client's affected side. How should the RN handle the situation?

① Make a note to talk with the LPN in private after the shift is over.
② Call the LPN in for counseling to determine why directions were not followed.

③ Find the LPN and review the importance of not taking the blood pressure on the affected side.
④ Write up a report regarding the incident and place it in the LPN's personnel folder.

3.41 The staff nurse of an acute pulmonary unit is preparing notes that will be necessary for a shift report on assigned clients. What information is critical to communicate in a shift report on this unit?

① Laboratory work drawn on the client, arterial blood gas reports, nutritional intake, and vital signs for the shift.
② Any respiratory difficulty client experienced, tolerance to activity, sputum production, and significant variances in vital signs during the shift.
③ Name of the client's provider of care, date client was admitted, dietary intake and client's general condition.
④ Urinary output, PO and IV fluid intake, visits by attending provider of care, vital signs each time evaluated, any respiratory problems encountered.

3.42 An LPN is securing a Foley catheter on a female client. As the nurse walks in the room, the Foley drops on the floor. Which action would be the highest priority?

① Review aseptic technique with the LPN.
② Complete an incident report.
③ Get a new Foley catheter and assist LPN with the procedure.
④ Report the incident in the continuous quality improvement (CQI) report.

3.43 A provider has ordered timolol 1 gtt to both eyes bid. Point to the location of the eye where the medication will be placed.

3.44 An elderly client is admitted to an inpatient psychiatric unit with an initial diagnosis of psychotic depression. What would be the priority nursing plan?

① Clarify perceptual distortions.
② Establish reality orientation.
③ Ensure client and milieu safety.
④ Increase self-esteem.

3.45 A client in an assisted living facility asks the nurse to sign as a witness for an advanced directive. What is the best intervention by the nurse?

① Notify the provider of care that the client needs a witness for the advanced directive.
② Politely decline the request by the client.
③ Sign the advanced directive as a witness.
④ Work with the client to find someone who is an unrelated third party.

3.46 A client diagnosed with a lower GI bleed has an order for 1 unit of packed red blood cells. What information is most important to be documented during this procedure?

① Vital signs prior to procedure
② Confirmation that the nurse alone verified the blood label information
③ The total volume that is to be infused
④ Vital signs before, during, and after procedure, date and time started and completed

3.47 Which of these clients should be seen immediately after report?

① A client who is 10 hours postpartum and presents with fundus midline and 1 cm above the umbilicus.
② A client who is 18 hours postpartum with a T—100.1°F (37.8°C), and has lochia rubra as a discharge.
③ A client who is 30 hours postpartum with a T—101.2°F (38.4°C), and has dark vaginal drainage.
④ A client who is 48 hours postpartum and is awakened during the night several times to urinate and noted that gown and bedding were wet from profuse diaphoresis.

3.48 What would be the plan of care for a client who has a blood sugar of 200 mg/dL (11 mmol/L) at 7:00 AM?

① Increase the PM dose of NPH insulin.

② Increase the AM dose of regular insulin.
③ Have the client wake up at 3:00 AM and evaluate the blood sugar.
④ Decrease the PM dose of NPH insulin.

3.49 Which nursing action represents the best technique to set up a sterile field?

① Place all supplies as close to the edge as possible.
② Wear gown and gloves at all times.
③ Set up the field above waist level.
④ Open supplies with sterile gloves.

3.50 During the shift report, a client's ventilator alarm is activated. Which action would the nurse implement first?

① Notify the respiratory therapist.
② Check the ventilator tubing for excess fluid.
③ Deactivate the alarm and check the spirometer.
④ Assess the client for adequate oxygenation.

3.51 What nursing intervention should be implemented within an hour prior to surgery?

① Administer an enema.
② Verify that the signed consent form is on chart.
③ Perform preoperative shave and scrub.
④ Evaluate for food or medication allergies.

3.52 What would be the priority assessment for a client who is taking a sulfonylurea and prednisone?

① Monitor hemoglobin.
② Monitor platelets.
③ Monitor photosensitivity.
④ Monitor serum glucose.

3.53 Which response by the client indicates an understanding of how to collect a 24-hour urine specimen?

① "I will discard the first morning voided specimen, and then collect the urine for 24 hours into one container."
② "I will start collecting all of the urine into one container after 8:00 AM and continue until 8:00 PM tonight."
③ "I will place urine specimens in a separate container."
④ "I will notify the nurse so a call can be made to the lab to start this test."

3.54 Which fluid would be the most appropriate for a client receiving furosemide and digoxin?

① Milk
② Gatorade
③ Orange juice
④ Water

3.55 One hour after a bronchoscopy is completed on a client, which nursing observation would indicate a complication?

① Depressed gag reflex
② Sputum streaked with blood
③ Tachypnea
④ Widening pulse pressure

3.56 Which instruction would be included in the teaching plan for a client on oral steroids regarding when and how the medication should be taken?

① With 8 oz. (237 ml) of orange juice once each morning.
② With meals.
③ Between meals.
④ On an empty stomach.

3.57 An older adult client begins choking while eating dinner. Organize the steps in chronological order when performing the Heimlich maneuver. **All options must be used.**

① Thrust upward 6-10 times.
② Position nurse's thumb toward client, above the waist and below the rib cage wrapping one arm around the client.
③ Assess by asking client if he is choking.
④ Position self behind client.
⑤ Form a fist with one hand.
⑥ Other arm should be wrapped around the client placing that hand on top of the nurse's fist.

3.58 The nurse is assessing the emotional support available to an adolescent client who is starving herself. Which question would be most important for the nurse to ask in the assessment interview?

① "What do you consider your ideal weight?"
② "How does your eating habit change when you are around other people?"
③ "What happens at home when you express opinions that are different from those of your parents?"
④ "What do you think about your present weight?"

3.59 Which symptoms might alert the nurse to an alcohol problem in a client hospitalized for a physical illness?

① Depression, difficulty falling asleep, decreased concentration.
② Elevated liver enzymes, cirrhosis, decreased platelets.
③ Tremors, elevated temperature, complaints of nocturnal leg cramps, complaints of pain symptoms.
④ Flu-like symptoms, diarrhea, night sweats, elevated temperature, decreased deep tendon reflexes.

3.60 An 87-year-old client with terminal cancer requests that the nurse give him a second dose of Morphine, so he "can get it over with." What is the nurse's next action?

① Give the client Morphine to help the client out of misery.
② Call the provider of care for an order for the extra dose.
③ Ask the client to read their Living Will document before the nurse makes a decision.
④ Gently refuse as this is beyond the nurse's scope of practice.

Category Analysis – Pretest

1. Pharmacology	21. Physiological Adaptation	41. Management of Care
2. Reduction of Risk Potential	22. Basic Care and Comfort	42. Safety and Infection Control
3. Pharmacology	23. Pharmacology	43. Pharmacology
4. Physiological Adaptation	24. Reduction of Risk Potential	44. Psychosocial
5. Basic Care and Comfort	25. Management of Care	45. Psychosocial
6. Reduction of Risk Potential	26. Management of Care	46. Basic Care and Comfort
7. Management of Care	27. Pharmacology	47. Health Promotion
8. Management of Care	28. Health Promotion	48. Basic Care and Comfort
9. Management of Care	29. Physiological Adaptation	49. Safety and Infection Control
10. Physiological Adaptation	30. Safety and Infection Control	50. Physiological Adaptation
11. Basic Care and Comfort	31. Reduction of Risk Potential	51. Basic Care and Comfort
12. Basic Care and Comfort	32. Basic Care and Comfort	52. Pharmacology
13. Basic Care and Comfort	33. Reduction of Risk Potential	53. Basic Care and Comfort
14. Pharmacology	34. Pharmacology	54. Pharmacology
15. Physiological Adaptation	35. Physiological Adaptation	55. Physiological Adaptation
16. Pharmacology	36. Physiological Adaptation	56. Pharmacology
17. Health Promotion	37. Pharmacology	57. Reduction of Risk Potential
18. Health Promotion	38. Pharmacology	58. Psychosocial
19. Management of Care	39. Basic Care and Comfort	59. Psychosocial
20. Physiological Adaptation	40. Management of Care	60. Management of Care

Directions

1. Determine questions missed by checking answers.
2. Write the number of the questions missed across the top line marked "item missed."
3. Check category analysis page to determine category of question.
4. Put a check mark under item missed and beside content.
5. Count check marks in each row and write the number in totals column.
6. Use this information to:
   - identify areas for further study.
   - determine which content test to take next.

We recommend studying content where most items are missed—then taking that content test.

Number of the Questions Incorrectly Answered

Pretest	Items Missed																													Totals
C Management of Care																														
O Safety and Infection Control																														
N Health Promotion and Maintenance																														
T Psychosocial Integrity																														
E Physiological Adaptation:Fluid Gas																														
N Reduction of Risk Potential																														
T Basic Care and Comfort																														
Pharmacology and Parenteral Therapies																														

Answers & Rationales

3.1 ④ Option #4 is correct. As a client ages the kidney perfusion decreases. Metformin may result in a major complication with lactic acidosis. This should not be routinely administered to the geriatric client due to potential renal complications. **I CAN HINT:** The *"6 P's of Geriatrics" (Polypharmacy, Poor infiltration of the liver, Poor absorption of the intestine, Poor kidney perfusion, Protein poor, Pain has a blunted response)* will help organize facts. Renal function declines with age, along with a lot of other systems! The result is that many medications may lead to renal toxicity. This is the reason so many drug-drug interactions and undesirable effects with renal toxicity occur with the elderly client. This strategy will assist you in answering many of these type of questions related to the geriatric client. Option #1 is incorrect. If digoxin is taken with metformin, then digoxin may increase metformin concentrations. Option #2 does need to be monitored, but with the age of the client and the potential risk with lactic acidosis, Option #4 is still a priority. HbA1c was most likely elevated for metformin to be ordered. It does need to be monitored while client is taking the medication. Option # 3 is incorrect. For this option to be correct, it would need to read *"monitor renal function tests."* This medication is eliminated almost entirely unchanged by the kidneys.

3.2 ② Option #2 is the correct answer. Elderly clients who have a complication of pneumonia typically present with some behavioral problems or changes along with appetite changes. Typically, elderly clients have a blunted response to pain. Options #1, #3 and #4 address pain and discomfort. Refer to the *"6 P's of Geriatrics"* in the rationale for question #1 to assist you in answering future questions regarding the elderly client. Questions do evaluate the NCLEX® Activity, *"Provide care and education for adults over 85 years of age."*

3.3 ③ Option #3 is correct. The client should wait for 2 minutes prior to taking the second dose of medication. Option #1 is incorrect. The client should hold the breath as long as possible and then exhale through pursed lips. Option #2 is incorrect because pulse rate versus the respiratory rate should be monitored, since the medication may result in tachycardia. The key in this option is that it reads 60 seconds. The rate of the RR is important; however, it is important to assess the breath sounds to evaluate the effectiveness. Option #4 is not the correct procedure. The client should push the top of the medication canister while taking a deep breath.

3.4 ② Option #2 would be the priority of care for this client since the elderly client already has very thin skin, and it is fragile without all of these other complications. The poor capillary refill may be a result of decrease oxygen. This can result in a decrease in oxygenation to the skin which may lead to skin breakdown. Skin care becomes very important to prevent complications from skin breakdown. Ongoing evaluation is of paramount importance! With the complication of lethargy, the client may not move a lot in bed or in the chair. The urinary incontinence presents a major complication with risk for breakdown, since the client may be too lethargic to realize the skin is wet which precipitates an increase in this process for skin breakdown. Option #1 is incorrect in this clinical situation. The characteristics of the lips, mucous membranes, and skin turgor do not address the clinical presentation for this client. Even if it did, the normal physical changes that occur with the aging process and the elasticity of the skin changing make the assessment of the skin turgor less effective for evaluating the hydration status. Option #3 is important, but since the client is lethargic this would not be an appropriate plan of care due to client safety. Option #4 is an important intervention; however, it does not address the complete clinical presentation with this client. **I CAN HINT: "SKIN"** will assist you in recalling priorities for skin care for the elderly client. Skin—maintain clean, dry skin and wrinkle-free linens. Know the importance of repositioning client in bed at least q 2 hr and every 1 hr when sitting in chair; know to maintain HOB at or below 30-degree angle unless contraindicated, to relieve pressure on sacrum, buttocks, and heels. Intake (hydration)—2,000 to 3,000 mL/day. Nutrition—meet protein and calorie needs. If serum albumin levels are <3.5 g/dL (35g/L), this puts client at a high risk for skin breakdown and may result in a decrease in healing and risk for infection. Provide nutritional support such as vitamin and mineral supplements, nutritional supplements, enteral nutrition, and parenteral nutrition.

3.5 ① Option #1 is the correct answer since the nurse would need to intervene because this is not the Standard of Practice for this condition. Elevating legs would be appropriate for venous insufficiency. The other options are appropriate for PAD.

I CAN HINT: A good way to remember arterial insufficiency is to remember the "5 P's": pallor, pulse, pain, paresthesia, and paralysis. In comparison to "VENOUS" insufficiency which is: Varicose veins may be visible. Edema may be present in lower legs. No temperature decrease; actual extremity may be warm to touch if there is a blood clot. Often the ulcer may be painful. Ulcers may be present. Skin color—"brawny" leathery in appearance to skin of the lower extremities. Remember the physiology will also assist you on future concepts between arterial and venous insufficiency: "Arterial" is taking blood AWAY from the heart; Veins "Venous" is bringing blood back "TO" the heart. So in other words, the venous is more like pooling of blood in the lower extremities and not getting back to the heart. Arterial is having problems getting blood from the heart, so the extremities become pale, weak pulses, cool to touch, etc. Now, see how easy the positioning is! If blood cannot get down to the extremities as in "peripheral arterial disease" then dangle the legs. If blood cannot get back to the heart from the extremities, then elevate them.

3.6 ① The question focuses on tachypnea, tachycardia, and a drop in the oxygen saturation. Even if you do not know the medical problem, you know this concept is about hypoxia. You also know that in the stem of the question, the client has chronic atrial fibrillation and has been on bed rest for three days which puts the client in the high risk category for developing a pulmonary emboli. The client is presenting with a, life-threatening hypoxic condition caused by a collection of particulate matter that enters the venous circulation and lodges in the pulmonary vessels resulting in an obstruction in the pulmonary blood flow. Clients high risk for pulmonary emboli include: long term immobility, oral contraceptive use and estrogen therapy, pregnancy, tobacco use, hypercoagulability, obesity, orthopedic surgery of the lower extremities or pelvis, heart failure or chronic atrial fibrillation, long bone fractures, etc. The clinical assessment findings for a pulmonary embolism may include: tachypnea, tachycardia, diaphoresis, decreased in the SaO_2, crackles and cough and pleurisy. Position client in the high Fowler's in order to facilitate oxygen exchange. Option #2 would be appropriate if client was in shock from hypovolemia. Option #3 is inaccurate for this client. This position would be appropriate if client was going to get an enema or was unconscious. Option #4 would be for a client who had a spinal cord injury.

3.7 ① Any suspicion of child abuse should be reported to the Child Protection Agency. Options #2, #3, and #4 do not provide nor plan for protection of the child.

3.8 ④ Option #4 is correct. The priority plan for the nurse manager is to determine the source of conflict, recognize the issues that have developed, and progress through resolving the conflict. It is important to remain positive with both staff members. Option #1 is incorrect. It is important to review the conflict with the person or persons with whom there is a conflict prior to going to the superiors. The ultimate goal is to achieve a win-win solution for both staff members. Option #2 is incorrect. There needs to be an assessment made initially to determine the actual issue causing the conflict. Option #3 is not the priority over #4. Prior to any intervention, it is imperative for an assessment be made to have an understanding for the conflict.

3.9 ④ This option is the most diplomatic response and considers cost effectiveness. Many insurance companies view extra supplies on the day of discharge as stockpiling, and the client may be stuck with the bill. While some companies may still pay the entire bill as presented, many are becoming dollar-wise and view each bill with a critical eye. Options #1 and #3 do not consider cost effectiveness. Option #2 is an inappropriate response.

3.10 ① Fluid retention is best detected by weighing daily and noting a gaining trend. Options #2 and #3 are incorrect and will not provide information regarding fluid retention. Option #4 can provide an estimation of the amount of urine output but not about fluid retention.

3.11 ④ This represents the appropriate process in collecting a "sterile" urine specimen. Options #1 and #2 open a closed system which allows bacteria to be introduced. Option #3 is incorrect information.

3.12 ③ Option #3 is correct. Kawasaki's disease is the leading cause of heart disease in children. I&O are important assessments for any client with heart disease. Option #1 is incorrect. This would be more of a priority for a child with tracheoesophageal fistula (TEF). Option #2 is important but not a priority. Option #4 could lead to complications with heart disease due to fluid and sodium excess.

3.13 ③ Aseptic techniques decrease the possibility of contamination with organisms. Options #1, #2, and #4 are incorrect. Option #1 is incorrect; there is no need to call lab prior to collecting the specimen. Option #2 is not specific to this urine for culture and sensitivity. Option #4 would be appropriate if the client was collecting a 24-hour urinalysis.

3.14 ① The elderly are particularly prone to digoxin-induced confused states which can occur in the presence of subtoxic digoxin levels and without other signs of toxicity. Option #2 occurs as a late side effect. Options #3 and #4 are incorrect.

3.15 ② Option #2 is correct. Bronchophony may be auscultated with a consolidation. Option #1 would be present with a prolapsed lung. Option #3 would be auscultated over the majority of the lung fields. Option #4 would be auscultated with conditions such as asthma due to swollen alveoli.

3.16 ② Options #2 and #5 are correct. Dry mouth
⑤ and urinary retention are anticholinergic symptoms that may occur when taking this medication. Other anticholinergic symptoms may include visual disturbances, constipation, and orthostatic hypotension. Option #1 is incorrect since the undesirable effect would be constipation, not diarrhea. Option #3 is incorrect. Diphenhydramine (Benadryl) is occasionally prescribed to treat a nonproductive cough and also is prescribed for skin rash (Option #4) caused by allergies.

3.17 ③ Option #3 should be reported. The head circumference should be 2 cm larger than the chest circumference. 4 cm larger is not normal and requires further assessment. Options #1, #2, and #4 are normal clinical findings.

3.18 ④ The normal respiratory rate of a neonate is 30–50. Tachypnea is a sign of sepsis or hypoxia with a neonate. Option #1 is incorrect because it is within the normal range. Option #2 is not significant. Option #3 is incorrect. Neonates normally experience between a 5–10 percent loss of weight within the first few days of life.

3.19 ① Option #1 is correct. The LPN did not follow the standard of care for a client for the use of restraints. There should be an order written every 24 hours. Options #2, #3 and #4 do not require immediate intervention by the charge nurse, since these are consistent with safe care for clients using restraints.

3.20

3.21 ① Metabolic alkalosis results in neuromuscular excitability. Alkalosis causes calcium to bind with albumin making less available for contraction of smooth skeletal muscle leading to muscle cramps and twitching.

3.22 ① A decreased production of urea nitrogen can be achieved by restricting protein. These metabolic wastes cannot be excreted by the kidneys. Options #2 and #3 decrease the non-protein nitrogen production; therefore, these foods are encouraged. Option #4 is incorrect.

3.23 ① The glycosylated hemoglobin will indicate the overall glucose control for approximately the past 120 days. This allows evaluation of control of the blood sugar regardless of increases or decreases in blood sugar immediately prior to drawing the sample. Option #2 is not a priority to #1. Option #3 would be evaluating the response to an antihypertensive medication. Option #4 is evaluating for pancreatitis.

3.24 ② A high-pitched cry is one of the first signs of an increase in intracranial pressure in infants. Option #1 is normal for the first year of life. Option #3 is incorrect because the fontanel should be closed by the third month. Option #4 is incorrect because with increased pressure, the pupils may respond to light slowly rather than with the usual brisk response.

3.25 ③ This information must be respected and remain confidential. Under the Invasion of Privacy, it states that the client has the constitutional right to be free from publicity and exposure to public view. Option #4 does not benefit the client in any constructive way.

3.26 ② The maintenance of a patent airway for a post-operative larnygectomy client would be a priority. Options #1, #3, and #4 would not be a priority to a potential airway issue.

3.27 ② Option #2 is correct. Severe hypotension or bradycardia are signs of adverse reaction with this medication. Options #1 and #3 are not typically adverse effects from this medication. Option #4 is within the defined limits.

3.28 ④ Clients who are immobilized from a spinal cord injury are high risk for developing pneumonia. Options #1 and #2 are not high risk. A postoperative client who is ambulating and has no direct insult to the respiratory system is not high risk. The infant is in traction, but is frequently expanding the lungs with the crying. Option #3 is a concern, but not a priority to Option #4.

3.29 ② The daily weight is the best way to evaluate for fluid volume deficit. Options #1, #3, and #4 provide information regarding the fluid volume level, but are not the best actions for evaluation.

3.30 ④ Turning client at frequent intervals is one of the most effective methods of preventing the development of skin breakdown caused by pressure, friction, or shearing forces. Option #1 encourages independent moving, but does not relieve pressure. Option #2 is an incorrect standard of practice. Skin inspection should be carried out at least once every 8 hours. Option #3 does not offer any prevention.

3.31 ② Elevation after surgery will minimize edema and optimize venous return. This would not be done for more than 24 hours due to the potential development of a contracture. Option #1 is not correct because some bloody drainage is expected. The nurse should outline the drainage and assess again in 5 minutes. Options #3 and #4 contain incorrect information.

3.32 ② Ambulation increases the return of peristalsis and facilitates the expulsion of flatus. Option #1 should not be encouraged until the bowel sounds have returned. Option #3 does nothing to increase peristalsis, but may make the client more comfortable. Option #4 doesn't provide anything.

3.33 ① The objective is to minimize eye movement in order to prevent further injury. Options #2, #3, and #4 would lead to further injury.

3.34 ③ Option #3 is correct. Since an undesirable effect from hydromorphone (Dilaudid) may be urinary retention, this option is demonstrating a downward trend with the urine output over the last 8 hours. This clinical finding should be reported to the RN to alert the nurse for a need to do further assessments. Option #1 is an appropriate action for a client who is one day post-op. The client needs to cough and deep breathe in order to decrease the risk of developing alteration in gas exchange. There is no need for the LPN to report this finding. Option #2 is an appropriate behavior; there is no reason to report this to the RN. This is a safe action and will minimize the risk of being dizzy. Option #4 is an expected finding from the anesthesia, and does not need reporting at this time.

3.35 ④ This allows optimum pulmonary expansion. Sitting decreases the venous return to the heart which assists in lowering the ventricle's output and pulmonary congestion. Options #1, #2, and #3 do not enhance ventilation.

3.36 ① Option #1 helps establish if there is equal, bilateral lung expansion. Intubation of the right mainstem bronchus would cause decreased or absent sounds in the left lung. Option #2 is not the appropriate first action. Waiting for this result will cause a delay in adjusting tube placement. Option #3 will also cause a delay in adjusting tube placement. Option #4 is not diagnostic.

3.37 ③ Antacids are the most effective after digestion has started but prior to the emptying of the stomach. Option #1 will not be beneficial because they must be taken several times a day to be effective. Option #2 contains incorrect information. Option #4 is incorrect because antacids are used to prevent pain through protecting the gastric mucosa.

3.38 Answer: $\underline{10}$ gtts/min.
First convert 1 hour to 60 minutes to fit the formula.

Then set up a fraction. Place the volume of the infusion in the numerator. Place the number of minutes in which the volume is to be infused as the denominator.

$$\frac{40\text{mL}}{60 \text{ min}}$$

To determine X, or the number of drops per minute to be infused, multiply the fraction by the drip factor. Cancel units that appear in both the numerator and denominator.

$$X = \frac{40 \text{ mL}}{60 \text{ min.}} \times \frac{15 \text{ gtt}}{\text{mL}}$$

$$X = \frac{40 \times 15}{60 \text{ min.}}$$

$$X = \frac{60}{6} \qquad X = 10 \text{ gtts/min.}$$

On the NCLEX®, you may have a box for your answer. Put only the number in the box.

3.39 ① This option is low both in sodium and fat. Option #2 contains selections (hot dog and canned soup) high in sodium. Option #3 is incorrect due to the avocado salad which is high in fat. Option #4 includes baked ham which is high in sodium.

3.40 ③ The problem needs to be taken care of now. If the LPN continues to make mistakes in client care, then a counseling report should be done. An LPN is expected to understand the importance of this requested procedure. Options #1, #2, and #4 are not appropriate at this time.

3.41 ② This option lists critical information that is significant to the safety and quality of the client's care. Other items are important, but not a priority to #2.

3.42 ③ This indicates the action of a client advocate and dealing with the immediate situation. Option #1 would not be done in front of a client. Options #2 and #4 are not addressing the immediate problem.

3.43

3.44 ③ The The initial nursing priority for all psychiatric clients is to ensure their safety and the safety of all members of the milieu. Options #1, #2, and #4 are extremely important, but secondary to safety issues.

3.45 ④ An advanced directive needs to be witnessed by two individuals that are unrelated to the client. The two individuals will need to witness the client signing the advanced directive. Option #1, there is no reason to call the provider of care unless the client has any additional medical questions. Option #2 is not acting in the best interest of the client. Option #3, the nurse does not need to sign because it is considered a conflict of interest.

3.46 ④ Option #4 is correct. Option #1 is not as inclusive as #4. Option #2, blood should be verified with another nurse. Option #3 should be actual volume versus projected amount since the infusion may need to be discontinued prior to total amount being infused.

3.47 ③ Option #3 is correct. This client is presenting with infection. Options #1, #2, and #4 are expected findings. Option #1 is a correct finding. At approximately 12 hours, the fundus may be palpated at 1 cm above the umbilicus. Every 24 hrs the fundus should descend approximately 1 to 2 cm. By the sixth postpartum day, the fundus should be halfway between the symphysis pubis and the umbilicus. By the tenth day, the uterus should lie within the true pelvis and should not be palpable. Option #2 is also an expected finding. If temp, was above 101 and lochia rubra was brown or had a foul odor, then this would be a complication. Option #4 is also an expected finding. While it would be imperative for the nurse to go in and provide physical care due to the discomfort from the diaphoresis, it still would not be a priority over Option #3 which is a postpartum complication with infection.

3.48 ③ It is important to evaluate the 3:00 AM blood sugar to determine if the hyperglycemia is from the somoygi effect. Options #1 and #4 will be adjusted after knowing if the AM blood sugar is the accurate reading or a rebound response to a low blood sugar at 3:00 AM. Option #2 is incorrect.

3.49 ③ Sterile fields should be set up above the waist. Option #1 will not maintain sterility. Option #2 is incorrect because gowns are not always necessary. Option #4 is incorrect because supplies can be opened with bare hands, but touched inside the package with sterile gloves.

3.50 ④ The priority intervention is to assess the client's airway. Option #1 is done only if the nurse is unable to determine the problem. Option #2 would be appropriate after the client assessment. Option #3 contains inappropriate information. The alarm should not be deactivated or silenced.

3.51 ② The surgical consent should be verified that it is on the chart prior to going to surgery. Notice, it does not read that the consent needs to be signed or obtained. This should have already been done. In some clinical situations the consent has been signed, but for some reason does not get put on the chart. This is just going through the check offs to make certain the form is on the chart. OR will not accept the client without a signed consent. Options #1, #3, and #4 should be done prior to one hour before surgery. **I CAN HINT:** If the consent has not been signed and/or is not on the chart, then this leads into a new question because the client is not able to sign a consent once they have been pre-medicated for surgery. It is a great habit to verify the consent is on the chart prior to the client receiving pre-op medication.

3.52 ④ An undesirable effect of prednisone may be hyperglycemia. It is important to monitor the glucose since prednisone is working in direct opposition to the action of sulfonylureas. Sulfonylureas stimulate insulin release from the beta cells in the pancreas resulting in a lower serum glucose. Options #1, #2, and #3 are incorrect.

3.53 ① The initial specimen is to remove the residual urine prior to the collection. Options #2, #3, and #4 contain incorrect information.

3.54 ③ This will assist in restoring potassium which is depleted through diuresing. Option #1 is inappropriate since it does not have any potassium to assist in correcting the depletion. Option #2 is too high in sodium, and it counteracts the effectiveness of giving Lasix. Option #4 is ineffective in restoring the potassium.

3.55 ③ After a bronchoscopy, the client should be assessed for symptoms of respiratory distress from swelling due to the procedure. Signs of respiratory distress include tachypnea, tachycardia, respiratory stridor, and retractions. Option #1 does occur and could become a complication if the client is given fluids before reflex has returned. Option #2 is common for a few days after a bronchoscopy. Option #4 is not associated with the procedure, but is a sign of increased intracranial pressure.

3.56 ② Oral steroids have ulcerogenic properties and need to be administered with meals. Options #1, #3, and #4 contain incorrect information for the administration of steroids.

3.57

③ The first step is to assess by asking client if he is choking.
④ The second step is to position self behind client.
⑤ The third step is to form a fist with one hand.
② The fourth step is to position nurse's thumb toward client, above the waist and below the rib cage wrapping one arm around the client.
⑥ The fifth step is wrap other arm around the client placing that hand on top of the nurse's fist.
① The sixth and last step is to thrust upward 6–10 times.

3.58 ③ This is the question that identifies the ability of parents to support the emotional needs of their children as separate human beings. Options #1, #2, and #4 are important questions to ask during the assessment, but are not directly related to the issue of emotional support.

3.59 ③ When a client is admitted to a general medical, surgical, or critical care unit for another physical problem, the nurse may become the case finder and must be alert for subtle symptoms of an alcohol-related problem. The client who has several complaints of pain that do not appear related to the admissions problem requires a further investigation. Tremors, elevated temperature, and pain may be indicative of an alcohol-related problem. Option #1 is more indicative of a dysphoric or depressed, medically ill client. Option #2 could warrant further exploration of alcohol use. Option #4 is more indicative of withdrawal from narcotics or an infective problem such as tuberculosis.

3.60 ④ Option #4 is the only correct answer. Options #1 and #3 are outside the nurse's legal scope of practice. Option #2 is also outside the provider of care's scope of practice although the provider should be apprised of the situation.

CHAPTER 4

*Time management is
life management.*
    –ROBIN SHARMA

Management of Care

✔ **Clarification of this test …**

Note this percentage has remained 17–23% with the revised NCLEX-RN®. The minimum standards include performing and directing activities that manage client's care such as: the provision of care within the legal scope of practice, practicing in a manner that is consistent with the code of ethics for RNs, client rights, confidentiality, establishing priorities, ethical practice, legal rights and responsibilities, collaboration with an interdisciplinary team, quality improvement, referrals, resource management, informed consent, staff education, and supervision.

- ☛ Provide care within the legal scope of practice.

- ☛ Practice in a manner consistent with a code of ethics for registered nurses.

- ☛ Maintain client confidentiality/privacy.

- ☛ Prioritize the delivery of client care.

- ☛ Organize workload to manage time effectively.

- ☛ Use approved abbreviations and standard terminology when documenting care.

- ☛ Collaborate with inter-professional team members when providing care (e.g., language interpreter, healthcare professionals).

- ☛ Provide cost-effective care.

- ☛ Advocate for client rights and needs.

- ☛ Provide and receive report on assigned clients.

- ☛ Receive and/or transcribe healthcare provider orders.

- ☛ Assign and supervise care provided by others (e.g., LPN/VN, assistive personnel, other RNs).

- ☛ Utilize valid resources to enhance the care provided to a client (e.g., evidence-based research, information technology, policies and procedures).

- ☛ Recognize limitations of self and others and seek assistance.

- ☛ Initiate, evaluate, and update plan of care (e.g., care map, clinical pathway).

- ☛ Perform procedures necessary to safely admit, transfer, or discharge a client.

- ☛ Verify that the client received appropriate procedure education and consents to care and procedures.

- ☛ Provide education to clients and staff about client rights and responsibilities.

- ☛ Recognize the need for referrals and obtain necessary orders.

- ☛ Participate in performance improvement/quality improvement process.

- ☛ Integrate advance directives into client plan of care.

- ☛ Manage conflict among clients and healthcare staff.

- ☛ Recognize ethical dilemmas and take appropriate action.

- ☛ Report unsafe care of healthcare personnel and intervene as appropriate (e.g., substance abuse, improper care, staffing practices).

4.1 Which of these nursing actions should the nurse delegate to an unlicensed assistive personnel (UAP) on a medical nursing unit? **Select all that apply.**

① Assisting a client to ambulate on the second post-operative day.
② Bathing a client experiencing respiratory distress.
③ Educating a client about the importance of deep breathing and coughing to prevent post-op pneumonia.
④ Reminding a client to use an incentive spirometer (IS) every 1 to 2 hours while awake.
⑤ Setting up lunch trays for clients who have orders for regular meals.

4.2 Which of these antidepressant medication orders should the nurse question for an elderly client?

① Amitriptyline
② Haloperidol
③ Sertraline
④ Aripiprazole

4.3 Which of these nursing actions reflect the ethical principle of justice?

① The nurse administers a blood transfusion to a young adult client with leukemia who consented to the transfusion against the wishes of the family, who are all Jehovah Witnesses.
② The nurse establishes a plan to ambulate the post-op client as ordered by the provider of care even when the client would prefer staying in bed all day due to discomfort.
③ The nurse provides the same caring approach along with the nursing interventions for both the client who is the CEO of his company and a client who is homeless.
④ The nurse notifies the healthcare provider regarding a client that is not receiving any outcomes from the pain medication and has an alteration in the sensation in the foot with a cast.

4.4 Which of these nursing actions by the LPN should the RN intervene with due to the violation of the Privacy Rules outlined by HIPAA? **Select all that apply.**

① Discussing the client's condition during a telephone conversation with an individual who has provided the nurse with the client's code information.
② Refusing to share any information with a family member who is out of town.
③ Answering questions about a client's condition for the client's son.
④ Reviewing client's condition and medical information outside the client's room in rounds.
⑤ Photocopying client's lab reports for the medical team to have during rounds.

4.5 The nurse assessed a trend in the prevalence of falls among older clients in a Rehab Unit. The nurse documented the findings and collaborated with the unit manager to develop and implement a new policy using a *Fall Risk Indicator and Risk for Injury* Reference. Which of these plans would include this process?

① Advocacy
② Case Management
③ Collaboration
④ Quality Improvement

4.6 Which of these actions by the nurse demonstrates ethical practice for a nurse working on a Rehabilitation Unit?

① Discusses the inappropriate behavior only with the nurse who was seen taking part of a client's narcotics for personal use versus discarding it as per protocol.
② Encourages a client to take a walk to the recreation room, and explains the reason is so the healthcare provider will have some privacy to discuss the bad results of the biopsy.
③ Explains an answer to a client's question to the best of the nurse's ability due to limited knowledge about the medical condition.
④ Notifies the healthcare provider that a client has refused the chemotherapy treatment and wants to discontinue the treatment.

4.7 What would be the priority plan for a young child's parents that are Jehovah Witness who clearly state they do not want to make a decision that might kill their child, but are unable to give permission to administer blood due to hemorrhaging from an accident?

① Contact case management while administering fluids to maintain BP.
② Consult the ethics committee while administering fluids to maintain BP.
③ Call the hospital attorney while administering fluids to maintain BP.
④ Realize that this is the family's religious belief and support their decision.

4.8 A client is admitted with a kidney stone. The client is moaning in pain and vomiting. ABGs are: pH—7.54; PaO$_2$—78 mm Hg; PCO$_2$—26 mm Hg; and HCO$_3$—25 mEq/L (25 mmol/L). What is the nursing priority?

① Administer pain medication.
② Administer albuterol.
③ Administer an antiemetic.
④ Prepare for intubation.

4.9 Which of these clients should the nurse see first after report?

① A middle-aged client with liver failure and an INR of 3.0 who is complaining of IV site leaking.
② A middle-aged client who is complaining of shortness of breath.
③ An older client with Type II diabetes mellitus who is complaining of feeling weak and shaky.
④ An elderly client who is scheduled for surgery.

4.10 The nurse has not received training in the use of a new type of wound-drainage machine, but the charge nurse assures the nurse that it is easy to operate. What is the next action?

① Let client demonstrate how the device functions.
② Notify the charge nurse that the nurse has not been checked off in the use of this equipment.
③ Read the instruction manual and accept care of the client.
④ Care for the client, but call for help whenever there is a question about the machine's functioning.

4.11 Which of the following clients would be best to delegate to the LPN (licensed practical nurse)?

① A client who needs to be taught administration of enoxaparin.
② A client who has hypertension and is being managed with IV enalapril.
③ A client with potassium level of 3.0 mEq/L (3.0 mmol/L) and needs oral potassium replacement.
④ A client who is on a nitroglycerin drip and has complaints of chest pain.

4.12 During the admission physical, the nurse notes multiple bruises on a client, particularly on the breasts, back, and arms. When the nurse asks the client how the bruises occurred, the client begins to cry and states, "I fall down a lot." The nurse suspects domestic abuse. What is the priority nursing action?

① Do a referral to case management.
② Contact the healthcare provider for guidance.
③ Ask the client if anyone is hurting her.
④ Contact law enforcement.

4.13 The nurse is caring for a client with end stage COPD. The client has an advanced directive that specifies no ventilator. The client is in acute respiratory distress and states, "I need some relief. I want the machine!" The spouse states, "No, we are not doing that again!" What is the priority nursing action?

① Notify the healthcare provider (HCP) that the client has rescinded the advanced directive, but that the spouse is in disagreement.
② Prepare for intubation and mechanical ventilation.
③ Inform the spouse that the client has a legal right to change their mind about the advanced directive.
④ Administer anti-anxiety medication and call respiratory therapy to give the client a breathing treatment.

4.14 A client has pulled out the IV and Foley and has climbed out of bed. When attempting to get the client back into bed, the client begins to shout and tries to punch the nurse. What is the priority nursing action?

① Tell the client to stop in a strong, confident voice.
② Call security.
③ Run out of the room.
④ Restrain the client.

4.15 What is the priority nursing action for the manager to initiate on a medical unit for a nurse who is frequently late for work even after a verbal warning?

① Notify Human Resources about this problem and ask for advice.
② Ask the nurse why this behavior of being frequently late for work continues.
③ Give the nurse a written warning informing the nurse of the plan for termination if this behavior occurs again within the next three months.
④ Terminate the nurse effective immediately.

4.16 What is the initial action for an elderly client who is very agitated, confused, and frequently attempts to climb out of bed?

① Restrain the client to prevent injury.
② Call a family member to sit with the client.
③ Ask the healthcare provider for an order to administer a sedative.
④ Turn on the bed alarm.

4.17 What is the priority nursing action for a client's angry spouse who comes to the nurses' station shouting and demanding that his wife be seen by a healthcare provider (HCP) immediately?

① Contact security because of the potential of injury to staff.
② Contact the client's HCP and inform the spouse of the situation.
③ Check on the client to see what is needed.
④ Ask the spouse to sit down and try to talk with the client.

4.18 What is the priority nursing action for a client who was admitted with GI bleeding and has removed the IV, and is insisting on signing self out of the hospital against medical advice?

① Give the client the AMA paper to sign and help gather client's belongings.
② Encourage the client to stay in the hospital until client is more stable, but do not prohibit client from leaving.
③ Call security to prevent the client from leaving the hospital room.
④ Tell the client not to leave the hospital since it is prohibited until client is discharged by the HCP.

4.19 What is the priority nursing intervention for an estranged wife and current girlfriend who are loud, disruptive at the client's bedside, and arguing about who is to blame for the overdose?

① Ask them to leave until the client is able to communicate.
② Call security to escort them out.
③ Tell the girlfriend to leave, but allow the estranged wife to stay.
④ Close the door to the room and let them finish the argument.

4.20 Which of the following assignments would be appropriate for the unlicensed assistive personnel (UAP) to perform?

① Give a bed bath to a newly admitted client with chest pain.
② Evaluate a client's tolerance to activity while ambulating.
③ Document a client's intake and output.
④ Feed a client who has had a CVA and a history of aspiration.

4.21 A nurse from the oncology unit is floated to the ICU. Which assignment is most appropriate for the oncology nurse?

① A newly admitted client with respiratory failure on a CPAP machine.
② A post-operative client who needs two units of blood transfused before being transferred to the surgical unit
③ A client with sepsis who has been on the ventilator for 5 days.
④ A client who has post-op delirium and is removing his tubes and attempting to climb out of bed.

4.22 What would be the first action for the nurse who has received a healthcare provider's (HCP's) order that reads: "100ml D₅W with 80 mEq (80 mmol) of KCL to infuse in 1/2 hour"?

① Assess urine output.
② Ensure the patency of the IV line.
③ Request an order for Lidocaine to be added to the IV.
④ Check the accuracy of the order.

4.23 The nurse is caring for a client with Type 1 diabetes who is being treated with insulin glargine. The MAR reads 10 units SubQ twice daily. What is the priority nursing action?

① Check the client's glucose level.
② Administer the medication as prescribed.
③ Provide the client with a 15g carbohydrate snack.
④ Verify the appropriateness of the order.

4.24 What is the highest priority of care for a client with a new order for cefaclor who has a history of penicillin allergy?

① Immediately start an IV.
② Identify wrist bracelet for correct client identity.
③ Verify accuracy of order.
④ Monitor BUN and creatinine prior to administering the medication.

4.25 A client with chronic lung disease is admitted to the acute pulmonary unit with: respiratory rate of 50; pulse of 140 and irregular; skin pale and cool to touch; client confused as to place and time. Orders are: oxygen per nasal cannula at 4L/minute, bed rest, soft diet and pulmonary

function tests in the AM. What is the best sequence of nursing activities?

① Place in semi-Fowler's position, begin the oxygen, have someone stay with the client, then notify the healthcare provider regarding the current status of the client.
② Begin the oxygen, call the nursing supervisor, keep the bed flat to maintain blood pressure, and stimulate client to take deep breaths.
③ Call the nursing supervisor, discuss with the family if the client has experienced this problem before, offer the client sips of clear liquids.
④ Advise respiratory therapy of the client's problem, place the client in semi-Fowler's position, and begin the oxygen.

4.26 The nurse arrives for the day shift and receives the assignments around 7:30 AM. The assignment includes:

- A man with a diagnosis of rule-out MI who is on a monitor and having 4–6 premature beats per hour.
- An elderly client who is confused and has constant urinary dribbling.
- A client with pneumonia who is presenting with an increase in the confusion and a temperature of 104°F (40°C) at 6:30 AM.
- A client with diabetes mellitus who experienced a restless night and 7:00 AM serum glucose was 170 mg/dL (9.44 mmol/L).

Which client is a priority and how should the nurse plan the care?

① The client with pneumonia has priority; the client's condition should be assessed immediately.
② The elderly client is probably wet and uncomfortable and should be taken care of first. Then obtain a stat blood glucose to determine the diabetic client's current serum glucose level.
③ The client with cardiac symptoms should be assessed immediately as the monitor indicates cardiac irritability. Then the temperature on the client with pneumonia should be reassessed.
④ The client with diabetes should be seen immediately to assess for evidence of hyper-glycemia. Then the client with pneumonia should be assessed for patency of airway.

4.27 After the nurse administered Lidocaine from a verbal order for a cardiac client who experienced numerous premature ventricular contractions, the healthcare provider entered the order for procainamide into the electronic medical order instead of Lidocaine. What should be the priority nursing action?

① Request a meeting with the healthcare provider when making rounds.

② Notify healthcare provider; discuss the order, and request a change in order if it is appropriate.

③ Discuss situation with the manager and ask if she/he could call healthcare provider regarding the situation.

④ Complete an incident report.

4.28 At 5:00 PM, the nurse on the evening shift opens the nurses' notes and discovers that the last entry was at 9:00 AM. The day nurse did not complete the charting and did not sign the nurses' notes. What is the priority nursing action?

① Leave a note on the front of the chart for the day nurse to make a late entry and begin charting on the line below the last entry on the nurse's notes.

② Leave enough space for the day nurse to complete the charting when the day nurse comes in the next morning.

③ Not chart anything until the day nurse returns to complete the charting for the care delivered that morning.

④ Call the day nurse and ask about the care the day nurse gave that morning so the evening nurse can complete the chart.

4.29 Which assignment would be appropriate for the Labor and Delivery (L&D) nurse who will be working for one shift on the Medical Surgical unit?

① A toddler with croup

② A young adult with malignant hypertension

③ A middle-aged client with unstable angina

④ An older adult client with heart failure

4.30 Which of these clients with spinal cord injury (SCI) should be assessed immediately following shift report?

① A client with a C6 SCI presenting with partial paralysis of hands, arms, and lower body.

② A client with a T6 SCI presenting with a BP 170/68, severe headache, and HR—48 bpm.

③ A client with a L1 SCI presenting with paralysis below the waist.

④ A client with a C4 SCI presenting with paralysis below the neck and is on ventilator.

4.31 After establishing IV access, what is best for the nurse to document immediately after the procedure?

① The type of catheter used and number of venipuncture attempts.

② The type of IV fluid hung and equipment used.

③ The date, time, venipuncture site, type and gauge of catheter, and IV fluid hung.

④ Type, amount, and flow rate of IV fluid, condition of IV site.

4.32 Which of these clients should be triaged first?

① A client who is taking NSAIDs for arthritic pain, experiencing epigastric pain, HR—90 bpm.

② A client who has a decline in the cranial nerve #1, reporting a problem with presbyscusis and presbyopia.

③ A client with thin skin, alteration in depth perception, and episodes of incontinence.

④ A client with fixed, dilated pupils, and is asystole.

4.33 Which would be the most appropriate to assign to the LPN?

① A client who is being discharged and needs new diabetic teaching.

② A client who is a new admission with chest pain.

③ A client who is receiving chemotherapy.

④ A client who has the diagnosis of Myasthenia Gravis.

4.34 Which would have the highest priority when caring for a terminally ill client during the final stage of dying?

① Encourage family to discuss legal matters with an attorney.

② Provide privacy for the client and his family to spend time together.

③ Keep client sedate.

④ Encourage family to limit visiting hours, so they can rest.

4.35 Which of these clients should be seen first after shift report?

① The husband of a cardiac client who indicates that the IV pump is alarming and his wife is not receiving the appropriate amount of medication.

② A cardiac client who is presenting with multifocal, trigeminal premature ventricular contractions on the ECG monitor.

③ A post-op appendectomy client 2 days ago; T—102°F (38.9°C); HR—104 bpm; and Respirations—30 breaths/min and is complaining of chest discomfort when coughing.

④ A newly admitted client with gastroenteritis: T—100°F (37.8°C); HR—100 bpm; and Respirations—20 breaths/min and a BP—114/76.

4.36 After the nurse receives report, which of these clients should be assessed first?

① A client with COPD who is experiencing some shortness of breath with exertion.

② A client who had a CVA and has been hospitalized for 1 week.

③ A client who had a laminectomy 2 days ago and is complaining of pain.

④ A client with diabetes who is diaphoretic, with nausea, and is vomiting.

4.37 The nurse comes out of report and has several orders to initiate with a client who has R—28 and is congested; HR—90; and T—102.4°F (39.1°C). Which of these orders should be implemented first?

① Blood cultures.

② Evaluate vital signs.

③ Start an IV.

④ Start ceftriaxone.

4.38 Which assignment would be most appropriate to assign to the pregnant nurse?

① A client with HIV.

② A client with a cervical radium implant.

③ A client with syphilis.

④ A client with cytomegalovirus (CMV).

4.39 After the nurse receives shift report, which of these clients should the nurse assess first?

① A 30-year-old female client refusing to take cimetidine before breakfast.

② A 40-year-old male client scheduled for a cholecystectomy and complaining of chills.

③ A 50-year-old female client with right-sided weakness, asking to go to the bathroom.

④ A 60-year-old male with an NG tube who had a bowel resection 2 days ago.

4.40 Which sequence is correct when providing care for a client immediately prior to surgery?

① Administer preoperative medication, client signs operative permit, determine vital signs.

② Check operative permit for signature, advise client to remain in bed, administer preoperative medication.

③ Remove client's dentures, administer preoperative medication, client empties bladder.

④ Verify client has been NPO. Client empties bladder; family leaves room.

4.41 Which assignment is the most appropriate for a client in the burn unit who has a cytomegalovirus (CMV) infection?

① A nurse who has an upper respiratory infection.

② A nurse who is eight weeks pregnant.

③ A nurse who is CMV negative.

④ A nurse who has thirty years of experience.

4.42 Which nursing action should be done initially for a middle-aged client who is admitted with tertiary syphilis and is exhibiting signs of marked dementia and disorientation?

① Place the nurse call bell within reach.

② Frequently observe client behavior.

③ Apply a vest-type restraint.

④ Provide an around-the-clock sitter.

4.43 The nurse observes that a fire has started in the client's room. Which action should be implemented first?

① Confine the fire to the client's room.
② Extinguish the fire.
③ Pull the fire alarm.
④ Rescue the client.

4.44 Which room assignment is most appropriate for an adult male client who has sustained a second degree burn over 10% of the body?

① A semi-private room with a male client undergoing chemotherapy.
② A semi-private room with a male client who is three days post abdominal surgery.
③ A semi-private room with a male pediatric client.
④ A semi-private room with a male client admitted for chest pain.

4.45 Which observation indicates the need for a nurse to stay with a client admitted to the emergency room following a car wreck?

① Disorientation and irregular vital signs.
② Irregular vital signs and hostility.
③ Rapid respirations and agitation.
④ Elevated vital signs and apprehension.

4.46 What should be included in the documentation for a client who has returned from surgery with a new, fine, reddened rash noted around the area where Betadine prep had been applied prior to surgery?

① The time and circumstances in which the rash was noted.
② Explanation to client and family the reason for rash.
③ Notation on an allergy list and notification of the healthcare provider.
④ Application of corticosteroid cream to decrease inflammation.

4.47 A client is admitted with acute pancreatitis. The pain level is 9 on a 0–10 scale and vital signs are BP—78/54; HR—148 beats per min; and RR—32/min. What should be the priority nursing action from protocol?

① Administer pain medication.
② Administer antibiotics.
③ Administer a fluid bolus.
④ Insert a nasogastric tube.

4.48 The charge nurse demonstrates an understanding of appropriate delegation when which client assignment is made to the LPN?

① A psychotic client
② A client receiving chemotherapy
③ A client in Buck's traction
④ A client receiving a blood transfusion

4.49 Which nursing action regarding intubation equipment/supplies is most appropriate following intubation of a postoperative client who had a respiratory arrest?

① Soak the intubation equipment in concentrated Betadine solution.
② Place intubation blade in a container and arrange for steris sterilization.
③ Soak intubation blade in Cidex solution.
④ Wash with soap and water and allow to air dry.

4.50 A client with active multi-drug resistant TB is admitted to the unit and placed in the negative pressure room. The client is insistent upon smoking and states "If I can't smoke, I will sign myself out of the hospital against medical advice!" What should be the priority nursing action?

① Allow the client to leave because it is the client's right.
② Notify security and the charge nurse since this represents a public health hazard.
③ Permit the client to smoke in his room to protect the community.
④ Confiscate the client's cigarettes.

4.51 A client with bacterial endocarditis is being discharged home on IV antibiotics through a PICC line. Which statement by the client indicates the need for further teaching?

① "I will need antibiotics for at least the next six weeks."
② "I will be able to have lab drawn through the PICC line."
③ "I need to keep the occlusive dressing over the insertion site and cover it with plastic when I shower."
④ "I should check my blood pressure on the arm with the PICC line at least once a day."

4.52 Which of these clients would be most appropriate to discharge early in order to have a bed for a new client that is being admitted from the Emergency Unit?

① A client who had a cholecystectomy 4 days ago. Currently has active bowel sounds, is taking po fluids with no problems, and has an abdominal drain.
② A client who had an epidural bleed and is currently lethargic. Vital signs: HR—62 bpm; BP—160/92 mm Hg; Respirations—26 breaths/min; and Temperature—99.4°F (37.4°C).
③ An elderly client with some acute confusion and a new onset of incontinence.
④ A one-day post thyroidectomy client who has been stable and is now presenting with an increase in hoarseness.

4.53 A client who has an allergy to Penicillin has an order to receive ceftriaxone. What would be the priority of care for this client?

① Question the order.
② Administer the drug as ordered.
③ Call the pharmacy.
④ Ask the client if they have a history of any hypersensitivity to ceftriaxone or any other cephalosporin drug.

4.54 The charge nurse on a medical unit admitted a client in the early AM who had developed a diffuse macular rash and a fever. The healthcare provider suspects rubella. What would be the priority nursing action?

① Notify the infection control practitioner.
② Check the immunization status of the employees on the unit.
③ Place the client on contact precautions.
④ Place the client on airborne precautions.

4.55 A postoperative client is receiving bupivacain hydrochloride for pain through an epidural catheter. Which response should the nurse recognize as desirable for this pain management technique?

① Decreased respirations
② Somnolence
③ Decreased restlessness
④ Decreased blood pressure

4.56 What would be the priority nursing action for the spouse of a client with dementia who confides in the nurse a concern about being able to handle the client following discharge from the hospital?

① Make a case management referral.
② Reassure the spouse that management of the husband's care can be done at home.
③ Notify the healthcare provider (HCP) that the client needs long-term care placement.
④ Tell the spouse that the client will improve after being discharged and returns home.

4.57 There is an order to administer 1000 mL. 0.9 NS over 10 hours. The tubing calibration factor is 10 drops/mL. To deliver this, set the infusion at _____ gtts/min.

4.58 One of the clients is a male admitted with dehydration. The client has an IV infusing at 150 mL/hr. The client's vital signs are: BP—82/98; HR—36; and RR—6. The pulse oximeter reads 87%. The client is in acute distress, coughing up pink, frothy sputum. What would be the first nursing action?

① Raise the head of the bed.
② Apply oxygen at 4 L/min.
③ Inform the provider of care.
④ Slow the IV rate.

4.59   In planning the debridment of a burn for a client, which action would be the nursing priority?

① Assemble all necessary supplies and medications.
② Organize time for dressing change and provide emotional support.
③ Prepare the client and family for the pain the client will experience during and after the procedure.
④ Limit visitation prior to procedure to reduce client stress.

4.60   There is a shortage of rooms, and the nurse must assign two clients to the same room in order to accommodate the newly admitted client. Which of these clients should the nurse assign to the same room?

① A 25-year-old female who is one day postoperative hysterectomy and an 80-year-old female who is confused and agitated.
② A 35-year-old male who is two days postoperative cholecystectomy and a 40-year-old male with pain due to fibromyalgia.
③ A 40-year-old female who has gastroenteritis and occasional vomiting with a 45-year-old female who is receiving corticosteroids for nephrotic syndrome.
④ A 50-year-old male with a MRSA infection and a 55-year-old female client with a Clostridium difficile infection.

Answers & Rationales

4.1 ① Options #1, #4, and #5 are correct. These
④ assignments are all within the legal scope of
⑤ practice for the UAP. Refer to "*Bart*" in the book, *Nursing Made Insanely Easy*, in order to assist in remembering this concept. A quick **I CAN Hint**: "BART" will assist you in remembering the actions the UAP can implement within their scope of practice. A UAP can Bathe clients who are stable, Ambulate clients who are stable, conduct Routine tasks, and Tasks that do not require clinical decision making. Option #2 is incorrect because client is in distress, and the UAP will not have the knowledge to know the importance of discontinuing the procedure for this client. The procedure should not actually even be started when a client is in distress. Option #3 is incorrect because teaching is not within the legal scope for UAPs.

4.2 ① Option #1 is correct. To begin down the path of success for answering this question, you must first know which of these drugs include antidepressants. The two antidepressants in these options include Amitriptyline and Sertraline. Amitriptyline has the most anticholinergic and sedating side effects of these two antidepressants. There may be pronounced effects on the cardiovascular system (hypotension) which may result in falls. This medication order should be questioned due to the risk to the client for injury from the falls. Option #2 is incorrect since it is an antipsychotic medication. Option #3 is a useful antidepressant due to the decrease in undesirable effects in comparison to the traditional tricyclic antidepressants. It has one of the shortest half-life of the currently marketed serotonin reuptake inhibitors. In other words, there would be no need to question this order. Option #4 is incorrect since it is an antipsychotic medication.

4.3 ③ Option #3 is correct. This is an example of justice which reflects fair treatment in matters related to physical and psychosocial care and use of resources. There should be no difference in the quality of care for any individual based on economics or professional accomplishments. Option #1 is incorrect. This is an example of autonomy which allows the client to make personal decisions, even those decisions that may not be in the client's own best interest. Option #2 is incorrect. This is an example of beneficence which is the care that is in the best interest of the client. Option #4 is incorrect. This is an example of nonmalefiscence which is prevention of harm or pain as much as possible during treatment.

4.4 ③ Options #3, 4, and #5 are correct answers.
④ These demonstrate inappropriate
⑤ dissemination of client information as outlined by HIPAA. These would require intervention by the RN since these actions demonstrate a violation in the Privacy Rules. Option #1 does not require intervention since the individual has the client's code information. Option #2 does not require intervention since this is appropriate practice.

4.5 ④ Option #4 is correct. Quality Improvement includes activities such as assessing opportunities and developing plans/policies for improving the quality of nursing practice. Identifying an increase in the trend of falls and implementing a policy focused at improving the assessment and prevention of falls among the older clients fulfills the focus of quality improvement. Option #1 is incorrect since advocacy refers to the nurse's responsibility to act on behalf of the client. Option #2 is incorrect since this refers to the coordination of care to minimize costs and fragmentation. This also assists with the improvement in outcomes and quality. Option #3 is incorrect. While the nurse did collaborate with the unit manager, this plan goes beyond collaboration to assessment and policy development based on high-volume risks.

4.6 ④ Option #4 is the correct answer. This demonstrates respect for the client autonomy, even if the decision may not be in the client's own best interest. Option #1 is incorrect. Taking narcotics from a client demonstrates unethical practice. Most employers have protocols for reporting of witnessed theft or conduct that is unprofessional. The nurse needed to report this behavior to the manager due to unethical practice. Option #2 is incorrect. This action is a violation to client confidentiality. The nurse shared the fact the client had a biopsy and also that there were bad results from the biopsy. Option #3 is incorrect. The nurse violated veracity (truth telling); the nurse should have indicated the truth which was a lack of knowledge regarding the answer to the question, and would be happy to go and find out the correct information.

4.7 ③ Option #3 is correct. The child is a minor and cannot make own medical decisions. By contacting the hospital attorney there can be a decision made by the court to allow the life-saving administration of blood in this circumstance. This will also support the family who is unable to make the decision due to the support system. Option #1, while case management can be supportive, and there is a need for the ethic committee to meet and give their opinion it is essential to have a legal opinion regarding the treatment. Option #4 is incorrect. It clearly indicates the family is in a dilemma, and in this situation would welcome medical and/or legal support.

4.8 ① Option #1 is correct. The ABGs indicate respiratory alkalosis, uncompensated. By relieving the client's pain, the respiratory rate should decrease and should stop blowing off the CO_2. Option #2, the albuterol, is not a standard of practice for the clinical presentation. Option #3, an antiemetic can be administered after the pain medication. Option #4, there is no indication that client should be intubated.

4.9 ② The priority assessment will be Option #2 (possible hypoxia), followed by Option #3 (possible hypoglycemia), Option #1 (bleeding due to increased PT/INR) and finally Option #4. Each of these clients need to be seen by the nurse.

4.10 ② Option #2 is the correct choice. A nurse should not use new equipment until there has been training in the use and documentation that the nurse can safely use the equipment. Options #1, #3, and #4 could put the nurse in legal jeopardy.

4.11 ③ Option #3 is correct. Option #1, LPNs do not do initial teaching, and the Options #2 and #4 are unstable situations.

4.12 ③ Option #3 is correct. Options #1 and #2 are using the provider to make a nursing judgment. Option #4 would be appropriate if the client admits that she is being physically harmed and is willing to involve the legal system. Whether or not the client admits that abuse is occurring, careful documentation of bruising and the client's response is important.

4.13 ① Option #1 is correct. The client has a right to rescind the advanced directive. The nurse needs a HCP's order to reverse the Do Not Resuscitate order on the chart, and the HCP needs to know about the conflict between the client and spouse. Option #2 is dependent upon the HCP's order. Option #3 would be best handled by the HCP. Option #4 could provide relief to the client, but could also suppress the client's respirations and postpone their wishes.

4.14 ① The first nursing action would be Option #1. The client is out of control and at risk of harming self and the nurse. That might be enough to enable the client to regain control. Option #2, security then needs to be called. Option #3 is inappropriate. Option #4, restraints should be used only as a last option and requires a healthcare provider's (HCP's) order.

4.15 ③ Option #3 is correct. The manager is responsible for responding to employee problems. This is not the role of the Human Resources Department as stated in Option #1. The nurse has already had a verbal warning, so the next step is a written warning. Option #2 is incorrect. Asking why nurse is late does not resolve the problem. A written warning (Option #3) precedes termination (Option #4).

4.16 ④ Option #4 is the correct answer. The best initial response is to turn on the bed alarm. The sound will notify staff if the client is climbing out of bed. Option #2, while it will be helpful to have a family member sit with the client, this would still not be the best initial action. Option #1, restraints should be a last resort. A physical assessment and labs should be obtained before medicating the client. Option #3, medications can cause delirium to get worse.

4.17 ① Safety is the priority in this situation. Contacting security will decrease the risk of injury to staff. The spouse appears to be out of control. Contacting the HCP in Option #2 will not take care of the immediate problem. Leaving the scene (Option #3) to check on the client could increase the risk of injury to staff. Option #4, asking the spouse to sit down and talk may not be possible due to spouse's level of agitation.

4.18 ② Option #2 is the best choice. The client has not been involuntarily committed and has every right to leave the facility. Option #1 is encouraging the client to leave. Options #3 and #4 may be considered as false imprisonment.

4.19 ① Option #1 should be attempted first. If they refuse to leave, then Option #2, call security to escort them out of the building. Options #3 and #4 are not appropriate.

4.20 ③ Option #3 is the correct answer. Documenting vital signs and I&O are within the UAP's scope of practice. Option #1 is not appropriate to give a bed bath to a newly admitted client with chest pain. Option #2 is not within the UAP's role. The client in Option #4 is at high risk for aspiration and needs to be fed by a licensed care giver.

4.21 ② Option #2 is correct. The client is stable enough to be transferred to the surgical unit, and the oncology nurse frequently administers blood products. Option #1 is a newly admitted client and therefore requires very close monitoring and may not be stable. Option #3, care of a ventilator client is not in the usual scope of practice for the oncology nurse. Option #4, a client with delirium needs frequent and close assessment to determine if the treatment is working.

4.22 ④ Option #4 is correct. Potassium chloride must be diluted and administered at a rate not to exceed 10mEq/hr (10 mmol/hr) for adults with a serum potassium level > 2.5 mEq/L (2.5 mmol/L) or if serum potassium is < 2 mEq/L (2 mmol/L) the rate is not to exceed 20 mEq/hr (20mmol/hr). Checking the accuracy of the order would be the first action. Options #1 and #2 are correct after the order has been corrected. Option #3, Lidocaine, should not be added to this IV.

4.23 ④ Option #4 is correct since Lantus is administered one time a day versus twice daily. Option #2 is incorrect since the order is inappropriate, the nurse needs to focus on collaborating with the HCP to revise the order, so it is safe. While it is important to monitor the client's glucose (Option #1), this option does not answer the question. The question is evaluating the understanding for "safe medication administration." *Remember, the key to successful testing is to focus on what the question is asking.* Option #3 is not correct for this question. There is no indication in the stem of the question that the client is experiencing hypoglycemia which would then indicate a need for the nurse to administer a carbohydrate.

4.24 ③ Option #3 is correct. Clients who have a hypersensitivity to penicillin may experience the same reaction to Cefaclor (Ceclor). Option #1 is incorrect. Option #2 is important but Option #3 is a priority in this situation. Option #4 is a consideration for this drug, but is not a priority when drug order may be unsafe.

4.25 ① The healthcare provider's orders do not address the seriousness of the client's condition. The healthcare provider should be notified immediately. However, the client should not be left alone. Options #2, #3, and #4 do not address the seriousness of the client's immediate needs.

4.26 ① The sickest client is the client with pneumonia, and the client's needs should be addressed first. This client has an increased temperature, which may indicate his pneumonia is getting worse; the confusion may be indicative of hypoxia. The client status should be evaluated immediately. Option #3, premature beats of 4–6 per hour are benign and not unusual for a cardiac client. Option #2, the elderly client may be uncomfortable, but the respiratory status of the client with pneumonia is priority. Option #4, a serum glucose of 170 mg/dL (9.44 mmol/L) is abnormally high and should be addressed. The respiratory status of the pneumonia client, however, remains the highest priority.

4.27 ② During emergency situations, verbal orders should be entered into the electronic medical record and signed. The nurse must notify the healthcare provider and explain the order. If the nurse did hear this order correctly, then a new order should be requested from the healthcare provider. Option #1 is incorrect since the nurse would be waiting for the healthcare provider to make rounds, and this needs to be completed as soon as possible. (Not later!) Options #3 and #4 are incorrect. Option #3 is asking another nurse to intervene which is nurse avoidance. Option #4 is incorrect, since this may not be necessary if the nurse did hear the verbal order correctly.

4.28 ① The best way to handle the situation is to begin charting on the line below last entry, and have the day nurse make a late entry for the omitted information. Options #2, #3, and #4 would be illegal.

4.29 ② Option #2 is correct. The L&D nurse provides care for clients with pregnancy induced hypertension. These assessments and plans of care would correlate with the nurse's skills. Options #1, #3, and #4 would not be appropriate for this nurse. L&D nurses do not routinely provide care for children. Options #3 and #4 require an understanding of cardiology.

4.30 ② Option #2 is correct. This is an emergency and requires immediate intervention. The client is presenting with assessments of autonomic dysreflexia. Options #1, #3, and #4 are expected findings for the level of SCI.

4.31 ③ Option #3 is the most correct answer. Options #1 and #2 are appropriate but not as inclusive as Option #3. Option #4 should be included in the once-per-shift documentation. This question states "after establishing IV access."

4.32 ① Option #1 is correct. This client is presenting with symptoms of a bleeding ulcer with the history of the NSAIDs and the location of the pain and elevated heart rate. Options #2 and #3 are normal findings and do not need to be triaged. In Option #4, the client is dead.

4.33 ④ Option #4 is most stable. Option #1 is incorrect because it requires initial teaching. The LPN can reinforce teaching, but it is currently not in the scope of practice to do the initial teaching. Option #2 would require initial assessment. LPNs can do ongoing assessment, but it is not in the scope of practice to complete the initial assessment. Option #3 would require IV management and specialized assessment skills, so it is not a priority to Option #4.

4.34 ② A priority is to provide privacy. Options #1 and #3 are inappropriate at this time. Option #4 is partially correct about rest, but incorrect regarding the limiting of visiting hours.

4.35 ② Option #2 is correct. The cardiac client is the most unstable and is presenting with cardiac irritation which requires immediate assessment. Option #1 is not life-threatening. This can wait for an assessment. Option #3 is incorrect. This client may be experiencing some pneumonia and may require some revision in the plan of care, but does not mandate immediate assessment following report. Option #4 is dehydrated, but is not in any acute situation that would mandate immediate assessment over the priority client that is presenting with trigeminal premature ventricular contractions.

4.36 ④ The diabetic client is presenting with hypoglycemia. This can be dangerous. Option #1 may be expected with COPD. Options #2 and #3 are not priorities to Option #4.

4.37 ① The priority is to determine the organism the client is growing in order to determine the correct antibiotic. If the antibiotic, Option #4, is implemented first, then the blood cultures will not be accurate. Option #2 has been reported in the stem of the question and is not necessary to duplicate at this time. Option #3 is not a priority to Option #1.

4.38 ① An HIV client would not present a risk to the pregnant woman if she does not come in contact with the body secretions. Options #2, #3, and #4 could result in teratogenic effects to the fetus.

4.39 ② Option #2 is correct. The client is scheduled for surgery and has a sign of infection (chills)! Option #1 does not give any indication of any complications or any specific information about the client to indicate he would be a priority. Option #3 does not require a nurse. This client does need assistance, but the RN is not required for this client. Option #4 is high risk for potential complications, but none are indicated at this time. Option #2 has already developed a complication.

4.40 ② The operative permit must be signed prior to the client receiving his preoperative medication. The client is considered incapacitated after receiving a narcotic. Option #1, administer the medication prior to the permit being signed, is incorrect. Option #3 is incorrect because medication was given before emptying bladder which leads to a risk for falls. Option #4 is important information, but it is unnecessary for the family to leave the room.

4.41 ④ Option #4 is most appropriate due to a decreased risk of being infected. Option #1 is incorrect because those with a cytomegalovirus positive titer are often immunosuppressed clients who should be protected from other pathogens. Option #2 is incorrect because CMV is fetotoxic, and those who are pregnant should not care for CMV clients. Option #3 is incorrect because those with no protective titer are an increased risk for developing the disease if exposed.

4.42 ② Placing the client on frequent observation status would be the first action to ensure the client's safety. Option #1 is incorrect because it should not be assumed that the client will be able to use the call light appropriately. Option #3 should never be the first option used by a professional nurse. Current standards require not only a physician's order, but a time limit, exact type of restraint to be used, and the specific rationale for restraint. Option #4 may be suggested to the family at a later time.

4.43 ④ Option #4 is correct. Rescuing the client is always the priority. "RACE" will assist you in remembering fire safety. R = rescue client; A = activate an alarm; C = confine the fire; and E = extinguish the fire.

4.44 ① Both clients have lost major protective mechanisms and are at risk for infection. Options #2 and #3 are incorrect due to the infection risk they pose. Option #4 is incorrect due to the need to decrease stimulation to conserve oxygen, and does not need the same isolation precautions.

4.45 ① A disoriented client with irregular vital signs represents a grave safety risk. Options #2, #3, and #4 may increase the need for nursing interaction/assessment and are secondary to Option #1.

4.46 ③ Option #3 is correct. Any suspected reaction to drugs should be reported to the healthcare provider, and noted on the list of possible allergies. Option #1 would be noted, but is not as high a priority as Option #3. Option #2 would be important to implement, but would not be a priority over Option #3. Option #4 does not address the fact that the rash is new and occurred following the Betadine prep.

4.47 ③ Option #3 is priority as failure to treat the hypotension could result in acute renal failure and shock. Option #1 could further drive the BP down, but should be administered as soon as possible after the bolus. Options #2 and #4 are important, but are not a priority.

4.48 ③ This client is the lowest acuity out of the group and requires the least specialized care. The scope of practice would allow the LPN to care for this client. Options #1, #2, and #4 require care from the RN which is out of the LPN's scope of practice.

4.49 ② Sterilization of equipment after exposure to body fluids of a client is protocol. Options #1, #3, and #4 are incorrect because they do not provide sterility.

4.50 ② Option #2 is correct. This represents a public health hazard. Infection controls standards will require notification of security to keep the client in the negative pressure room until the health department determines the best course of action. Option #1 would endanger the community, Option #3 is not a possible action due to smoke free facilities, and Option #4 could endanger the nurse if it angered the client.

4.51 ④ Option #4 indicates a need for further teaching. Blood pressure should not be taken on the arm with a PICC line. The other options indicate effective teaching.

4.52 ① Option #1 is correct. This client is the most stable out of the four clients. Option #2 is incorrect since the client is lethargic and BP is elevated. Option #3 needs ongoing evaluation for a urinary tract infection. Elderly clients presenting with acute confusion along with incontinence may have an infection. Option #4 is not appropriate to discharge since the hoarseness may indicate a complication from laryngeal edema.

4.53 ④ Option #4 is correct. There is a possibility for cross-sensitivity between penicillin and cephalosporins. Asking the client about the previous use of a cephalosporin may indicate that there is no problem with cross-sensitivity. Option #1, the nurse should then call the provider of care to question the order and inform the provider about the client's previous use of cephalosporins. Options #2 and #3 are incorrect because they do not address the issue with the allergy in the stem of the question. This would be unsafe practice.

4.54 ④ The correct response is Option #4. Airborne precautions is most appropriate infection control precautions for a client who the healthcare provider suspects rubella. Option #1 is necessary, but in this cases not the first priority. Option #2 will require the assistance of employee health to check immunization records. Rubella is transmitted via the airborne route; therefore Option #3 is incorrect.

4.55 ③ A decrease in physiological shortness of breath and restlessness is a desired outcome criteria of pain management. Options #1, #2, and #4 are undesired responses.

4.56 ① Option #1 is the best choice. The case manager can work with the spouse to determine what resources are available in the community and make needed referrals. Options #2 and #4 are giving false reassurance. Option #3, this is not the staff nurse's role to inform the provider of care that the client needs long-term care placement.

4.57   17 drops/minute

Step 1: Volume to be infused =
Volume (mL) 1000 mL

Step 2: Time for the infusion =
Time (min) Convert hr to min

$\dfrac{60 \text{ min}}{1 \text{ hr}} = \dfrac{x \text{ min}}{10 \text{ hr}}$

10 hrs = 600 min

Step 3: What is the drop factor on the
IV tubing?
10 drops/ mL

Step 4: Equation

$1000 \text{ mL} \times 10 \text{ gtt/mL} = \dfrac{10{,}000 \text{ gtt}}{600 \text{ min}} = 17 \text{ gtts/min}$

4.58 ④ Option#4 is correct. The first action is to decrease the IV rate. All of these actions need to be taken. The client is most likely in pulmonary edema due to fluid overload. The next action would be to raise the head of bed, Option #1, then apply oxygen, Option #2. At that point, the provider of care needs to be notified for orders, Option #3.

4.59 ② Prior planning for burn wound treatment should include organizing and planning for the mechanics of the procedure as well as the emotional support necessary for the client. Options #1, #3, and #4 may be appropriate, but have a lesser priority over Option #2.

4.60 ② Option #2 is correct. Both of these clients would require ongoing pain assessment, pain management interventions, and there is no indication of an infection with either client. Option #1 is incorrect. The developmental needs are very different, and with a 25-year-old client most likely having numerous visitors, this may cause the agitation and confusion of the older client to be increased. Another concern with Option #1 is that the option does not say if this is a new onset of confusion. If it did state "new onset of confusion," this could be a sign of infection. This assignment then would not be appropriate for this client who had surgery one day ago. Of course, we NEVER want to read into the options or the questions, so with the information available you can problem solve this option correctly by understanding the differences in the developmental stages. Option #3 is incorrect since the 40-year-old is presenting with vomiting and an infection, and the client taking corticosteroids may be immuno-compromised. Option #4 is in direct violation of the standard of practice for these clients. Based on the standards of care for these clients, they should not be in the same room.

Notes

Far out in the ocean
On a moonlit night,
A circle of dolphins
Slips out of sight.
They're on a mission
Of the grandest scale,
To spread the word
To every minnow and whale:
That life's an illusion
Just waiting for you—
To believe in your dreams
So that they can come true!
—MICHAEL DOOLEY

CHAPTER 5

Safety and Infection Control

*The rung of a ladder was never meant to rest upon,
but only to hold a foot long enough to enable the
person to put the other somewhat higher.*
— Thomas Henry Huxley

✔ **Clarification of this test …**

Note this percentage has remained 9–15% on the new NCLEX-RN®. These minimum standards include performing and directing activities that manage client care such as: ensuring proper identification, applying principles of infection control, protecting client from injury due to (falls, electrical hazards), applying ergonomic principles, safe use of equipment, accident prevention, error prevention, handling hazardous and infectious materials, incident reports, use of restraints, disaster planning, emergency response plan, and home safety.

☛ Apply principles of infection control (e.g., hand hygiene, surgical asepsis, isolation, sterile technique, universal/standard precautions).

☛ Ensure proper identification of client when providing care.

☛ Protect client from injury (e.g., falls, electrical hazards).

☛ Evaluate appropriateness and accuracy of medication order for client.

☛ Use ergonomic principles when providing care (e.g., safe patient handling, proper lifting).

☛ Facilitate appropriate and safe use of equipment.

☛ Verify appropriateness and/or accuracy of a treatment order.

☛ Assess client for allergies and intervene as needed (e.g., food, latex, environmental allergies).

☛ Follow procedures for handling bio-hazardous and hazardous materials.

☛ Assist client to compensate for a physical or sensory impairment (e.g., assistive devices, positioning, compensatory techniques).

☛ Educate client on safety issues (e.g., home, school, transportation).

☛ Educate client and staff regarding infection-control measures.

☛ Assess client ability to manage care in home environment and plan care accordingly (e.g., equipment, community resources, etc.).

☛ Follow security plan and procedures (e.g., newborn nursery security, violence, controlled access).

☛ Follow requirements for use of restraints and/or safety devices (e.g., least restrictive restraints, timed client monitoring).

☛ Acknowledge and document practice errors (e.g., incident report for medication error).

☛ Implement emergency response plans (e.g., internal/external disaster, bomb threat, community planning).

5.1 What nursing actions indicate the nurse understands how to safely provide care for a client with herpes zoster? **Select all that apply.**

① The nurse who hasn't had chickenpox or vaccine should not be assigned to the client.
② The nurse puts on sterile gloves when entering the client's room.
③ The nurse puts on a gown when entering the client's room.
④ The nurse only puts on gloves when starting an IV.
⑤ The nurse maintains the client in isolation precautions for the duration of visible lesions.

5.2 What is the correct order for the nurse to remove the personal protective equipment (PPE) following the care for a client in isolation? Organize the steps in chronological order. **All options must be used.**

| ① Mask |
| ② Gloves |
| ③ Goggles/Face Shield |
| ④ Gown |

| |
| |
| |
| |

5.3 Two Rehab nurses are preparing to transfer a client from the bed to the chair. Which of these nursing actions should the nurse implement to assure a safe transfer for the client?

① Instruct client to depend on the nurse whenever possible during the transfer.
② Position bed in highest position if client is able to tolerate.
③ Position chair so client is moving toward the strong side.
④ Instruct client to pivot prior to standing.

5.4 What is the priority of care for the Rehab nurse prior to administering atenolol as prescribed?

① Verify the identity of the client by asking the client to state first name.
② Verify the client's name and room number with the medication order.
③ Scan the hospital code along with the medication name and compare to wrist bracelet.
④ Verify the full name of the client and medical record number on the wrist bracelet with appropriate documentation.

5.5 Which of these actions by the older adult, who is being discharged from Rehab with a cane following a fall, indicate the client understands how to safely use the cane?

① The client places the cane on the affected side to provide support to that side.
② The client advances the cane simultaneously with the opposite affected lower limb.
③ The affected lower limb assumes the first full weight-bearing step on level surfaces.
④ The client places the cane on the unaffected side and moves before the affected lower limb.

5.6 Which of these nursing actions indicate an understanding of how to safely provide care for a client with Vancomycin-Resistant Enterococci (VRE)?

① The nurse puts on a mask and gown when entering the client's room.
② The client's roommate is located > 2 feet (61 cm) from the client.
③ The client will remain in isolation until there are three negative cultures from infection site 1 week apart.
④ The nurse will wear an N95 respirator when providing care for client.

5.7 A client arrives in ER with a chief complaint of very dark urine and swelling around the eyes. Client's blood pressure is 160/92 and is complaining of fatigue. In taking the client's history, what would be most important for the nurse to ask?

① "Have you had a recent strep infection?"
② "Have you had a recent staph infection?"
③ "Have you been camping recently?"
④ "Is anyone else in your home sick?"

5.8 What would be the priority of care for the nurse to implement when drawing blood cultures on a client with acute renal failure (ARF) on dialysis who has a temporary access catheter and spikes a temperature of 104°F (40°C)?

① Draw a sample from the dialysis catheter.
② Obtain 2 culture bottles from the same stick.
③ Use alcohol and Betadine to prep the skin.
④ Wait until the cultures are drawn to start the antibiotics.

5.9 What is the priority nursing action for a client in airborne precautions with the diagnosis of active tuberculosis who is refusing to eat or make eye contact?

① Limit contact with the client to reduce the risk of transmission of infection.
② Place a "No Visitors" sign on the door to give the client privacy.
③ Request a psychiatric consult because the client is obviously depressed.
④ Spend extra time with the client to assess the client's emotional status.

5.10 In order to best prevent infection in the NICU, the nurse should implement what nursing action?

① Use meticulous hand washing technique.
② Wear sterile gowns and gloves when in direct contact with an infant.
③ Administer ordered antibiotics.
④ Avoid contact with the infant unless absolutely necessary.

5.11 A client is admitted to the Emergency Department with complaints of abdominal pain and bloody diarrhea. The client has been traveling and eating in restaurants for the past week. What should the nurse implement first?

① Be certain blood cultures and a CBC are obtained.
② Institute IV therapy and IV antibiotics.
③ Obtain a stool specimen for culture and WBCs.
④ Administer antidiarrheal medication.

5.12 The teacher sends a first grader to see the school nurse. The child's eyes are red, and there is a small amount of purulent discharge. The nurse phones the parent and the parent says, "My child has been on antibiotic eye drops for 24 hours." What should the nurse implement?

① Permit the child to return to the classroom, but encourage frequent hand washing.
② Tell the parent the child must stay out of school until all the symptoms are gone.
③ Tell the teacher to prevent contact with other children and encourage frequent hand washing.
④ Demand the parent pick up the child immediately.

5.13 What is the priority of care for the nurse to implement after finding an elderly client on the floor during AM nursing rounds?

① Document that client fell out of bed due to side rails being low and place the description of the incident in the client's chart and on the medical record.
② Advise the supervisor on night shift to complete the incident report prior to leaving since supervisor was in charge on the previous shift.
③ Complete the incident report at the end of day, when nurse is less busy, and can think in a logical manner, so the provider of care can review it on the medical records.
④ Complete an incident report including an objective description of the incident and actions taken to safeguard the client, as well as assessment and treatment of injuries.

5.14 The nurse is changing a dressing on an infected abdominal wound with Penrose drains and a large amount of purulent drainage. What is the best way to perform this procedure?

① Obtain clean gloves and dressings, remove the soiled dressing, and use another pair of clean gloves to dress the wound.
② Use clean gloves to remove the soiled dressings, change to sterile gloves and use sterile dressings to cover the wound.
③ Use the sterile gloves to remove the dressing, obtain clean gloves and sterile dressing to reapply to the wound.
④ Initiate protective isolation, utilize only sterile gloves when removing the dressing, and reapply using sterile technique.

5.15 What observations indicate a potential risk and need modification for a client with dementia secondary to Alzheimer's disease who is being cared for by family at home? **Select all that apply.**

① There is a nightlight between the client's bedroom and the bathroom.
② Throw rugs on hard wood floor in front of the entry door and sinks.
③ Client wears nonskid shoes when up and walking in the home.
④ The client only wears glasses when attempting to read fine print.
⑤ Protective door handle covers opening to the outside.

5.16 A client with a necrotizing spider bite is to perform dressing changes at home. Which statement made by the client indicates a correct understanding of aseptic technique?

① "I need to buy sterile gloves to redress this wound."
② "I should wash my hands before redressing my wound."
③ "I should not expose the wound to air at all."
④ "I should use an over-the-counter antimicrobial ointment."

5.17 During the insertion of a central venous pressure monitor device, the tip brushes the underside of the sterile field. Which nursing action is most appropriate?

① Wipe the tip with alcohol before connecting to system.
② Notify the physician of the occurrence, so an antibiotic can be given.
③ Back-flush catheter for several seconds before connecting.
④ Obtain a new monitor device, and prepare for a second attempt.

5.18 During the post-op period for a cardiac client, the graduate nurse is providing dressing care for the client receiving total parenteral nutrition (TPN) through a single-lumen percutaneous central catheter. Which of these observations would require intervention by the charge nurse to review the standard of practice with the graduate nurse?

① The client is weighed daily per hospital protocol.
② The client has a mask on during dressing changes over the TPN site.
③ The client's dressing is changed daily using standard precautions.
④ The nurse discards a bag of TPN after it was hanging only 24 hours and hangs a new bag.

5.19 The nurse is changing the dressing on a client with a large abdominal wound. There are two Penrose drains in place. What is the priority information for the nurse to include when recording this procedure?

① Condition of the surrounding tissue, time necessary to change the dressing, the type of dressing used.
② Client's tolerance of the procedure, time the dressing was changed, amount of wound drainage.
③ Client's response to the dressing change, status of Penrose drains, type of drainage from Penrose drains.
④ Time dressing was changed, description of the wound, color and amount of drainage from Penrose drains.

5.20 While assessing the incision of a 2-day postoperative client, a shiny pink open area is noted with underlying visible bowel. Which action should the nurse take first?

① Cover gaping area with sterile gauze soaked in normal saline.
② Reapply sterile dressing after cleaning with peroxide.
③ Pack opened area with sterile ¾-inch (19 mm) gauze soaked in normal saline.
④ Apply Neosporin ointment and cover with Tegaderm dressing.

5.21 An older client has been recently diagnosed with Clostridium difficile following hospitalization for an elective surgery. Which of these nursing actions by the LPN requires further intervention by the charge nurse?

① The nurse places the client in a private room.
② The nurse refuses to share the dynamap and stethoscope with the nurse providing care for another client.
③ The nurse cleans hands with the hand antibacterial foam that is outside the client's room.
④ The nurse disposes the infections dressing material into the nonporous bag.

5.22 Which nursing implication is important regarding spinal anesthesia?

① The client should be adequately hydrated in order to prevent hypotension after anesthesia is established.
② The client must be NPO at least 12 hours prior to the initiation of the anesthesia to decrease the risk of aspiration.
③ Assess the client for any allergies to Betadine or iodine preparations.
④ Determine the specific gravity of the urine and prepare the client for a central line.

5.23 Which of these plans is most important for reducing the risk of falling for an elderly client admitted to the medical unit?

① Provide the client with long pajama bottoms and assist with tying them around waist, so they do not drag on the floor.
② Place the phone and personal items on the dresser in the client's room.
③ Provide client with a bed alarm if received sleeping medicine within 10 hours.
④ Verify bed alarm works every 24 hours.

5.24 To evaluate the adverse reactions from antibiotic therapy in a client with a postoperative infection and receiving ceftriaxone sodium IVPB every day, what should the nurse monitor?

① Surface of the tongue.
② Hemoglobin and hematocrit.
③ Skin surfaces in skin folds.
④ Changes in urine characteristics.

5.25 After taking the vital signs of a client returning from abdominal exploratory surgery, which action should be taken next?

① Position the client on their left side supported with pillows.
② Check the chart and determine the status of fluid balance from surgery.
③ Check the client's abdominal dressing for any evidence of bleeding.
④ Monitor the incision and pulmonary status for presence of infection.

5.26 When irrigating a draining wound with a sterile saline solution, which sequence is most appropriate for the nurse to follow?

① Pour solution, wash hands, and remove soiled dressing.
② Wash hands, prepare sterile field, remove soiled dressing.
③ Prepare sterile field, put on sterile gloves, and remove soiled dressing.
④ Remove soiled dressing, flush wound, wash hands.

5.27 To protect a post heart transplant client from potential sources of infection, what is the priority nursing intervention?

① Keep client in total isolation.
② Limit participation in unit activities.
③ Adhere to and monitor strict hand-washing techniques.
④ Monitor vital signs, especially temperature, every 2 hours.

5.28 Which instruction is correct regarding the colletion of a specimen from a 4-year-old suspected of having pinworms?

① Collect the specimen 30 minutes after the child falls asleep at night.
② Save a portion of the child's first stool of the day, and take it to the physician's office immediately.
③ Collect the specimen in the early morning with a piece of scotch tape touched to the child's anus.
④ Feed the child a high-fat meal; then save the first stool following the meal.

5.29 What is the priority of care for a young adult client who was found unconscious with several empty medicine bottles at side with a breath that smelled like alcohol and BP—120/72, HR—64 bpm, R—10/min and shallow, T—97.8°F (36.6°C)?

   ① Keep client on a backboard and apply neck brace.

   ② Have respiratory therapy paged for ventilation support.

   ③ Call poison control for instructions and set up charcoal infusion.

   ④ Obtain the empty medicine bottles from the EMTs and notify the ER provider.

5.30 Which observation indicates a mother needs further teaching regarding protecting the newborn from infection?

   ① Applies alcohol to the umbilical cord after a diaper change.

   ② Positions the diaper below the umbilicus.

   ③ Does not wash her hands prior to handling the newborn.

   ④ Applies sterile gauze with petroleum jelly to the circumcision.

5.31 What is the priority plan of care to promote client safety when they are receiving internal radiation therapy?

   ① Restrict visitors who may have an upper respiratory infection.

   ② Assign only male care givers to the client.

   ③ Plan nursing activities to decrease nurse exposure.

   ④ Wear a lead lined apron whenever delivering client care.

5.32 What is the priority nursing intervention to promote safety in the environment for a client with a marked depression of T cells?

   ① Keep a linen hamper immediately outside the room.

   ② Use sterile linens.

   ③ Provide masks for anyone entering the room.

   ④ Discard any standing water left in containers or equipment.

5.33 Which nursing observation indicates a major complication in a client who suffered a thermal injury two weeks ago?

   ① Increased heart rate and elevated blood pressure.

   ② Temperature of 100.6°F (38.1°C) and decreased respiratory rate.

   ③ Increased heart rate and decreased respiratory rate.

   ④ Increased respiratory rate and decreased blood pressure.

5.34 Which statement concerning the transmission of head lice is most important for the nurse to teach?

   ① Head lice occur primarily in lower socioeconomic groups.

   ② Transmission is airborne through insect vectors.

   ③ Infestation is reduced in cold weather.

   ④ Transmission is most common where there are crowded living conditions.

5.35 What is the correct procedure for obtaining a throat culture from a client with pharyngitis?

   ① Quickly rub a cotton swab over both tonsilar areas and posterior pharynx.

   ② Obtain a sputum container for the client to use.

   ③ Following irrigation with warm saline, the pharynx is swabbed.

   ④ Hyperextend the client's head and neck for the procedure.

5.36 Prior to the insertion and after contact with a vascular access device for a client, what is the priority of care?

   ① Apply on a mold mask and goggles.

   ② Educate client regarding the procedure.

   ③ Initiate scrupulous hand hygiene.

   ④ Initiate vigorous friction to central catheter hubs with betadine prep x 10 seconds.

5.37 Which nursing observation indicates a serious complication of impetigo?

   ① White patches on buccal mucosa.

   ② Hearing loss.

   ③ Respiratory wheezes.

   ④ Periorbital edema.

5.38 How should the nurse administer the DPT immunization to a 6-month old?

① By mouth in three divided doses.
② As an IM injection into the gluteus maximus.
③ As an injection into the vastus lateralis.
④ As a Z track injection into the deltoid.

5.39 Which action is necessary to maintain asepsis during a sterile dressing change?

① After scrubbing for the procedure, hold your elbows close to your body.
② Unused sterile dressing tray can be used for the next client if used within 15 minutes.
③ If you splash a liquid on the sterile field, start over again.
④ If you drop a dressing, leave it until you have completed the procedure.

5.40 Which statement made by a parent indicates a correct understanding of poison prevention at home?

① "We store gasoline for the lawn mower in the garage."
② "All our medications are kept in their original containers."
③ "We keep all our cleaning products in the bathroom."
④ "I keep most of our medications in my purse."

5.41 A client with a diagnosis of ulcerative colitis is receiving sulfasalazine. What is the desired response to the medication?

① A decrease in the anemia
② Relief of the diarrhea
③ Exacerbation of anorexia
④ Diminish the retention of fluids

5.42 Which clinical finding should be reported prior to administering gentamycin IV piggyback?

① Temperature—101.2°F (38.4°C)
② Intake 65 mL in one hour
③ BUN—29 mg/dL (10.4 mmol/L), creatinine—2.1 mg/dL (186 µmol/L)
④ WBC—12,000/mm³

5.43 What is the appropriate nursing action for the client on the first postoperative day after a cholecystectomy who has 375 mL of dark serosanguineous fluid draining from the gastric tube?

① Notify the provider of care immediately.
② Prepare for a blood transfusion.
③ Document information in notes.
④ Replace fluid to prevent dehydration.

5.44 A school-aged child is being treated for Hepatitis A which was diagnosed two weeks ago. The client plans to return to school this week with a provider of care's permit. What plan for client's return is appropriate?

① Isolating client from the other children.
② Talking with the provider of care about the reason for return so soon.
③ No specific health requirements are necessary.
④ Not allowing participation in any sports.

5.45 A client with a colostomy wants to know if other people will be able to smell him. What is the best response by the nurse?

① "Keep your bag clean to reduce this possibility."
② "You can eat onions, beans and cucumbers."
③ "You could eat oranges, yogurt and drink buttermilk."
④ "You can take a nonprescription medicine that controls smell."

5.46 What is the priority nursing action to teach the client and close associates to prevent the spread of Hepatitis A?

① Wash their hands every time they go to the bathroom.
② Refuse to use any blood products.
③ Teach drug addicts never to share their used needles.
④ Always use condoms during sexual intercourse.

5.47 A client is four days postoperative abdominal perineal resection. Which sign is most important for the nurse to report to the healthcare provider?

① Moderate amount of serosanguineous drainage on abdominal dressing.
② Nausea, vomiting, and increased abdominal distention.
③ Moderate amount of yellow-green nasogastric drainage and decreased urine output.
④ Urinary output via Foley catheter 200 mL over a 4-hour period.

5.48 Which measure should be explained to the staff to maintain safety while using the defibrillator?

① Remain clear of the bed when using the defibrillator.
② Check the defibrillator every 24 hours.
③ Ask staff not to leave the defibrillator plugged in.
④ Do not defibrillate over the electrodes.

5.49 What would be the priority plan of care for an elderly client with diabetes, hypertension, BUN—23 mg/dL (8.2 mmol/L); creatinine—2.1 mg/dL (186 μmol/L); who is scheduled for a CAT scan with and without contrast?

① Hydrate well prior to the procedure.
② Monitor BP before and after procedure.
③ Make client NPO six hours prior to procedure.
④ Recommend to provider that the scan is only done without contrast.

5.50 A client with renal cancer will be discharged home with a central venous catheter in place. Which of the following statements made by the client indicates a correct understanding of aseptic technique?

① "I should not take showers."
② "I must wash my hands after changing the dressing."
③ "I can reuse my equipment from the day before."
④ "I must wash my hands before changing the dressing."

5.51 What is the desired response to intestinal antibiotics such as neomycin sulfate?

① Decrease gas formation by anaerobic bacteria.
② Work as an adjunct to systemic antibiotics therapy.
③ Decrease postoperative wound infection by decreasing incidence of peritonitis.
④ Prevent ulcerative colitis in young adults.

5.52 At a health screening clinic, an adult male client's total plasma cholesterol level is reported to be 200 mg/dL (5.17 mmol/L). Based on this assessment, which nursing action is most appropriate?

① Refer the client to a physician for appropriate medication.
② Ask the client to lie down immediately.
③ Encourage the client to follow a low-fat diet.
④ Recheck the cholesterol level in two years.

5.53 What is the priority plan of care when teaching a newly diagnosed diabetic client how to give insulin injections?

① Demonstrate how to give an insulin injection on self.
② Provide the client with a pamphlet on how to give injections.
③ Provide the client with a doll to practice the injection technique.
④ Let the client practice giving the injection to the nurse.

5.54 When teaching a newly diagnosed diabetic client about regulating diabetes at home, the nurse would include which instructions?

① Limit vigorous exercise.
② Eliminate sugar from the diet.
③ Test blood sugar at regular intervals.
④ Limit carbohydrates in the diet.

5.55 The healthcare provider orders wrist restraints for an elderly client pulling at the Foley catheter. The client refuses to allow the nurse to put the restraints on arms. What is the priority nursing intervention?

① Chart the refusal, remove the restraints, and check the client frequently.
② Apply a vest restraint rather than wrist restraints.
③ Obtain the assistance of the UAP to apply the wrist restraints.
④ Administer client PRN for pain and apply restraints after client is asleep.

5.56 A client receiving patient-controlled analgesia (PCA) complains of no pain relief. Which is the safest action by the nurse?

① Check the programming of the pump for correctness.
② Replace the pump with a new one. Have the old one checked.
③ Report the pump dysfunction to the charge nurse.
④ Replace the pump. Send the old one to soiled utility.

5.57 Workplace violence especially in the ER Department is an increasing safety issue. Which are the best plans to reduce this type of violence? **Select all that apply.**

① Provide fast service to remove clients from ER as soon as possible.
② Provide hospital security in the ER department.
③ Maintain communication with clients in the waiting room.
④ Allow providers of care to carry guns.
⑤ Educate admitting staff regarding communication and caring.

5.58 What should be the priority discharge instructions for a client with hemiplegia from a stroke who is being discharged home with use of a cane?

① Rent a hospital bed with an overhead frame, so that the client can get up easily without falling.
② Remove throw rugs and other obstacles on the floor as canes can easily slip.
③ Build a ramp for easy access to the outside.
④ Insert handrails in the shower and beside the toilet for easy use.

5.59 The female client gets out of the bed and a cervical implanted radiation device falls to the floor. What is the nurse's best action?

① Call the hazardous materials department to remove the device immediately.
② Have the client take a shower and return to bed.
③ Remove the device from the room, so that the client will not be harmed.
④ Call the provider of care to inform of the situation.

5.60 What is the priority action if the hospital area becomes filled with smoke from a fire?

① Remove the clients from the smoke.
② Sound the fire alarm.
③ Use fire extinguisher to put out the fire.
④ Contain fire to prevent the spread to other clients.

Answers & Rationales

5.1 ① Option #1 is correct. Nurses who have not
③ had chickenpox or the vaccine should not
⑤ provide care for this client due to the risk
of transmission. Option #3 is correct. The
precautions used for this organism include
standard/airborne/contact precautions. Part
of contact precautions includes gown, gloves,
and as needed mask and goggles. Option #5
is a correct statement. Option #2 is incorrect,
since sterile gloves would be used for protective
isolation which would include clients who are
receiving chemotherapy, immunosuppressed or
neutropenic, and clients who have an increased
susceptibility to infection. Option #4 is
incorrect, since gloves are part of the isolation
precautions for this infectious agent. It would
violate the standard of care if the nurse ONLY
put on gloves for this client when starting an
IV.

5.2

② Gloves: The first step would be to extend arms and slowly peel one glove downward, turning it inside out. With the ungloved hand, slide a finger under the inside portion of the remaining glove, turning inside out, and discard.
③ Goggles/ face shield: The second step in this process is to remove the goggles/face shield by grasping the ear pieces or headband to remove.
④ Gown: The third step is to remove the gown by unfastening the neck, then the waist ties; pull gown forward away from the body, folding it inside out and rolling it into a bundle for disposal.
① Mask: The fourth step is to remove the mask by only touching the ties. It is important the front of the mask is not touched.

5.3 ③ Option #3 is correct. During a transfer from
the bed, always remember "*Strong side leads.*"
Option #1 is incorrect. The client should be
advised how to assist when possible versus
depending on the nurse. Option #2 is incorrect
since the bed should be lowered to the lowest
position to decrease the risk for falls. Option #4
is incorrect since the client should be standing
first and then pivot.

5.4 ④ Option #4 is correct. The 2009 National
Patient Safety Goals mandate reviewing and
using a minimum of two client identifiers.
This goal is to prevent medication errors and
optimize the delivery of safe care to the clients.
Option #1 is not a complete answer. While
asking a client who is alert and coherent to
state name is correct, the new National Patient
Safety Goals mandate using a minimum of two
client identifiers prior to administering the
medication. Option #2 is incorrect. While it
is imperative to verify the name of the client
prior to administering a medication, the room
number is not an acceptable client identifier.
Option #3 is incorrect. If the hospital has a
bar coding system, then it may be correct to
scan the medication label and the client's wrist
bracelet; however, not the hospital code and
this would not be a priority over Option #4.

5.5 ② Option #2 is correct. The client should
advance the cane simultaneously with the
opposite affected lower limb to promote
safety and prevent from falling. Option #1 is
incorrect since the cane should be placed on
the unaffected side to provide support to the
opposite lower limb. Option #3 is incorrect
since the unaffected lower limb should assume
the first full weight-bearing step on level
surfaces. Option #4 is incorrect even though
the first part of the answer is correct regarding
placing the cane on the unaffected side, it
should be moved simultaneously with the
opposite affected lower limb not before the
affected lower limb.

5.6 ③ Option #3 is correct. Until there are three negative culture reports from infectious site (1 week apart), the client will remain in standard/contact precautions. Option #1 is incorrect since there is not a need for a mask unless there is an anticipation of splashing of body fluids. The gown would be correct if in contact with contaminated material. Hand hygiene and gloves are definitely part of these precautions for this infectious agent. Option #2 is incorrect; CDC recognizes situations may occur necessitating the roommates. If this becomes necessary, then the guidelines are that clients should be located > 3 feet (91.4 cm) apart from each other. It is also imperative that protective attire is changed and hand hygiene is performed between contact with clients in the same room, regardless of the disease status. Option #4 is incorrect for this client. This N95 respirator is necessary for clients with tuberculosis (TB) who are in airborne precautions.

5.7 ① Option #1 is correct. The client is showing symptoms of APSGN (acute post-streptococcal glomerulonephritis). Other symptoms for APSGN may include: oliguria, proteinuria, orthopnea, bibasilar rales, weight gain; an elevation in the serum BUN and creatinine; decrease in the creatinine clearance; hematuria, increased urine specific gravity; hyperkalemia, hypermagnesemia, dilutional hyponatremia if urine output is decreased. Throat culture will be positive for streptococcus infection. Options #2, #3, and #4 do not directly relate to the client's symptoms.

5.8 ④ Option #4 is correct. Starting an antibiotic prior to obtaining the culture can alter the results. Option #1, staff nurses and lab personnel do not use the dialysis catheter to obtain blood samples. Option #2, when cultures are ordered x 2 they should be drawn from 2 different sites. Option #3, clorhexadine is the preferred skin prep.

5.9 ④ Option #4 is the correct answer. It is important to further assess the emotional state to determine the cause of the behavior. It may be that when the nurse does additional assessment that the nurse learns the behavior is from some inappropriate concerns regarding isolation, and it can be improved with specific knowledge. In reality, there is a lot of different emotional concerns that the client may be experiencing. The key is for the nurse to assess, in order to unlock the appropriate plan to provide support for the client. Options #1 and #2 could worsen the situation. Option #3 is a possible correct answer, but the nurse should first assess the situation.

5.10 ① Option #1 is correct. The best method to reduce the risk of infection is hand washing. Option #2 is not usually necessary, Option #3 will not prevent infection. Option #4 could cause harm to the infant and result in failure to thrive.

5.11 ③ Option #3 is the priority action. This will determine the necessity of antibiotic use. Option #4, if this is bacterial gastroenteritis, antidiarrheals are contraindicated. Option #1 is not a priority over Option #3.

5.12 ① If the child has been under treatment for 24 hours, the child should no longer be contagious, so Option #1 is correct. Option #2 is not necessary as symptoms can last for several days after treatment begins. Option #3 is not practical to prevent contact among children in a classroom, and Option #4, there is no need for the child to be picked up immediately. Hand washing is the best method to reduce the spread of infection.

5.13 ④ Option #4 is correct. The nurse should complete an incident report including an objective description of the incident and actions taken to safeguard the client, as well as assessment and treatment of injuries. This report should be included as soon as possible and within 24 hours of the incident. These are considered confidential and are not shared with the client (nor does the nurse inform the client that one has been completed.) These incident reports should not be in the chart of the client nor in the medical record. A description of the incident should be documented in clear concise and factual language in the client's record. This report should be forwarded to the risk management department after being reviewed by the nurse manager. Option #1 is incorrect, since the nurse is not certain as to the reason the client fell out of bed, and the report should not be placed in the client's chart nor in the client's medical record. The report should include a factual description of the incident and injuries incurred, avoiding any assumptions as to the cause of the incident. Option #2 is incorrect. The incident report should be completed by the person who identifies that an unexpected event has occurred. Option #3 is incorrect since the report should be completed as soon as possible and within 24 hours of the incident.

5.14 ② Sterile gloves and dressings are used in the application of dressings to wounds. Option #4 is incorrect because protective isolation is not appropriate for this client. Sterile gloves are not necessary for removing the soiled dressings.

5.15 ② Options #2 and #4 are correct. Throw rugs
④ should be removed since they can lead to falls. If the client has glasses, these should be worn on a routine basis. These can assist in the prevention of falls. Option #1 is not an answer since this is not a risk. This is a good practice to assist the client to see when going to bathroom. Option #3 will decrease the risk for falls, Option #5, the protective door handle covers will prevent the client from going outside and wandering outdoors unattended.

5.16 ② The hallmark of asepsis is hand washing. Option #1 is incorrect because the question addresses medical aseptic technique, not sterile procedure. Option #3 is not necessary. Option #4 is incorrect because the client should use only prescribed medications on the wound.

5.17 ④ Contamination of equipment mandates new equipment be employed. Options #1 and #3 are not adequate because the catheter is still contaminated. Option #2 may be appropriate later, but obtaining a new monitoring device is a priority.

5.18 ③ Option #3 is correct. The technique should be surgical aseptic technique versus standard precautions. Typically, based on hospital protocol, the dressing is changed every 48 to 72 hours. This would require further intervention by the charge nurse to review the standard of practice with the graduate nurse. Option #1 would not require intervention by the charge nurse. Option #2 would be considered part of the standard of practice for this procedure, and would not require intervention due to lack of understanding. Option #4 would not require further intervention since this is included in the standard of care for toal parenteral nutrition. Solutions hanging for 24 hours should be discarded and a new bag of solution should be hung.

5.19 ④ The information in Option #4 best describes the essential information that should be charted after a dressing change for a wound of this type. Options #1, #2 and #3 contain important information. However, the information in Option #4 is more important.

5.20 ① Evisceration is treated immediately by application of sterile gauze soaked in sterile normal saline followed by notification of the physician. Options #2, #3, and #4 are not correct responses to this complication.

5.21 ③ Option #3 is correct because the charge nurse needs to explain to the LPN that this antibacterial foam has alcohol in it which does not kill the spores from Clostridium difficile. Hand washing with soap and water are the preferred nursing action to prevent infecting other clients. Option #1 is correct practice for a client with Clostridium difficile, and does not need intervention by the charge nurse. While the private room is the priority plan for this client, if there are no other rooms, the clients can be put in a room together with Clostridium difficile. The nurse, however, will need to change PPE and perform hand washing in between client care since they can be growing different spores. Option #2 is also correct practice and requires no further intervention. Equipment should be dedicated for the client or disinfected after each use. Option #4 is also correct practice, and does not require any further intervention by the charge nurse.

5.22 ① It is important that the client be well hydrated to prevent hypotensive problems after the spinal anesthesia is initiated. Option #2 is unnecessary. Option #3 is not necessary as iodine dyes are usually not used. Option #4 is irrelevant to the procedure.

5.23 ③ Option #3 is correct. Clients should have a bed alarm in place for the first 24 hours of their hospital stay based on their unit protocol and client population. After the first 24 hours, then the need to continue with the alarm will be based on the following: confusion, impulsive, impaired mobility, recent fall, and/or sleeping med within 10 hours. Option #1 is incorrect since they can become loose after being in bed and sleeping. It would be much better to provide clients with capri-length pajama bottoms versus having long bottoms that can cause falls. Option #2 is incorrect. It is not the most important plan for fall prevention in comparison to Option #3. Even if the dresser was closer to client, it still would not be the priority over #3. Option #4 is incorrect since the alarm should be verified every shift for safe care.

5.24 ① Long-term use of Rocephin can cause overgrowth of organisms such as Candida albicans; therefore, monitoring of the tongue and oral cavity is recommended. Options #2, #3, and #4 do not reflect a problem with this medication.

5.25 ③ The dressing should be checked on admission to the room and frequently for several hours. Options #1 and #2 are not priority at this time. Option #4 is inappropriate as it is too soon for infection to occur secondary to surgery.

5.26 ② Hand washing should be done prior to beginning any procedure—especially irrigating a wound. Options #1, #3, and #4 are in the incorrect sequence.

5.27 ③ One of the most important nursing strategies with a client who is immunosuppressed is adherence to, and monitoring hand-washing of self and others to prevent transmission of sources of infection. Option #1 is not necessary although a private room might be helpful. Option #2 would allow the client to further withdraw and limit their opportunities for corrective milieu experiences. Option #4 is more often than necessary unless there is a temperature elevation.

5.28 ③ Pinworms crawl outside the anus early in the morning to lay their eggs. This specimen should be collected early in the morning before the child awakens. Option #1 is not the optimum time for collecting the eggs and may result in a false negative test. Option #2 is incorrect because pinworms are rarely found in the stool. Option #4 is incorrect protocol for this test.

5.29 ④ Option #4 is correct. The bottles will likely determine the next step in the emergency treatment. Option #1 is incorrect. There is nothing in the stem of the question indicating a risk for a neck injury. Option #2 may be the second step. Option #3 is premature since the bottles are a mystery until they are examined.

I CAN HINT: This question is evaluating your understanding of the general principles for poison control. A way to help you remember this is by using the mnemonic "SIRES":

Stabilize the client's condition. Assess condition and provide respiratory support, IV access.

Identify the toxic substance. Obtain history and retrieve any available poison. Notify HCP.

Remove the substance to decrease absorption. Shower or wash off radioactive substance.

Antidotes: for heroin or other drug overdose. Ingested substances: lavage, absorbents (activated charcoal), or cathartics.

Eliminate the substance from client's body.

Support client both physically and psychologically.

5.30 ③ Proper hand washing is a priority in preventinginfection. Options #1, #2, and #4 are correct and do not indicate a need for further teaching.

5.31 ③ The principles for radiation safety include: time, distance, and shielding. The nurse should decrease the time spent at a close distance to the client. Option #1 is incorrect because all visitors must keep distance from the client. Option #2 is incorrect since radiation is as harmful to males as to females. Option #4 is used when the nurse has to spend any length of time at close distance with the client—not for routine care.

5.32 ④ Water should not be allowed to stand in containers, such as respiratory or suction equipment, because this could act as a culture medium. Option #1 is incorrect because the protocol for handling soiled articles is accomplished within universal/standard precautions guidelines using double biohazard bags. Option #2 is incorrect because sterile linens are used for clients who are burned or immuno-compromised. Option #3 is not protocol unless the client or visitor has an active pulmonary infection.

5.33 ④ Increased respiratory rate and decreased blood pressure may indicate burn wound sepsis—a life-threatening complication of thermal injury. Options #1, #2, and #3 should be investigated further, but alone do not represent significant compromise.

5.34 ④ Crowded living conditions where there is sharing of clothing and physical closeness increases the likelihood of transmission. Option #1 is incorrect because head lice occur in all socio-economic levels. Option #2 is incorrect because lice are transmitted by close contact. Option #3 is incorrect because weather is not a deterrent although more cases are seen in the winter in some areas due to the sharing of hats.

5.35 ① The tonsilar and pharyngeal areas are quickly swabbed to avoid client discomfort. Option #2 is incorrect because this would not reflect throat bacteria. Option #3 should not be done to obtain an adequate sample for culture. Option #4 is incorrect because the client should hold his head upright—not hyperextended.

5.36 ③ Option #3 is correct. When answering questions about preventing Central Line (CVC) Associated Blood Stream Infection (CLABS) with insertion and maintenance— I CAN HINT: Follow the "SAVE" Precautions. This is an easy way to remember the care. Scrupulous hand hygiene: Prior to insertion & before & after contact with vascular access device. Aseptic Technique- During CVC catheter insertion & care. Vigorous friction to central catheter hubs with alcohol prep x 15 seconds & allow to air dry – whenever a break to the connection is made with administering medication, obtaining a blood sample, flushing, changing tubing/port, or adding a device. Ensure CVC lumen patency. Positive pressure cap must be used on all CVC lumens, including PICC's. (Maximum Clear Access cap). Flush each lumen with 20 ml (2 pre-filled 10 ml syringes) preservative free NS after each medication or every 12 hours if lumen not in use or infusion rate <25 ml/hr. Do not force flush a line. CVC flush technique: 1. Flush line. 2. Disconnect syringe. 3. Clamp lumen. Change injection cap if unable to clear all blood from port after blood samples (do not leave blood in access cap).

5.37 ④ Periorbital edema is indicative of post-streptococcal glomerulonephritis, a possible complication of impetigo. Option #1 describes a fungal infection. Options #2 and #3 can be caused by many other factors.

5.38 ③ Because the muscle mass of an infant is small, the intramuscular injection should be given in the lateral aspect of the thigh (vastus lateralis). Option #1 is incorrect since the injection is not administered PO. Option #2 is incorrect because the gluteus does not have enough muscle mass. Option #4 is not necessary, and the deltoid is an incorrect area for this method of administration.

5.39 ④ To maintain a sterile field, all items in that field must remain sterile. Leave the contaminated dressing until the procedure is completed. Option #1 is incorrect because elbows are held away from the body. Option #2 is incorrect because sterile materials can be used only for one client; and if unused, must be discarded, or re-sterilized. Option #3 is unnecessary because a liquid can be covered with a sterile towel.

5.40 ② All medications should be kept in their original container and out of reach. Options #1, #3, and #4 are not appropriate safety measures to prevent accidental poisonings.

5.41 ② Azulfidine is used to decrease diarrhea. Option #1 is incorrect because one of the side effects of prolonged use of this drug is anemia. Option #3 is incorrect because nausea and vomiting are common reactions. Option #4 is incorrect because this drug has no effect on fluid retention.

5.42 ③ Option #3 is important to report since gentamycin can be nephrotoxic. Options #1 and #4 are indications of an infection which is the reason for administering the antibiotic. Option #2 is a normal clinical finding.

5.43 ③ Option #3 is correct. The amount of drainage for the first postoperative day is approximately 300 to 500 ml. It is important to keep accurate records of the output. Options #1, #2, and #4 are incorrect. I CAN HINT: If you did not know the drainage amount, then you could have clustered Options #2 and #4 together, since these both address too much drainage. Option #2 indicating the need to prepare for a blood transfusion is implying the client is bleeding or low in blood volume. Option #1 also indicates there is a problem if the provider of care has to be notified. Critical reasoning is not just effective for clinical decision making, but is also great for test taking strategies!

5.44 ③ Type A Hepatitis is not infectious within a week or so after the onset of jaundice, and the child can return to school. Options #1 and #2 are not necessary. Option #4 depends on the child's energy level.

5.45 ① Cleanliness is known to control odor. Option #2 causes gas production. Option #3 is ineffective. Option #4 is incorrect because the client should check with the provider of care before taking any over-the-counter drugs.

5.46 ① Type A Hepatitis is spread by oral-fecal route, so it is important to teach effective hand washing every time the client uses the bathroom, or has genital-rectal contact. Options #2, #3, and #4 are not true for Hepatitis A. I CAN HINT: Notice that options #2 and #3 both address blood/needles. Since this is not a *Select all that apply* question, you can cluster the similar options together. This will provide you with a 50% chance of getting the right answer even if you have no idea what the correct answer is!

5.47 ② Abdominal distention, along with the nausea and vomiting, indicate potential development of an ileus, or decreased peristalsis, and should be brought to the attention of the physician as soon as possible. Options #1, #3, and #4 might also be reported as additional data, but are normal findings.

5.48 ① This is a priority to prevent accidental countershock. Option #2 is incorrect because the equipment should be checked every 8 hours. Option #3 is incorrect because the equipment should remain plugged in at all times. Option #4 is correct information, but is not a priority.

5.49 ④ Protecting the client's safety is a priority for the nursing care plan. Options #1, #2, and #3 are not necessary for this client and do not address safety.

5.50 ④ The foundation of aseptic technique is meticulous hand washing prior to a procedure. Options #1 and #3 are inappropriate. Option #2 is incomplete.

5.51 ③ Neomycin sulfate is a bowel sterilizer and is used to prevent wound and abdominal infection in the postoperative intestinal surgery client. Options #1, #2, and #4 are incorrect.

5.52 ③ The total cholesterol level for an adult male should be under 200 mg/dL (5.17 mmol/L). Higher levels require a low-fat diet. Levels higher than 250 mg/dL (6.47 mmol/L) may require medication, if diet therapy is not effective. Option #1 is not necessary prior to working on diet. Option #2 is incorrect. Option #4 is incorrect because blood levels should be checked sooner than 2 years.

5.53 ③ A client should be given a doll to practice injection technique. Options #1 and #2 may be appropriate, but Option #3 provides the best teaching method. Option #4 is not recommended.

5.54 ③ Testing blood sugar levels several times each day gives the client information about the regulation of insulin and blood sugar. This information would be important in assessing the control of this disease process. Option #1 is incorrect because regular exercise should be encouraged. Option #2 is correct for a diabetic; however, Option #3 is a higher priority. Option #4 is not correct for the diabetic diet.

5.55 ① Option #1 is the only answer that does respect the client's right to refuse. Options #2, #3, and #4 may be considered malpractice.

5.56 ② Option #2 is correct. If faulty equipment, client's treatment is interrupted, and for safety it is imperative for the PCA pump to be replaced. Option #1 is incorrect; the settings will have been checked by 2 RN's prior to initiating PCA. Option #3 is incorrect, reporting does not address the issue of client not receiving medication. Option #4 is incorrect, replacing is correct; however, the faulty one must be investigated for safety.

5.57 ①
② Options #1, #2, #3 and #5 are ways to keep
③ the waiting clients from becoming belligerent.
⑤ Hopefully we will never get to Option #4 as being the only answer.

5.58 ② Option #2 is the priority instruction. Option #4 may be necessary if the client is having trouble with balance. Options #1 and #3 should not be necessary at this time.

5.59 ① Option #1 is the only safe answer. The device must be removed by special handling materials, so that the person touching the radiation will not be exposed. Options #2 and #4 are secondary. Option #3 is an incorrect statement and a safety hazard to other clients, employees, family members, etc. that may come in contact with the radiation.

5.60 ① Option #1 should be priority. The rest is as easy as "RACE"—Rescue client, Activate the alarm, Contain fire, and Extinguish. This is a strategy to assist in remembering the sequence of events for fire safety.

CHAPTER 6

Health Promotion and Maintenance

It is not how much you do but how much love you put in the doing.
– Mother Teresa

✔ **Clarification of this test ...**

There have been no changes in percentages. This chapter still represents 6–12% of exam items. The minimum standards include performing and directing activities that promote and maintain the health of client/family. This includes performing a comprehensive health assessment, provide care and education throughout the growth and development stages and through the aging process, disease prevention, health promotion programs, ante/intra/postpartum/newborn care and immunizations, plan and/or participate in community health education programs. Activities in this chapter are not as heavily weighted as many of the activities in pharmacology and management.

- ☛ Provide care and education for the adult client ages 18–64 years.
- ☛ Perform comprehensive health assessments.
- ☛ Provide care and education for the adult client ages 65–85 years and over.
- ☛ Assess readiness to learn, learning preferences, and barriers to learning.
- ☛ Educate client regarding acute or chronic condition.
- ☛ Perform targeted screening assessments (e.g., vision, nutrition).
- ☛ Provide information about health maintenance recommendations (e.g., physician visits, immunizations).
- ☛ Provide information for prevention and treatment of high-risk health behaviors (e.g., smoking cessation, safe sexual practice, needle exchange).
- ☛ Assess and teach clients about health risks based on family, population, and/or community characteristics.
- ☛ Provide care and education for the newborn less than 1 month old through the infant/toddler (client through 2 years).
- ☛ Provide care and education for the preschool, school-age, and adolescent client ages 3 through 17 years.
- ☛ Provide care and education to a client in labor or antepartum client.
- ☛ Provide postpartum care and education.
- ☛ Provide prenatal care and education.
- ☛ Plan and/or participate in community-health education.

6.1 What would be the priority to include in the health promotion plan for an older adult client with a diagnosis of multiple sclerosis?

① Discuss the importance of decreasing antioxidants (vitamins C and E, beta-carotene) due to the risk of losing the myelin sheath.
② Educate client to consume a low-fat, high-fiber diet, with a calcium supplement, and daily cranberry juice.
③ Review importance of keeping warm due to improving the neurologic function.
④ Teach about the importance of avoiding aerobic exercise due to muscle weakness.

6.2 What plan would be most appropriate for the common complaint in pregnancy during the third trimester with the problem with leg cramps? **Select all that apply.**

① Discuss the importance of doing Kegel exercises.
② Demonstrate the pelvic rocking exercises.
③ Increase broccoli in diet.
④ Increase dairy products in diet.
⑤ Increase raisins in diet.

6.3 In preparation for discharge of a client with arterial insufficiency and Raynaud's phenomenon, what is the priority to include in the teaching plan?

① Walk several times each day as a part of an exercise routine.
② Keep the heat up, so that the environment is warm.
③ Wear thromboembolic disease (TED) hose during the day.
④ Use hydrotherapy for increasing oxygenation.

6.4 What would be the priority of care for a client with Stage 2 Alzheimer's Disease who becomes agitated and refuses to answer further questions during an interview?

① Ask client if questions are upsetting in any way.
② Discontinue the interview.
③ Explain that the questions are necessary to complete plan of care.
④ Give client a small break and reconvene in five minutes.

6.5 Which of these plans would be most appropriate to incorporate while educating the family members of an older Asian American client regarding the discharge teaching?

① Avoid making eye contact with authority figures during the teaching.
② Touch client on the head to demonstrate respect.
③ Hug family after the teaching session is complete to demonstrate caring and acceptance.
④ Direct most of teaching plan at the women in the family and the grandparents.

6.6 A female client is diagnosed with human papilloma virus (HPV). Which client statement illustrates an understanding of the possible sequelae of this illness?

① "I will take all of the antibiotics until they are finished."
② "I will use only prescribed douches to avoid a recurrence."
③ "I will return for a pap smear in 6 months."
④ "I will avoid using tampons for 8 weeks."

6.7 Which of these questions is the highest priority for the nurse when discussing safety for a pre-school child with the parents?

① "Do you have all of your kitchen cabinets locked?"
② "Do the parents in your neighborhood feel comfortable reporting strangers?"
③ "Are you able to discuss your child's disagreements while playing with his friends to other parents?"
④ "Does your child have appropriate safety equipment for the games he plays?"

6.8 Which intervention would be most important to implement during a teaching session for an elderly client who has bilateral hearing loss and macular degeneration?

① Frequently touch client when speaking.
② Maintain a dimly lit environment.
③ Remain on the side of the client.
④ Use a lower tone of voice when speaking.

6.9 The family members of an elderly client think their father is masturbating. Which response by the nurse is best?

① "I understand your concern because this is not a normal part of aging."

② "I would not worry about this behavior. He will stop soon."

③ "This is considered a normal behavior."

④ "The best thing you can do is talk to your father about this behavior."

6.10 Which clinical situation indicates the nurse has an accurate understanding of how to complete a physical assessment?

① The nurse uses the diaphragm of the stethoscope to auscultate S3 and S4.

② The nurse uses the Snellen chart to evaluate the first cranial nerve.

③ The nurse uses the bell of the stethoscope to auscultate S1 and S2.

④ The nurse assesses the abdomen by inspecting, auscultating, percussing, and palpating.

6.11 A mother tells the nurse that the school-age sibling of a child with cystic fibrosis is having difficulty in school, fights frequently with playmates and throws his toys. Which response by the nurse is best?

① "Did he have these behaviors before his sister was diagnosed?"

② "That is typical of school-age children."

③ "Spend time with each child daily, and it will stop."

④ "He is jealous of the attention his sister is receiving."

6.12 Which of these plans for Screening Guidelines indicates the nurse understands the current guidelines for Health Promotion and Disease Prevention?

① Colorectal screening should begin at age 50 and plan should include a colonoscopy every 5 years.

② Blood cholesterol screening should begin at age 20 and be evaluated on a minimum of every 5 years.

③ Blood glucose screening should begin at age 25 and be evaluated on a minimum of every 5 years.

④ Mammograms should begin at age 50, yearly.

6.13 When performing nursing care for a newborn after delivery, which of the following nursing interventions would be the highest priority?

① Adhere to Droplet Isolation precautions.

② Conduct a full physical assessment.

③ Suction the nose prior to the mouth.

④ Cover the newborn's head with a cap.

6.14 A hypertensive client returns to the clinic for reevaluation of his medication. His blood pressure is 180/100. The nurse questions the client regarding how he is taking his medication. What response by the client indicates that he understands and has been taking the medication as prescribed?

① "I take my medication every morning. If my blood pressure is high, I take another dose in the evening."

② "I take my medication every day at the same time regardless of how I feel. I have not missed any doses."

③ "I take my medication every day and make sure that I drink a large amount of liquid each time I take it."

④ "If I have a headache, I don't take my medication. If I miss the morning dose, then I take two pills in the evening."

6.15 Which statement made by the parents of an infant with hydrocephalus indicates they understand how to care for a child with a new ventriculoperitoneal shunt?

① "We will position our child on the operative side to facilitate draining."

② "We will report if our child starts vomiting."

③ "We understand the home health nurse should pump shunt daily."

④ "We will position our child in the semi-Fowler's position after surgery."

6.16 What question is most important to ask a male client who is being evaluated for a digital rectal examination?

① "Have you noticed a change in the force of the urinary stream?"

② "Have you noticed a change in tolerance of certain foods in your diet?"

③ "Do you notice polyuria in the AM?"

④ "Do you notice any burning with urination or any odor to the urine?"

6.17 A young female client has just been told by the healthcare provider that her biopsy results indicate breast cancer. What is the next appropriate action for the nurse to take?

① Ask the client if she has any questions.
② Encourage client to talk about her feelings.
③ Leave client alone for awhile.
④ Call the chaplain for the client.

6.18 A female client reports that for the last 4 months a lump in her right breast has been growing larger. The nurse should recommend the client take which action?

① Notify her physician to schedule a mammogram.
② Begin taking large doses of vitamins.
③ Limit sodium intake.
④ Immediately stop any hormone treatment.

6.19 The nurse is preparing a middle-aged client for diagnostic tests to determine if she has a malignancy in her reproductive system. The client is having difficulty concentrating, appears tense, and is wringing her hands constantly. Which response should the nurse make?

① "You seem to be anxious about the tests. Tell me what you are thinking about."
② "You need to pay more attention to what I'm saying. You'll be less anxious if you understand these tests."
③ "Why are you so restless? Your physician is very good."
④ "I know you're worried about these tests, but I'm sure everything will be fine."

6.20 The nurse assesses a prolonged late deceleration of the fetal heart rate while the client is receiving oxytocin to stimulate labor. What is the priority nursing intervention?

① Turn off the infusion.
② Turn client to left side.
③ Change the fluids to Ringer's Lactate.
④ Increase mainline IV rate.

6.21 Which plan would best promote bonding between the mother and her newborn that is in pediatric intensive care for jaundice?

① Allow the mother to visit and participate in the newborn's care.
② Take the infant to the mother's room for feeding.
③ Place a picture of the infant at the mother's bedside.
④ Provide the newborn with an article that bears the mother's scent.

6.22 What clinical finding would cause the nurse to be concerned with the quality of home care for the toddler?

① Has a bruise on the knee.
② Cries and is fearful when parents leave.
③ Is lacking required immunizations.
④ Throws a temper tantrum during an injection.

6.23 Which assessment is a priority in documenting the nursing history of a toddler upon admission to the hospital?

① The child's rituals and routines at home.
② The child's understanding of hospitalization.
③ The child's ability to be separated from parents.
④ The parent's methods for dealing with temper tantrums.

6.24 While doing a physical examination with a toddler, which assessment should be done last?

① Rectal temperature
② Breath sounds
③ Apical heart rate
④ Motor functions

6.25 Which nursing approach would be most appropriate to use while administering an oral medication to an infant?

① Place medication in 45 mL of formula.
② Place medication in an empty nipple.
③ Place medication in a full bottle of formula.
④ Place in supine position. Administer medication using a plastic syringe.

6.26 What is the priority of care for an infant in this type of traction?

① Notify provider of care regarding the traction set up.
② Assess the infant for signs of infection under the ace wraps.
③ Evaluate brachial pulses and document in the chart.
④ Encourage the mom to assist with care and stroke and talk with infant during care.

6.27 Which statement made by the new mother indicates an understanding of screening for PKU for her newborn son who she is breastfeeding?

① "I will have him tested 24 hours after birth."
② "I will return to the clinic in 48 hours for the screening."
③ "I will return in 1 week to obtain blood samples."
④ "I will return in 1 month for the screening."

6.28 While performing a physical examination on a newborn, which assessment should be reported to the physician?

① Head circumference of 40 cm.
② Chest circumference of 32 cm.
③ Acrocyanosis and edema of the scalp.
④ Heart rate of 160 and respirations of 40.

6.29 To assist the mother in providing appropriate foods for her toddler, the nurse would identify which priority as being the highest?

① Provide the child with finger foods.
② Allow the child to eat favorite foods.

③ Encourage a diet higher in protein than other nutrients.
④ Limit the number of snacks during the day.

6.30 Which action by the mother of a preschooler indicates a disturbed family interaction?

① Tells her child that if he does not sit down and shut up she will leave him there.
② Explains that the injection will burn like a bee sting.
③ Tells her child that the injection can be given while he's in her lap.
④ Reassures child that it is acceptable to cry.

6.31 Planning anticipatory guidance for parents of a beginning school-aged child, what is most important for the nurse to include in the teaching plan?

① Teaching the child to read and write.
② Teaching the child sex education at home.
③ Giving the child responsibility around the house.
④ Expecting stormy behavior.

6.32 Which statement by the parent of a toddler indicates a lack of understanding of this child's nutritional needs?

① "I spend a lot of time planning and preparing my family's meals."
② "I realize she eats more at some meals than at others."
③ "She is a picky eater so I give her one of my vitamins every day."
④ "She likes starchy foods so I decorate them with vegetables."

6.33 What is the priority plan for preventing falls in the older adult?

① Recommend removing all the rugs in the home.
② Encourage installation of appropriate lighting in the home.
③ Review the normal aging changes that place one at risk.
④ Complete a comprehensive risk assessment.

6.34 What should the nurse emphasize when guiding parents teaching their children about human sexuality?

① Parents should determine exactly what the child knows and wants to know before answering questions.

② Parents' words will have more influence than their actions.

③ Anatomic terms should be avoided because they are difficult for the child to understand and learn.

④ Children should be allowed to play "physician" as it will satisfy their sexual curiosity.

6.35 What is most important to teach a child's parents about the treatment of pediculosis capitis (head lice) with Kwell shampoo?

① Treatment should be continued every other day for 1 week with a follow-up treatment in 14 days.

② Clothing and personal belongings require only normal cleansing with soap and water.

③ Application of the shampoo may be repeated at a later date to destroy any surviving live lice.

④ Never repeat the shampoo application as it is readily absorbed through the scalp.

6.36 A physician should be notified about which observation of a mother during her third trimester of pregnancy?

① Epigastric pain.

② Shortness of breath.

③ Increase in rectal pressure.

④ A total weight gain of 33 pounds (15 kg).

6.37 During the nursing history interview, a preschool client's mother reports frequent hospitalizations for gastroenteritis. Which question reveals the most information regarding the cause of these frequent readmissions?

① "Are there other children in the family?"

② "Does the child attend a day care center?"

③ "Does your child play with neighborhood children?"

④ "Is the child current with his immunizations?"

6.38 Which assessment indicates a need to order a magnesium sulfate blood level?

① Urine output decreased from 70 mL/hour to 30 mL/hour.

② Respiratory rate increased from 14/min to 18/min.

③ Hypertonic patellar reflexes.

④ Blood pressure 150/90 increased to 170/100.

6.39 Which client would be the most appropriate for the nurse to administer Rh immune globulin?

① A client with a husband who is Rh positive.

② A client with a positive indirect antiglobulin (indirect Coomb's) test.

③ A client who is sensitized to the Rh antigen.

④ A client who is Rh negative and has an Rh positive infant.

6.40 Which of these schedules is most appropriate to recommend to a pre-menopausal woman regarding her self breast exam?

① One week prior to the monthly period

② One week after the menstrual period

③ During every shower

④ The same day monthly

6.41 Which fetal monitor pattern indicates a problem with a cord compression?

① Early decelerations

② Late decelerations

③ Variable decelerations

④ Loss of variability

6.42 What is most important for the nurse to assess prior to administering calcium gluconate 10% 500 mg IVP stat to a pregnant client who has developed magnesium sulfate toxicity?

① Stability of the respiratory system.

② Adequacy of urine output.

③ Patency of the vein.

④ Availability of magnesium sulfate injection.

6.43 After the termination of pre-term labor, what action by a client indicates her ability to monitor herself at home for fetal well-being?

① Counts uterine contractions.
② Measures her urine output.
③ Counts fetal kicks.
④ Weighs herself daily.

6.44 Which of these nursing actions should be initiated when the nurse is evaluating the Rinne test?

① The nurse occludes one of the client's ears while the nurse whispers in the other ear from 30 cm away.
② The nurse places a vibrating tuning fork midline on top of the head and the client is asked when the sound is heard best.
③ The nurse places a vibrating tuning fork on the mastoid process and then placed near the ear until the sound is no longer heard.
④ The nurse evaluates the eyes for equality of pupil constriction.

6.45 After the anesthesiologist administers an epidural, which nursing action has the highest priority?

① Decrease IV fluid to prevent fluid overload.
② Assess fetal heart monitor for variable decelerations.
③ Place the client on their right side.
④ Evaluate the blood pressure.

6.46 A multigravida client presents to the labor and delivery area and has a precipitous birth with labor lasting only 45 minutes. Which should be the first nursing action for this client who now has a change in blood pressure from 120/70 to 94/50?

① Prepare client for surgery for retained placental fragments.
② Place the client in Trendelenburg position.
③ Massage uterus.
④ Apply oxygen.

6.47 A 28-hour-old newborn begins to exhibit a high pitched cry, irritability, diarrhea, sneezing, and frequent tremors. What is the priority assessment for the nurse to evaluate?

① Cardiac arrhythmias
② History of maternal drug abuse
③ Maternal sepsis
④ Newborn sepsis

6.48 During a health fair, which of these clients should be highest priority for receiving the seasonal influenza vaccination?

① A young adult client who is the mother of two young children.
② A young adult post-op client following an appendectomy.
③ A premenopausal female client with osteoporosis.
④ A middle-aged adult providing care for a spouse following a renal transplant.

6.49 Which of these pediatric clinical assessment findings should be referred to a specialist for further assessment?

① A 6-month-old infant who can only sit with support.
② A 12-month-old infant who is not walking.
③ A 2-year-old who has a vocabulary of 300 words, but only combines two or three words.
④ A 3-year-old who has a vocabulary of 400 words and can correlate these with objects.

6.50 What action should the nurse implement immediately for an OB client when at the peak of a contraction fluid gushes from a client's vagina?

① Evaluate for a prolapsed cord.
② Evaluate fetal monitor for early decelerations.
③ Perform a pH on the fluid to determine it is amniotic fluid.
④ Evaluate fetal monitor for an increase in the variability.

6.51 The mother of a 2-year-old reports that her son is becoming a very picky eater. What is the best response from the nurse?

① "This is a common behavior since he is becoming more autonomous. Try giving him some finger foods."
② "You may try setting better limits between meals regarding snacks."
③ "Try mixing his food together so there is not so much to select from."
④ "I will report this to the nurse practitioner. He may have a virus."

6.52 Which statement made by a mother who is breast feeding most indicates a need for further teaching about birth control?

① "I will go to my healthcare provider and get fitted for a diaphragm."
② "I will have my husband use a condom."
③ "I will get a prescription from my healthcare provider for the pill."
④ "I will practice abstinence during my fertile time."

6.53 Which statement by the parents of a newborn indicates a need for further teaching about newborn care?

① "We will notify the physician for absence of breathing for 10 seconds."
② "We will notify the physician for more than one episode of projectile vomiting."
③ "We will notify the physician if the infant's temperature is greater than 101°F (38.3°C)."
④ "We will rock and cuddle our infant to promote trust."

6.54 What would be a plan for a tertiary prevention activity for an older female client who had a cerebrovascular accident (CVA)?

① An annual mammogram.
② An annual influenza vaccine.
③ An annual ophthalmologic examination to evaluate for macular degeneration.
④ A physical therapy program.

6.55 A 3-month-old is placed in Bryant's traction for congenital hip dysplasia. Which toy is appropriate to offer the infant during hospitalization?

① Rattle
② Stuffed animal
③ Colorful blocks
④ Tape of nursery rhymes

6.56 Which of the following is a priority nursing referral for an elderly client who states, "I feel like I am looking through a tunnel?"

① Neurologist
② Ophthalmologist
③ Psychologist
④ Cardiologist

6.57 While planning care for an elderly client with dementia, which plan is a priority?

① Encourage dependency with activities of daily living.
② Provide flexibility in schedules due to mental confusion.
③ Limit reminiscing due to poor memory.
④ Speak slowly and in a face-to-face position.

6.58 Which observation would most likely represent caregiver burnout in the daughter of an older adult client with Alzheimer's disease?

① Failure of daughter to get parent into wheelchair daily.
② Home environment extremely cluttered at each visit.
③ Daughter remains involved in family's activities.
④ Husband is seen assisting in mother-in-law care.

6.59 During the newborn assessment, the nurse is evaluating the rooting reflex. Locate where the nurse would stroke to elicit this response.

6.60 While assessing cranial nerve 11, which part of the body would the nurse ask the client to move?

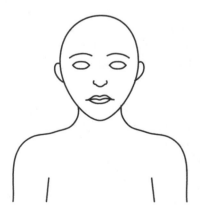

Answers & Rationales

6.1 ② Option 2 is correct. It is important to maintain an ideal body weight, have rest, and become informed about the need to supplement calcium and daily intake of cranberry juice. Option #1 is incorrect because a daily intake of multiple vitamins, antioxidants, and low-dose aspirin (81 mg) are recommended. Option #3 is incorrect. Keeping cool, not warm, is associated with improvement of the neurologic function. Option #4 is incorrect since clients should exercise routinely.

6.2 ③ Options #3 and #4 are correct. Leg cramps
④ during the third trimester may occur due to the compression of lower extremity nerves and blood vessels by the enlarging uterus. This can result in poor peripheral circulation as well as an imbalance in the calcium/phosphorus ratio. In this situation, the options are focusing more to the cause being from hypocalcemia. Both broccoli and dairy products are high in calcium. Additional foods high in calcium include kale, grains, egg yolks. Foods high in phosphorus include dairy, peas, soft drinks, meat, eggs, and some grains. Option #1 is incorrect. Kegel exercises are done to strengthen the perineal muscles and have nothing to do with leg cramps. Option #2 is incorrect since the pelvic rocking exercises stretch out the muscles of the lower back and help relieve lower back pain. Option #5 is incorrect. Raisins are high in iron.

6.3 ② Option #2 is correct. Raynaud's phenomenon consists of intermittent episodic spasms of the arterioles, most frequently in the fingers and toes. Symptoms are precipitated by exposure to cold, emotional upset, or nicotine and caffeine intake. The client's instructions should include keeping the environment warm to prevent vasoconstriction. Wearing gloves, warm clothes, and socks will also be useful in preventing vasoconstriction (option #3), but TED hose would not be therapeutic. Option #1 is incorrect. Walking will most likely increase pain. Option #4 is incorrect. Spasms are not necessarily correlated with other peripheral vascular problems.

I CAN HINT: Refer to the book *Nursing Made Insanely Easy* for a strategy to assist you in remembering the priority information!

6.4 ② Option #2 would be the most appropriate response due to the agitation and refusal to answer questions. The client may be getting overwhelmed. Option #1 is incorrect. The behavior of the client demonstrates that these questions are upsetting the client. Option #3 does not answer the question. The question indicates the client is becoming agitated and refuses to answer further questions. The answer needs to address the problem the client is experiencing versus what the nurse needs to get accomplished. Option #4 is not correct since this time frame will not allow the client to regroup.

6.5 ① Option #1 would be important since this behavior is viewed as a sign of respect and trust for the Asian Americans. Option #2 may be considered to be disrespectful since the head may be considered sacred. Option #3 is not correct, and is not typical with the Asian American culture. Client and family members may be very modest and public display of affection are not typical. The African American, on the other hand, shows affection by touching, hugging, and being close. Option #4 is incorrect since this group is more patriarchal. In the African American culture, however, the women typically head the household.

6.6 ③ Several strains of the human papillomavirus (HPV) are associated with cervical cancer. Option #1 is incorrect because antibiotics are not used for viral infections. Option #2 is incorrect because douches will not prevent recurrence. Option #4 is incorrect because tampons do not contribute to the problem as in toxic shock syndrome.

6.7 ④ Option #4 is a priority due to the developmental stage of the 4-year-old. They are into initiative vs. guilt. The 4-year-old is very active and safety is most important. Option #1 would be priority for the toddler. Options #2 and #3 are important but not a priority.

6.8 ④ Option #4 is correct. As the older clients age, they lose the ability to hear high tones. It is difficult for an older client to understand the voices of both children and women due to the high tones. Option #1 is incorrect since the touch may offend the client and actually be a distracter to the client. Options #2 and #3 are incorrect since the client may not be able to see.

6.9 ③ Masturbation is an activity that some elderly engage in. Options #1 and #2 are inappropriate. Option #4 might embarrass the father and may cause feelings of guilt and anxiety.

6.10 ④ Option #4 is correct. The diaphragm of the stethoscope is used to auscultate high pitch sounds such as S1 and S2. Option #1 is incorrect. Option #2 is used to evaluate the 2nd cranial nerve. Option #3 should be the diaphragm. The bell is used for S3 and S4.

6.11 ① Obtain information about his behavior before the diagnosis to be able to assess a cause for the disruptive behavior. Option #2 is not accurate. Options #3 and #4 may be correct; however, the nurse must assess behavior prior to his sibling's illness.

6.12 ② Option #2 is a correct plan for screening as outlined by the American Heart Association. Option #1 is incorrect; while colorectal screening should begin at age 50 is a correct statement, the plan should include a colonoscopy every 10 years or it may be adjusted based on the results as outlined by the American Cancer Society. Option #3 is incorrect. Blood glucose screening should begin at age 45 and should be evaluated on a minimum of every 3 years as outlined by the American Diabetes Association. Option #4 is incorrect. Mammograms begin at age 40, yearly, versus age 50 as the option reads.

6.13 ④ Option #4 is correct. The priorities immediately following delivery include: I CAN HINT: The 4 H's: hypoxia, hypothermia, hypoglycemia, and heart rate. One of the greatest risks to the newborn is cold stress. Due to the risk of developing hypothermia from the loss of heat from the head due to excessive evaporation, a priority in this question would be to cover the newborn's head with a cap. Option #1 is not required for the newborn unless the clinical situation indicates the growth of an organism that requires droplet isolation precautions such as: pertussis, streptococcal (group A) pharyngitis, pneumonia or scarlet fevers in infants, etc. Of course, standard precautions are practiced for all clients. Option #2 is not the highest priority following delivery. Yes, it is important to perform a full physical assessment, but the priority is safety during this time which would be the possible issue with hypothermia. Option #3 is incorrect since the mouth should be suctioned prior to the nose.

6.14 ② This option best describes how the client should take the medication for hypertension. It is important that he take it every day. However, it may be a problem if he is consuming a large amount of water during the day. If he is taking the medication correctly, he needs to have the medication reevaluated since his blood pressure remained high.

6.15 ② Option #2 is correct. Parents that understand how to provide care for their child with a ventriculoperitoneal shunt would need to know the signs and symptoms of increasing ICP. Refer to I CAN HINT below. Option #1 is incorrect. If the child had surgery, then infant would be positioned in the supine position with head turned operative side up to prevent pressure on the shunt valve and to prevent too rapid depletion of CSF. Option #3 is incorrect. The parents will learn how to provide care to the shunt. Option #4 is incorrect. This position would result in a rapid depletion of CSF.

I CAN HINT: An easy way to remember symptoms of increased intracranial pressure for the infant is "PIES." The book *Nursing Made*

Insanely Easy, has a fun image to assist you with this, but for now I will share with you the mnemonic memory tool "PIES":

Projecile vomiting, posturing

Irritability (early symptoms); high-pitched cry (headache)

Enlarged head (bulging fontanels, ↑ head circumference), eye changes (pupillary changes)

Suture separation (cranial), seizures

6.16 ① Option #1 is correct. This change would be most indicative of a potential complication with (BPH) benign prostate hypertrophy. Options #2, #3, and #4 are incorrect. Option #4 would be indicative of an infection.

6.17 ② Encouraging the client to talk about feelings allows the client to cry or express her reaction. Options #1, #3, and #4 do not allow for immediate expression of reaction to this crisis.

6.18 ① A mammogram is an x-ray of the breast. It usually shows the presence of a lesion if one is present. Positive zero radiography (type of mammogram) has the ability to detect carcinomas 1 to 2 years prior to formation of a palpable 1 cm. lesion. Option #2 is incorrect because specific vitamin therapy may be useful in some cases. It is not curative alone. Option #3 is incorrect because sodium has not been associated with breast cancer. Option #4 is incorrect because hormones have not been known to cause breast cancer.

6.19 ① This response acknowledges the client's concerns and allows exploration of her fears. Options #2, #3, and #4 provide false reassurance and do not allow the client an opportunity to express and deal with her feelings.

6.20 ① Stopping the infusion will decrease contractions and possibly remove uterine pressure off the fetus, which is a possible cause of the late deceleration. Option #2 may help the deceleration by removing the placenta off of the inferior vena cava and increasing blood flow to the fetus; however, the initial action should be to stop the infusion which is causing ongoing stimulation of the uterus. Option #3 would be appropriate if the nurse was going to bolus the client with isotonic fluid due to the epidural, but this is not addressed in the question. Option #4 would be appropriate if the late deceleration was from the decrease in blood pressure from the epidural, but NEVER read into the questions. There is NO indication that this is the clinical situation.

I CAN HINT: *Nursing Made Insanely Easy*, by Manning & Rayfield has a great acronym to assist in recalling how to answer this type of question in chronological order. There is an image of a fire truck uncoiling the hose to help put out "Fetal Distress." UN "COIL": #1 STOP OXYTOCIN, then, Change position to the left side, Oxygen, Increase IV fluids, then Lower the head of the bed.

6.21 ① Option #1 is the best intervention to promote contact and feedback needed for bonding between the mother and the newborn. Option #2 is not appropriate. Taking the infant back and forth to the mother's room does not provide optimal time for bonding. Option #3 does not replace the benefits of touch and eye contact needed for effective bonding. Option #4 only increases comfort for the infant and does not give feedback to the mother.

6.22 ③ This may indicate a lack of concern for child's well-being and may be a sign of poor quality of home care. Option #1 is a common assessment during the toddler years. Options #2 and #4 are expected behaviors for a toddler.

6.23 ① During a crisis such as hospitalization, children are able to establish a sense of security through a consistency of the rituals and routines from home. Option #2 is inappropriate for this age. Option #3 is incorrect because separation anxiety is a major fear during this age. Option #4 is not as high a priority as Option #1 in decreasing psychological trauma from hospitalization.

6.24 ① This, as any other invasive procedure, should be done last, so it doesn't alter the cardiopulmonary assessment of the child. Options #2, #3, and #4 should be done before Option #1.

6.25 ② This is a convenient method for administering medications to an infant. Options #1 and #3 are incorrect. Medication is not usually added to infant's formula feeding. Option #4 is partially correct. However, the infant is never placed in a reclining position during procedure due to potential aspiration.

6.26 ④ Option #4 is correct. This is Bryant's traction and the infant's buttocks are slightly off the bed with the legs suspended in the air bilaterally. This is typically used for infants with congenital hip dysplasia. This is an example of skin traction, so Option #2 is incorrect. The correct answer would have been to assess for skin integrity. Option #1 is incorrect since it is set up appropriately. Option #3 is incorrect since the pulses should be distal to the traction to evaluate arterial perfusion. The pulses that should be evaluated would be the dorsalis pedis and/or posterior tibial. Option #4 is correct since tactile stimulation is imperative for an infant's normal emotional development to continue to grow. Deprivation can result in a complication with failure to thrive.

6.27 ③ Option #3 is correct since the newborn is only getting colostrum for the first few days. This screening may have a possible false negative result with the initial screening. Options #1, #2, and #4 are inaccurate and would not provide valid information.

6.28 ① Average circumference of the head for a neonate ranges between 32 to 36 cm. An increase in size may indicate hydrocephaly or increased intracranial pressure. Options #2, #3, and #4 are normal newborn assessments.

6.29 ① The child is going through the autonomy versus shame and doubt stage. Finger foods allow the child the necessary independence for this stage. Options #2 and #4 may or may not be correct because the child may eat food without appropriate nutrients. Option #3 does not represent accurate nutritional information.

6.30 ① Threatening a child with abandonment will destroy the child's trust in his family. Option #2 is not necessarily accurate, but does not indicate a disturbed family interaction. Option #3 is inappropriate but does not indicate a disturbance in family interaction. Option #4 indicates a healthy interaction.

6.31 ③ Giving children responsibilities allows them to develop feelings of competence and self-esteem through their industry. Option #1 may require some assistance from the parents, but children this age learn at their own rate. Option #2 may be premature. Option #4 usually does not occur until about age 11.

6.32 ③ Children should not be given adult doses of vitamins because a child's need for vitamins is different than adults. Toddlers are picky eaters, and children's daily vitamins are appropriate. Option #1 shows concern about family nutrition. Option #2 is accurate because toddlers usually eat only one or two adequate meals each day. Nutritious snacks are helpful in assuring adequate nutritional intake. Option #4 is true because toddlers do prefer a "white diet" of starchy foods.

6.33 ④ Option #4 is priority in preventing falls. Options #1, #2, and #3 would be a part of doing a complete assessment.

6.34 ① Children often have misinformation about human sexuality; and if not identified, the child will incorporate the misinformation into the parent's answer. To be able to answer a question adequately, it is important to determine what the child wants to know. Option #2 is contra to human behavior. Option #3 is incorrect because most experts believe correct anatomic names are appropriate. Option #4, "Oh, please …"

6.35 ③ Kwell shampoo should be used as directed as it is an organic solvent and can be toxic as well as absorbed through the skin of the scalp. It may be repeated, but usually at least 5–7 days after the first application. Option #1 is too often for applying the shampoo. Option #2 is incorrect because very hot water and a special detergent (Rid) need to be used for cleansing clothing and personal belongings. Option #4 is incorrect because the shampooing must be repeated after the eggs hatch.

6.36 ① Epigastric pain is usually indicative of an impending seizure. Options #2 and #3 are expected observations. Option #4 is important to address but is not a priority to Option #1.

6.37 ② Environments where there are increased numbers of children, such as day care centers, are more likely to have infections due to close living conditions facilitating the transmission of disease. Options #1 and #4 do not pose a problem or solution regarding gastroenteritis. Option #3 is a possible source of infection but not as likely as a day care center.

6.38 ① Magnesium sulfate is metabolized and excreted by the kidneys. A decrease in the urine output can lead to toxicity. Option #2 indicates an improvement. Options #3 and #4 are incorrect because these assessments indicate a need to start magnesium sulfate.

6.39 ④ RhoGam is administered to this client to prevent sensitization to the Rh antigen. Option #1 is irrelevant because it is the mother and infant's Rh type that the decision is based on. Option #2 may or may not be correct depending on what specific antibody was detected. If the mother has anti-D and did not receive antenatal RhoGam, she is sensitized and not a candidate. Option #3 is incorrect because the client is sensitized and RhoGam is given to prevent sensitization from occurring.

6.40 ② Option #2 is correct because this is when the breasts are least congested. Option #1 is when the breasts are most congested. Option #3 is unnecessary. The recommended frequency is monthly. Option #4 is for post-menopausal women.

6.41 ③ Variable decelerations indicate a problem with cord compression. Option #1 indicates head compression. Option #2 indicates

uteroplacental insufficiency. Option #4 could indicate fetal acidosis, fetal neurological immaturity, or maternal medication.

6.42 ③ Option #3 is correct. If injected into the extravascular tissues, calcium gluconate can cause a severe chemical burn. Options #1 and #2 are the reason the client is receiving the antidote for magnesium sulfate. A few undesirable effects from magnesium sulfate include depressed respirations and absent patellar reflex. Since magnesium sulfate is excreted in the urine, if the output decreases then the client may become toxic and need to either decrease the magnesium sulfate or receive calcium gluconate. If the patellar reflex is absent and magnesium sulfate is still infusing, the client needs to have the magnesium sulfate decreased or stopped and/or receive calcium gluconate due to toxicity. Option #4 is incorrect since this is the reason the client is receiving calcium gluconate due to the toxicity of magnesium sulfate. I CAN HINT: The key to answering this correctly is to focus on the words "prior to administering calcium gluconate".

6.43 ③ Being able to count fetal kicks assures the fetus is moving and makes the mother aware of the importance of monitoring fetal movement daily. Option #1 might indicate the onset of premature labor. Options #2 and #4 relate to maternal, more than fetal well-being.

6.44 ③ Option #3 is correct. This accurately describes the Rinne test. Option #1 is incorrect. This is the description for the Whisper test. Option #2 is incorrect since this is the description for the Weber test. Option #4 is incorrect. This describes the evaluation of the 3rd cranial nerve which is the oculomotor cranial nerve.

6.45 ④ A side effect of an epidural is hypotension from the vasodilation which occurs. Option #1 is incorrect because the client must be well hydrated before and after the procedure. Option #2 may be done as ongoing management but is not a priority. Option #3 is incorrect because the client would be placed on her left side to promote uterine perfusion.

6.46 ③ Option # 3 is correct. Massaging the uterus will make it less boggy and more firm, reducing the bleeding that may be causing the decrease in blood pressure. The three major causes of bleeding following delivery are boggy fundus, cervical lacerations, and retained placenta. The answers for this question could be what is currently written or other options may include starting oxytocin or placing the neonate to the breast for the natural release of oxytocin while the neonate is nursing. Option # 1, a retained placenta is an emergency, but the way the question reads is "what would be the first nursing action," and it is unlikely that the nurse would begin by preparing for surgery prior to initiating the massaging of the uterus. This may correct the cause, since the most common cause of bleeding is insufficient uterine contractions. Option # 2, Trendelenburg position may help increase blood pressure, but does not address the etiology for the lowered blood pressure in a mutigravida client following a precipitous deliver. Option #4, applying oxygen may be indicated if the bleeding did not stop; however, this would not be the first nursing action.

6.47 ② Option #2 is correct. Signs of drug withdrawal are more frequently associated with central nervous system alterations, gastrointestinal disturbances, and tachypnea. Options #1, #3, and #4 are secondary to Option #2.

6.48 ④ Option #4 is correct. Individuals who provide care home care for a loved one who is immuno-suppressed and are at high risk for the flu need the vaccination. Options #1, #2 and #3 are not a priority over option #4 due to the risk involved.

I CAN HINT: Due to the treatment being increased immunosuppressive therapy; usually high- doses of steroids, polyclonal or monoclonal antibody therapy, it is imperative to prevent infection. This would also include any family member, friend, relative, etc. that will be having ongoing contact with the client.

6.49 ④ Option #4 is correct. A 3-year-old should have a vocabulary of 900 words and should be able to use a complete sentence of three or four words. This child needs a referral due to the developmental delay. Option #1 does not need a referral since a 6-month-old infant is only able to sit with support. By the time the infant is 8 months of age, the infant should be able to sit without support. Option #2 does not need a referral since this is normal. Not all children walk at 12-months-of age. Option #3 is an expected outcome for this age.

6.50 ① Option #1 is most important due to safety. Option #2 reflects head compression. This deceleration indicates a problem with cephalopelvic disproportion versus a prolapsed cord. Option #3 is not an immediate concern. The fetus is the priority! Option #4 is good; increase in oxygenation is not a problem. Variability = good oxygen! **I CAN HINT:** Remember, the question reads "immediately." The question to ask yourself is *"Do I need to immediately perform a pH on the fluid, or do I need to immediately intervene if the fetus has a prolapsed cord?"*

6.51 ① Finger foods will assist the child in establishing his autonomy. Options #2 and #3 are inappropriate. This age of child does not like food mixed together. In Option #4, there are no other concerns stated by the mother to make the nurse even consider a virus.

6.52 ③ The pill (oral contraceptive) will suppress production of breast milk. During breast-feeding, another method of contraception should be used. Options #1, #2, and #4 could be used and do not indicate a need for further teaching.

6.53 ① This is normal for a neonate. Apnea lasting longer than 15 seconds should be reported. Options #2, #3, and #4 do not indicate a need for further teaching.

6.54 ④ Option #4 is the correct answer. The physical therapy will assist client in restoring optimum level of functioning after a CVA. Options #1 and #3 are examples of secondary prevention activities nonspecific to a CVA. Option #2 is a primary prevention activity nonspecific to a CVA. The test taking strategy here is that Options #1, #2, and #3 are unrelated to the client with a CVA. Another approach is to use the **I CAN HINT:** Primary prevention has an "**i**" which can assist you in remembering immunizations. Secondary prevention has an "**s**" for screening. Tertiary prevention has an "**r**" for rehab or restore a function.

6.55 ① A 3-month-old can grasp a rattle. Options #2 and #4 are correct but not a priority to Option #1. Option #3 is for an older child.

6.56 ② Option #2 is correct. Tunnel vision can be a symptom of glaucoma and should be evaluated by an ophthalmologist. Options # 1, #3, and #4, a neurologist, psychologist and cardiologist are not the priority referrals for the symptom the client is experiencing.

6.57 ④ This is most effective when communicating with an elderly client. Option #1 is incorrect because independence is encouraged. Option #2 is incorrect because schedules need to be routine, reinforced, and repeated. Flexibility leads to confusion. Option #3 is incorrect because reminiscing helps the client resume progression through the grief process associated with disappointing life event and increases self-esteem.

6.58 ② Cluttered environment may represent depression and burnout. Option #1 may be impossible for the daughter to do alone. Options #3 and #4 are very healthy and desirable.

6.59

6.60 Cranial nerve 11 is the spinal accessory.

Notes

You're doing super!!

CHAPTER 7

Psychosocial Integrity

*To do what nobody else will do, a way that
nobody else can do, in spite of all we go
through; that is to be a nurse.*
— RAWSI WILLIAMS, BSN, RN

✔ **Clarification of this test …**

There have been no changes in percentages. This chapter still represents 6–12% of exam items. The minimum standards include performing and directing activities related to caring for client/family with emotional; mental; and; social problems, including behavioral interventions. These standards can be evaluated with any client; all clients need a therapeutic environment. All clients need a nurse who is supportive and uses therapeutic communication with clients. Spiritual factors and cultural practice and beliefs should be incorporated when planning and providing care. These activities also include reporting client conditions as required by law (e.g., abuse/neglect, communicable disease, gunshot wound). Assess the potential for violence and use of safety precautions. Standards such as assessing client for drug/alcohol dependencies, withdrawal, or toxicities; and intervening as appropriate are also included in this chapter.

- ☛ Provide a therapeutic environment.
- ☛ Use therapeutic communication techniques to provide support.
- ☛ Recognize nonverbal cues to physical and/or psychological stressors.
- ☛ Assess psychosocial, spiritual and occupational factors affecting care, and plan interventions.
- ☛ Assess family dynamics to determine plan of care (e.g. structure, bonding, communication, boundaries, coping mechanisms).
- ☛ Incorporate behavioral management techniques when caring for a client (e.g., positive reinforcement, setting limits, de-escalation techniques).
- ☛ Incorporate client cultural practice and beliefs when planning and providing care.
- ☛ Provide care and education for acute and chronic psychosocial health issues (e.g., addictions, dependencies, depression, dementia, eating disorders).
- ☛ Assess client in coping with life changes and provide support (e.g., palliative, amputation, new diagnosis).
- ☛ Assess the potential for violence and use safety precautions (e.g, suicide, homicide, self-destructive behavior).
- ☛ Assess client for drug/alcohol dependencies, withdrawal, or toxicities and intervene as appropriate.
- ☛ Assess client for abuse or neglect and intervene as appropriate.
- ☛ Provide care for a client experiencing visual, auditory, or cognitive distortions (e.g., hallucinations).
- ☛ Provide end-of-life care and education to clients.
- ☛ Report client conditions as required by law (e.g., abuse/neglect and communicable disease).

7.1　While the nurse is taking a history for an older client diagnosed with depression, what is the most important question for the nurse to ask?

① "Have you ever attempted suicide or thought about suicide?"
② "Do you take antidepressant medications or any other medications?"
③ "Have any of your family ever had a psychiatric disorder?"
④ "Are you currently experiencing delusions, illusions, or hallucinations?"

7.2　Which of these clinical findings would alert the nurse to suspect abuse for an elderly client who is admitted to the emergency department with injuries of unknown etiology?

① A diagnosis of a midshaft fracture of the femur.
② A daughter with the client who fills in the information that the client (her mother) is unable to recall.
③ Bruises and lesions on the inner aspects of the extremities.
④ Bruises on the extensor surfaces of the arms.

7.3　An elderly client is admitted to the emergency department (ED) with several bruises and cuts on body in various ages of healing. What is the nursing priority action after documenting these findings?

① Follow the agency policy for reporting elder abuse.
② Ask the client how the cuts and bruises occurred.
③ Notify the provider that abuse is suspected.
④ Immediately report to social worker.

7.4　What is the best initial treatment plan for a sleep disorder in an elderly client?

① Discuss the importance of including naps daily in the plan of care.
② Discuss the importance of decreasing noise and light in the environment.
③ Review the importance of taking trazodone as prescribed.
④ Review the importance of taking amitriptyline as prescribed.

7.5　A client rings the call bell requesting assistance to ambulate to the bathroom. The RN delegates this to the UAP. The UAP states, "I am so glad that I am the only one that is qualified to take someone to the bathroom. I guess they don't teach that in nursing school." How should the RN respond?

① "That was rude."
② "You sound like you are upset about something."
③ "Ambulating clients to the bathroom is within your scope of practice."
④ "We all have things about our job we do not like."

7.6　Which of these symptoms may be assessed for a client experiencing alcohol withdrawal? **Select all that apply.**

① HR—56 beats per minute
② BP—102/68
③ Fine tremor of both hands
④ Vomiting
⑤ Inability to sleep

7.7　A client with a severe thought disturbance has not been taking medication and appears to be more actively hallucinating. The client claims that the medicine makes him too drowsy during the day. Which action by the nurse is most likely to increase medication compliance?

① Ask the physician to schedule the client's entire dose at bedtime.
② Tell the client he is getting sicker and must take his medicine.
③ Teach the client about the side effects of the medication.
④ Ask the family to talk to the client about this problem.

7.8　A client, admitted for treatment of alcohol dependence, displays the following symptoms: slurred speech, ataxia, uncoordinated movements, and headache. Which nursing action should be taken first?

① Observe the client for 8 hours to collect additional data.
② Perform a complete physical assessment.
③ Collect a urine specimen for a drug screen.
④ Encourage the client to talk about whatever is bothering him.

7.9 When a client has dementia, which stressor would be identified as the most critical for the family?

① Client's unwillingness to eat food with the family.
② Client's inability to recognize and communicate with the family.
③ Lack of knowledge about community resources for day care.
④ Client's loss of continence.

7.10 What would be the most effective plan to assist with communication for a client who is being admitted to the medical unit, but only speaks Spanish?

① Notify the nursing assistant on another unit to come and interpret the questions for the client.
② Attempt to have the family interpret for the client to assist in understanding the questions the nurse is asking about client's history.
③ Notify the hospital's interpreter to assist client to understand the questions being asked in Spanish.
④ Since one of the client's friends speaks English, communicate with him.

7.11 Because of a borderline client's mood swings, limited problem-solving strategies, and self-concept disturbance, the treatment team has determined the client is at high risk for violence, either directed at self or others. The nurse should observe the client for early clues to which behavior?

① Intense but disruptive relationships
② Superficial interactions
③ Persistent sense of boredom and loneliness
④ Self-mutilation or suicidal gestures

7.12 What should be the priority plan of care following the death of a female client who is Muslim?

① Private room to gather the family for grieving
② A muslin wrap, preferably white, for the body
③ Post-mortem care of the body by a female nurse
④ Immediate referral to a crematory

7.13 An elderly man diagnosed with major depression is demonstrating decreased problem-solving ability, psychomotor retardation, and social isolation. In planning activities for this client during the early phase of hospitalization, which nursing action is appropriate?

① Prepare and give client a schedule of activities to follow and monitor participation.
② Encourage client to choose own activities.
③ Allow client some time to get acclimated to the milieu before scheduling activities.
④ Allow client to rest quietly to restore energy and fatigue level.

7.14 Which of these psychiatric clients should be evaluated first?

① Depressed client sitting on the floor rocking back and forth.
② Bipolar client pacing and clenching fist.
③ Psychotic client who is having a delusion that she is the Queen of England.
④ Schizophrenic client laughing and waving hands up in the air.

7.15 Which plan would be most important to assist a client to cope with sexual problems resulting from a chronic disease?

① Discuss the importance of decreasing sexual activity.
② Recommend counseling for the client's partner.
③ Recommend periods of abstinence after engaging in sexual activity.
④ Discuss alternate forms of sexual expression.

7.16 Which of these nursing interventions are appropriate for a client experiencing alcohol withdrawal? **Select all that apply.**

① Offer extra fluids and a nutritious diet.
② Place suction at bedside.
③ Place an airway at bedside.
④ Encourage to go to group therapy.
⑤ Place an ambu bag at bedside.

7.17 Which of these assessments is most important to report to provider of care for the wife of a spinal cord injury client with a C4 fracture?

① The wife indicates to the nurse that there may be a need for counseling to help cope with this current situation.

② The wife has elicited the support of family and friends in helping to provide care for the husband after discharge.

③ The wife has lost 10 lbs. (4.5 kg) since the accident, and shares with the nurse feelings of hopelessness about the future have resulted in an inability to sleep at night.

④ The wife reports going to bed one hour earlier to get the needed rest to assist in handling the current situation of with the husband.

7.18 What is the priority for an elderly client who has Alzheimer's disease and wanders the halls of the nursing unit during the day?

① Encourage client to watch television in room.

② Administer prn lorazepam as prescribed to calm client.

③ Assess client's gait to determine balance and steadiness.

④ Only allow client to wander in the unit with the assistance from a UAP.

7.19 Which plan is most appropriate for meeting the needs for a Hindu family after the loved one has died?

① Allow the family to wash the body.

② Allow the priest to touch the body.

③ Allow chanting to be done during the "last rites."

④ Do not consult with family about organ donations since it is considered a sin.

7.20 A client was minimally injured in a motor vehicle crash six months ago though client's friend was killed. The client comes to Student Health Services with complaints of not being able to study, not sleeping, and thinks "I'm going crazy." What is the most important information for the nurse to obtain?

① Complete physical and social history.

② Complete drug and alcohol history including reports from a drug screen.

③ Review of significant events in the last year.

④ Coping behaviors concerning the motor vehicle crash and friend's death.

7.21. What alternative plan of care would be most effective for clients with cancer who experience ongoing fatigue?

① Discuss the power of prayer and/or meditation as a regular part of plan of care.

② Drink several glasses of hot tea prior to lying down to go to sleep.

③ Encourage client to watch a favorite comedy on television.

④ Review the importance of taking an aspirin daily.

7.22 Which nursing action is of primary importance during the implementation of a behavior modification treatment program?

① Confirm that all staff members understand and comply with the treatment plan.

② Establish mutually-agreed-upon, realistic goals.

③ Ensure that the potent reinforcers (rewards) are important to the client.

④ Establish a fixed interval schedule for reinforcement.

7.23 Which of these statements made by a female client who has been abused by her spouse indicates the counseling has been effective?

① "I know my husband will never hurt me again."

② "I know it is my fault that he hits me."

③ "I promise I will get him to promise that he will not do it again."

④ "I have made arrangements to go to the battered women's shelter the next time he hits me."

7.24 An elderly client is frantically yelling for the nurse. The nurse enters the room as the client states, "See it? It's the devil!" What is the most therapeutic response?

① "The devil is here?"

② "Show me where the devil appeared to you."

③ "I don't see the devil, but I understand that it is real to you."

④ "The devil is not here. Your mind is playing tricks on you."

7.25 Which of these clinical findings is the first sign of opioid withdrawal?

① abdominal cramping
② diaphoresis
③ fever
④ nausea

7.26 An alcoholic client who occasionally uses marijuana and cocaine is attending his second group therapy meeting. The client comments, "I am having difficulty sitting still. Am I bothering some of the group members? Maybe I should stop coming to these group meetings." Which nursing action is most appropriate?

① Encourage client to share problem with the group.
② Remove client from the group and further assess needs.
③ Recognize that this is manipulative behavior and encourage client to remain in the group.
④ Tell client not to be concerned about the group members and to continue in the group.

7.27 Family members of clients with eating disorders should be instructed to watch for which of these possible problems?

① Aggressive behavior and feeling angry.
② Self-identity and self-esteem.
③ Focusing on reality.
④ Family boundary intrusions.

7.28 Which evaluation indicates a disoriented client with poor nutrition has made a positive response to the plan of care?

① Reports relationship of weight loss to change in mental status.
② Identifies basic four food groups.
③ States he needs to drink more water.
④ Feeds self when the nurse stays with and cues him.

7.29 A school-age client with AIDS asks if he is going to die. What is the best response from the nurse?

① "Let's talk about getting well instead of dying."
② "What do you think?"
③ "I don't know."
④ "Ask your doctor."

7.30 Policemen bring a client to the emergency room after standing barefoot in the rain for more than 2 hours. The policemen report that the client had to be restrained after resisting and becoming agitated. What is the first nursing action?

① Do a preliminary physical exam.
② Reassure and help maintain client safety.
③ Ascertain the client's mental status.
④ Orient the client to place and time.

7.31 An infant is scheduled for open-heart surgery. The mother begins to cry and says, "I'm a terrible mother!" What is the best nursing response?

① "Do you want to talk about the surgery?"
② To place a comforting arm around the mother.
③ "Is your family here to be with you?"
④ "You have done everything that you can, and the baby is in the best of hands."

7.32 An adolescent client is being discharged after an attempted suicide. What is the priority of care for this client?

① Schedule the follow-up visit for the family and client.
② Review the side effects of the prescribed anti-depressant medication.
③ Obtain the client's signature on the behavior contract.
④ Encourage client to attend group therapy every Wednesday evening.

7.33 A client admitted to the mental health unit experiencing hallucinations is not wearing an identification band. What is the best action before giving the client a scheduled medication?

① Compare the picture and the hospital identification number on the medication administration record (MAR) to the information in the client's chart.
② Ask the client to verify name and date of birth before giving the medication.
③ Ask another staff member who knows the client to give the medication for you.
④ Use the client's photograph and the hospital identification number on the client's chart and compare this to the client's physical appearance.

7.34 A psychiatric client with the diagnosis of schizophrenia tells the nurse that he is the President of the United States. What is the priority action for the nurse?

① Confront the client regarding this delusion and bring him back to reality.
② Reflect this statement back to the client to encourage therapeutic communication.
③ Respond with an open-ended response to get client to further discuss his thoughts.
④ Verify the identity of the client prior to administering his medications.

7.35 Before undergoing an electroconvulsive therapy (ECT), the client reports being very anxious. Which action by the nurse would be the most therapeutic?

① Allow the client to have a cup of coffee to calm down.
② Encourage the client to sit quietly in her room and listen to a relaxation tape.
③ Administer lorazepan 1 mg IM to the client.
④ Ask if you can remain with client and discuss any fears.

7.36 Which assessment data would indicate a severely paranoid client is likely to need nursing interventions to promote self-care abilities?

① Speaks in a low, monotone voice.
② Has had suicidal ideation on 2 previous admissions.
③ Is very fearful that people are putting poison in his food.
④ Is unable to make eye contact with the nurse.

7.37 A gardener goes to the physician with a complaint of a potential or occupational hazard. What clinical finding would the nurse anticipate to assess?

① Eggs (nits) attached to the hair shaft in the head.
② A painful local reaction of vesicles with an erythematosus louse on the upper lip.
③ Linear patches of vesicles with an erythematosus base.
④ A dark asymmetrical mole with an irregular border on the client's back.

7.38 Which nursing action is most appropriate in helping an elderly depressed client complete activities of daily living?

① Medicate the client before the activities are begun.
② Develop a written schedule of activities, allowing extra time.
③ Assist the client with grooming activities for her so it doesn't take so long.
④ Provide frequent forceful direction to keep the client focused.

7.39 Which plan would be most likely to help the family of an emotionally disturbed client in managing behavior at home after discharge from inpatient treatment?

① Refer the family to Alliance for the Mentally Ill meetings for educational programs and support groups.
② Provide the family with pamphlets that describe the desired action and side effects of medications the client is taking.
③ Tell the family that it is not their fault that the client behaves inappropriately.
④ Involve the family in the assessment of the client when he is first admitted to the hospital.

7.40 Which approach should be included in the nursing care plan for a client who displays the following: restless and tense behavior, complaints of feeling empty, history of several threats of self-mutilation?

① Monitor weight and dietary intake.
② Medicate with chlordiazepoxide for tremors.
③ Provide foods in client's own containers to decrease suspiciousness.
④ Take inventory of unit and remove hazardous or sharp objects.

7.41 Which nursing intervention is most important when caring for a client who has just been placed in physical restraints?

① Prepare PRN dose of psychotropic medication.
② Check that the restraints have been applied correctly.
③ Review hospital policy regarding duration of restraints.
④ Monitor client's needs for hydration and nutrition while restrained.

7.42 What would be the nurse's initial priority when managing a physically assaultive client?

① Restrict client to room.
② Place client on a 1-1 supervision.
③ Restore the client's self-control and help prevent further loss of control.
④ Clear the immediate area of other clients to prevent harm.

7.43 Which nursing action is most appropriate when a client presents a suicide plan and a request for confidentiality?

① Encourage client to think very carefully before being self-destructive.
② Agree to keep the information strictly confidential.
③ Inform client that confidentiality cannot be kept.
④ Encourage client to express her feelings.

7.44 Before giving medication to a client who identifies himself as Jesus Christ, which action by the nurse is necessary?

① Ask several UAPs to be available for safety.
② Ask the priest to come and speak with the client.
③ Check the client's name band to make sure of the client's identity.
④ Make sure the client has eaten a full meal.

7.45 A client on lithium therapy should be on which dietary plan to receive increased nutritional requirements?

① Restricted sodium diet with increased fluid intake.
② High calorie diet with sodium and potassium restriction and adequate fluid intake.
③ Regular diet with normal sodium and increased fluid intake.
④ Reduced calorie diet with a reduced sodium and reduced fluid intake.

7.46 What is the priority nursing action when coordinating a community placement for an alcoholic schizophrenic client who has been homeless?

① Collaborate with members of the client's family to explore placement options.
② Collaborate with healthcare team and the client to schedule a pre-discharge visit to residential placement facility.
③ Visit the placement facility alone to make an independent decision about the facility and report to the client and family.
④ Review with the client specific rules of the facility.

7.47 Which behavior indicates a client is beginning to develop a trusting relationship with the nurse?

① The client describes delusions to the nurse.
② The client can describe his feelings to the nurse.
③ The nurse feels more comfortable with the client.
④ The client states feeling less anxious.

7.48 Which post electroconvulsive therapy (ECT) treatment observations would the nurse report to the physician?

① Headache
② Disruption in short and long-term memory
③ Transient confusional state
④ Backache

7.49 Which information would indicate that the therapeutic interaction is in the working stage with a client who has an addiction problem? **Select all that apply.**

① The client reluctantly discusses the family history of addiction.
② The client addresses how the addiction has resulted in family distress.
③ The client experiences difficulty with identifying personal strengths.
④ The client discusses the financial burden related to the addiction.
⑤ The client is uncomfortable in meeting with the nurse.
⑥ The client discusses the addiction's effects on the children.

7.50 What should be the priority nursing action when dealing with a client who is a victim of interpersonal violence?

  ① Encourage the client to verbalize feelings.
  ② Assess for physical trauma.
  ③ Provide privacy for the client during the interview.
  ④ Help the client identify and mobilize resources and support systems.

7.51 What would be a positive outcome of treatment with a victim of paternal sexual abuse?

  ① Acknowledges willing participation in an incestuous relationship.
  ② Reestablishes a trusting relationship with mother.
  ③ Verbalizes that she is not responsible for the sexual abuse.
  ④ Describes feelings of anxiety when speaking about father and the sexual abuse.

7.52 A client was recently diagnosed with cancer. Which intervention is most appropriate to assist the client in dealing with his severe anxiety?

  ① During periods of stress, distract the client through activities.
  ② Review the stages of the grieving process.
  ③ Provide client with written information about chemotherapy.
  ④ Encourage client to discuss thoughts, feelings, and concerns with nurse.

7.53 Which nursing intervention is the highest priority for a client receiving aripiprazole for a diagnosis of schizophrenia?

  ① Recommend that the client reduces his alcohol intake to one drink per day.
  ② Instruct client to take the medication only before meals.
  ③ Review the importance of taking aripiprazole at bedtime since it causes sedation.
  ④ Advise to increase his exercising in order to optimize the drug action.

7.54 Which one of these plans indicates the nurse understands the characteristics of a therapeutic nurse-client relationship?

  ① Establishing priorities and goals for the client.
  ② Utilizing the nursing process to establish client goals.
  ③ Collaborating to establish mutually agreed upon goals and priorities.
  ④ Directing interactions to assist the client to meet needs.

7.55 A client with terminal cancer is nearing the end of life. Which plan best meets the client's emotional needs?

  ① Provide the client with a room where family can be present.
  ② Make sure that the client has an advanced directive on the chart.
  ③ Consult the hospital chaplain or client's personal spiritual advisor.
  ④ Provide the client with a journal to record final thoughts for family and friends.

7.56 A 17-year-old is beginning chemotherapy for her malignancy. Which statement indicates she has a realistic perception of her health status?

  ① "I will be cured after my therapy is completed."
  ② "I may need to get a wig during my chemotherapy."
  ③ "I will be able to continue my current school schedule."
  ④ "I must have done something to cause this illness."

7.57 Which is a positive response to fluoxetine HCL?

  ① Hand tremors and leg twitching.
  ② Increased ability to sleep.
  ③ Increased energy level and participation in unit activities.
  ④ Hypervigilance and scanning of the environment.

7.58 Which nursing intervention is most important when working with clients with a diagnosis of dementia?

① Reinforce the client's thought patterns.
② When speaking with the client, use simple, short sentences.
③ Administer anti-anxiety medications.
④ Facilitate an exercise program with the client's physical limitations.

7.59 Which assessment should have priority in an initial assessment of an alcoholic client?

① Has the client been taking over-the-counter medication?
② What has been the client's usual daily intake of alcohol?
③ When did the client have his last drink?
④ Has the client ever had a withdrawal seizure?

7.60 What would be the priority plan for a client diagnosed with dissociative disorder?

① Assist the client in understanding the relationship between anxiety and dissociation.
② Assess the client's level and reason for memory loss.
③ Assist the client to incorporate the dissociated material into conscious memories.
④ Establish an honest, non-judgmental and safe relationship with the client.

Answers & Rationales

7.1 ① Option #1 is correct. While the other options are important to assess during this initial history, it would be most important to assess if the client is at risk for injury related to suicide. Safety is a priority concern for depressed clients. Some assessments that are very valuable to determine if the client has a plan are giving away valuable possessions and if there has been an increase in the client's level of energy. Option #2 is not a priority over #1. It is important to assess the medications, but not more important than assessing for risk for suicide. Options #3 and #4 are not a priority over Option #1.

I CAN HINT: Testing strategy would be that Options #3 and #4 include general psychiatric disorders. The question is asking *"What would be the most important question to ask?" "Risk for suicide"* is a life and death assessment which makes this answer a priority.

7.2 ③ Option #3 is correct. Research has concluded that bruising on the inner surfaces of the extremities and areas with different stages of resolution are often found in the elderly client who has been abused. Option #1 is not conclusive of abuse. This could have resulted from a fall or an injury due to the complication from osteoporosis. Option #2 is not a finding for abuse. This is a finding of a caring daughter. Option #4 may be common findings for the elderly client, and does not indicate a complication with abuse.

7.3 ② Option #2 is correct. This question is evaluating the ability to *"Identify clients at risk for abuse."* The priority nursing action is to assess how the client perceives the cuts and bruises occurred. Option #1 is an important intervention, but would not come before assessment. Option #3 is also important, but not a priority over Option #2. Option #4 would not be a priority over Option #2 since the nurse should start with the client, and then evaluate if the stories are the same from both the client and family member accompanying client.

7.4 ② Option #2 is correct. The initial plan would be to correct environmental factors and treatment of underlying iatrogenic and medical conditions to incorporate with the initial treatment plan. Option #1 is incorrect; actually eliminating naps throughout the day may be useful in facilitating sleep. Option #3 is incorrect. Even though trazodone (Desyrel) may be useful if sleep deprivation is prominent, it would not be the initial treatment plan. Option #4 is incorrect. Amitriptyline (Elavil) may cause excessive somnolence.

7.5 ② Option #2 is the correct answer. This is an example of how to incorporate "therapeutic communication" with staff. This statement allows the UAP to know that the nurse is paying attention to the statement that was made. This will allow the UAP to ventilate the concerns to the RN and facilitate clarification as to the request. This will also still assist in understanding the feelings of the UAP. All human beings like to be heard and understood, and this is an excellent communication strategy. Option #1 is nontherapeutic. It is a statement, and does nothing to assist in understanding the reason the statement was made, even if in reality it was a rude statement. A strategy for *"therapeutic communication"* is that the goal is to assist the client, staff member (or anyone who is making the statement) to further discuss statement, know they are being heard, and take time to listen to their concerns. While Option #3 may be a true and valid statement, it does not address the feelings behind the statement. Stating this fact without addressing the feelings may escalate into inappropriate behavior in the future. Option #4 is not therapeutic and also does not address the feelings behind the question.

7.6 ③ Options #3, #4 and #5 are correct. This question
④ is evaluating the NCLEX activity: "*Assess*
⑤ *client for drug/alcohol withdrawal.*" These options include clinical findings for clients experiencing alcohol withdrawal. Additional clinical findings for client may include restlessness, depressed mood, irritability, vital signs are elevated, so the HR would be elevated and the BP would be increased (Options #1 and #2). A late symptom is tactile hallucinations of "bugs crawling" on the skin.

7.7 ① Medication dose non-compliance is often associated with negative side effects and a multiple dosing daily schedule. When the client has only one daily dose at bedtime, it is easier for him to remember to take the medication. The other advantage is that the sedative effects of the drug peak while the client is sleeping. Options #2 and #4 do not offer concrete solutions and may foster dependent behaviors. Option #3 may help to some degree, but a more concrete solution is possible.

7.8 ② The best way to identify possible physical complications of alcohol dependence is through a complete physical assessment. Option #1 is important but will not provide the data that a physical assessment would. This may be a medical emergency requiring an immediate intervention. Option #3 is also a helpful source of data but can be done after the physical assessment is finished. Option #4 is inaccurate since the symptoms are most likely caused by physical and not psychological stressors.

7.9 ② This confirms a deteriorating condition and increases feelings of loss among family members. Options #1, #3, and #4 are all stressors for those dealing with a family member with dementia but are usually less critical.

7.10 ③ Option #3 is correct. This will be more professional, more accurate, and will not violate any client confidentiality. The interpreter has a sense of accountability; whereas, the other options do not have this responsibility. Options #1, #2 and #4 are inaccurate due to confidentiality and accountability.

7.11 ④ This is a common form of behavior displayed by the borderline client, which places client at a great risk for violence. Options #1, #2, and #3 are behaviors the client is likely to display, but they are not as clearly related to the high risk for violent behavior.

7.12 ③ Option #3 is correct. The Muslim culture believes that the same gender should provide care after death. Option #1 is incorrect because the Muslim culture grieves at home. Option #2 is secondary to Option #3. Option #4 is incorrect because cremation is not typically practiced in the Muslim culture.

7.13 ① A regular daily routine of scheduled activities provides structure and decreases the degree of problem-solving. Depressed clients need to have structure provided because of impairment in decision-making and problem-solving. Options #2, #3, and #4 may promote further social isolation and increase the client's impairments. This may further decrease the client's self-esteem.

7.14 ② Option #2 needs to be evaluated first due to safety issues. Options #1, #3 and #4 are not going to hurt anyone.

7.15 ④ Option #4 is most important in encouraging client to fulfill an important part of life which is being intimate with his wife. Options #1, #2 and #3 do not support alternative plans.

7.16 ② Options #2, #3 and #5 are correct. This question
③ is evaluating "*Safe use of equipment*" for a
⑤ client who is experiencing alcohol withdrawal.

I CAN HINT: Always think about equipment for airway due to the risk of airway obstruction during the withdrawal activities such as delirious tremors. Think of equipment the nurse should have at the bedside for a client with seizure activity. This will assist in answering this question. Option #1 is incorrect for this question. The priority is safety for the client "experiencing alcohol withdrawal". Option #4 is incorrect for this question. This is the last thing the nurse will consider during this behavior with alcohol withdrawal.

7.17 ③ Option #3 is correct. This question is evaluating the NCLEX activity, "*Recognize impact of illness on individual/family.*" This assessment would be most important due to the feelings of hopelessness, insomnia, and significant weight loss. This assessment indicates a need for additional support. Option #1 is a healthy statement, indicating self-awareness with the need to seek additional support. Option #2 is also a healthy statement, indicating an awareness of not attempting to cope with this situation alone. Option #4 is also a healthy behavior.

7.18 ③ Due to medications, changes in eye sight, hearing, balance, etc., this client is at risk for falls. Option #1 is incorrect, since this does not allow client to ambulate and be independent. Option #2 is incorrect, since this may actually contribute to falls. Option #4 is unrealistic and unnecessary.

7.19 ① Option #1 is correct for the Hindu family. For an Islamic family member's death, only relatives or a priest may touch the body. The family washes the body and then turns it to face Mecca. Option #3 is appropriate for a Buddhist family. Option #4 is not true. Donation of organs may be done.

7.20 ④ All of these options are important and relevant to a thorough physiopsychosocial evaluation. However, initially ascertaining focused information about a very traumatic event, is helpful and provides the nurse with an opportunity to understand how this client has coped up to this point with a tragedy that has made client vulnerable.

7.21 ① Option #1 is correct. Studies show that cancer clients who practice meditation and/or pray experience a decrease in fatigue levels. These have been scientifically measured to be less than those clients who do not use these types of practice. Option #2 is incorrect due to the caffeine. This will not facilitate rest. Option #3 is going to result in laughing which can result in an increase in the endorphins that create more energy. Option #4 does not address the issue of fatigue.

7.22 ① To successfully implement a behavior modification plan, all staff members need to be included in the program development and to allow time for discussion of concerns from each nursing staff member. Consistency and follow-through are of utmost importance to prevent or diminish the level of staff manipulation by the client during the implementation of this program. Options #2, #3, and #4 are important in designing an effective behavior modification program. However, Option #1 is a priority.

7.23 ④ Option #4 is correct. Most abused women eventually leave the situation. Interventions may not produce quick outcomes, but they can begin to facilitate the process of healing. Options #1, #2, and #3 are incorrect. Option #1—the husband will not change without identifying cause of anxiety and altering the manner he deals with it. Options #2 and #3 do not indicate counseling was effective.

7.24 ③ The nurse does not want to reinforce the client's hallucinatory experiences. Option #1 is incorrect because reflection techniques usually do not work in this situation. Option #2 is incorrect because attempts to reason or argue with the client may entrench him more firmly into this distortion. Option #4 is a direct challenge to the client's belief about sensory-perceptual intake and may increase mistrust and conflict between the nurse and client.

7.25 ② Option #2 is correct. Diaphoresis can occur between 6–12 hours. Abdominal cramping, fever and nausea may occur later between 48–72 hours.

7.26 ① The client is probably experiencing some mild level of anxiety related to detoxification as well as his participation in the group process. He needs reinforcement and encouragement to continue attending the group meetings and to share his feelings. Options #2, #3, and #4 would not be therapeutic.

7.27 ② Clients with eating disorders experience difficulty with self-identity and self-esteem which inhibits their ability to be a self-advocate and act assertively. Some assertiveness techniques that are taught include: giving and receiving criticism, giving and accepting compliments, accepting apologies, being able to say no and set limits on what they can realistically do, rather than just doing what others want them to do. Options #1 and #4 are secondary because these clients may have problems with family boundary intrusion and having difficulty with feelings of anger. Family therapy sessions can be helpful in identifying some of these feelings and difficulties with family boundaries. Option #3 is usually not an issue.

7.28 ④ A disoriented client who is not able to be an independent self-care agent will need prompting from the nurse to accomplish self-feeding. Options #1, #2, and #3 are not usually indicative of a client who is disoriented. They are more characteristic of a client with a higher level of cognitive functioning.

7.29 ② One of the most important concepts is to listen to client concerns. Options #1, #3, and #4 will take away this opportunity.

7.30 ② The major priority of the nurse is to provide and maintain safety for the client who is unable to provide this for him/herself. A safe environment will generate trust and rapport. This will decrease resistance to the next critical steps. Options #1, #3, and #4 are important, but cannot be done effectively until Option #2 is accomplished.

7.31 ④ Option #4 is the priority answer. It is important to promote a sense of hope. Option #1 would provide for listening to client/family concerns, and Options #2 and #3 may provide comfort.

7.32 ③ Option #3 is a priority due to safety and placing some accountability with the client. Options #1, #2 and #4 are an important part of the plan but are not a priority to Option #3.

7.33 ④ Option #4 is correct. Using a client photograph for identification is acceptable in behavioral and long-term care areas. Option #1 compares one chart item to another. It does not identify the client. Option #2 is incorrect because a client experiencing hallucinations may not be able to respond reliably. Option #3 is inappropriate.

7.34 ④ Option #4 is a priority due to safety. Option #1 is partially correct, but nurses do not confront this client. Options #2 and #3 are part of therapeutic communication and are not answering the question.

7.35 ④ This allows the client some control over how to mutually deal with the anxiety related to ECT. The interpersonal contact provided by remaining with the client and discussing any fears will assist in anxiety reduction. Option #1 is inappropriate because the client must remain NPO before the ECT treatment, and coffee (especially caffeinated) is a CNS stimulant which could escalate her anxiety. Option #2 represents nurse avoidance but could be a beneficial strategy if the exercise had been instructed and practiced with the nurse. Option #3 is incorrect because medicating anxiety does not encourage the development of any additional coping strategies. Only if the level of anxiety were severe would psychopharmacologic intervention be necessary.

7.36 ③ When the client is fearful of being poisoned, he will not eat willingly and may suffer from problems with nutrition. Options #1 and #4 will have little bearing on his self-care abilities. Option #2 warrants further observation for depressive symptoms which might impair self-care, but at this point, there is no evidence to support this.

7.37 ④ Option #4 is correct. This is indicative of a melanoma and may occur to skin exposed to the sun frequently. Melanoma tend to be asymmetrical with border irregularity, color variegation, and a diameter greater than 6 mm.

7.38 ② A written schedule with built-in extra time will allow the client to understand what is expected and will allow her to participate at a slower pace. Options #1, #3, and #4 will not increase the client's independence and may interfere with the client's self-esteem.

7.39 ① This group provides ongoing support and educational information. People who attend have common needs and goals focused on managing the client's behavior at home. Options #2, #3, and #4 may be helpful, but will not have the ongoing impact that Option #1 would have.

7.40 ④ Option #4 is the correct answer. Protecting the client's safety is a priority for the nursing care plan. Options #1, #2, and #3 are not a priority for this client. Safety is the priority due to threats of self-mutilation.

I CAN HINT: The key to answering this question appropriately is to have an understanding of risk for suicide. "SUICIDE" will assist you in organizing these concepts for future questions.

Suicide precautions *(remove hazardous or sharp objects).*

Understand the need for adequate exercise and rest; encourage not to sleep during day.

Include hygiene and personal appearance as part of plan of care.

Contract agreeing not to harm self; provide an alternative plan of coping.

Interested approach (kind, pleasant) to client to promote a sense of dignity and self worth.

Depressed client often needs assistance with decision-making.

Evaluate weight; encourage increase bulk and roughage in diet along with sufficient fluids if constipated; encourage expression of angry, guilty, or depressed feelings.

7.41 ② While a client is restrained, physiological integrity is important. Monitoring the positioning, tightness and peripheral circulation are essential. The nurse documents the client's response and clinical status after being restrained. Option #1 is inappropriate for the client in restraints. Option #3 is important but secondary to Option #2. Option #4 is important after the client is safely restrained.

7.42 ④ Option #4 is correct. The most important priority in the nursing management of an assaultive client is to maintain safety of the client and others. A quick assessment of the situation, psychological intervention, chemical intervention and possible physical control are important when managing the physically-assaultive client. Option #1 may be a useful strategy before the client becomes assaultive. However, once the client is assaultive, this behavior may continue in room without any redirection and support. Option #2 may be unsafe to the other person. Option #3 is helpful, but not a priority.

7.43 ③ The nurse must let the client know that this information will be shared with the staff so the client's safety can be preserved. Options #1, #2, and #4 are inaccurate because they do not answer the client's immediate concern while giving accurate information about the nurse's responsibility.

7.44 ③ It is always necessary for the nurse to verify the client's identity before administering medications, particularly when the client cannot verbalize his identity. Options #1, #2, and #4 will be unnecessary.

7.45 ③ The client receiving Lithium needs to maintain a regular diet with a normal sodium intake and increased fluid intake (approximately 2–3 liters per day). Lithium is a salt preparation, and its retention within the body is directly related to the body's sodium and fluid salience. Option #1 is incorrect because a depletion of sodium is to be avoided because Lithium replaces sodium in the cells, therefore precipitating Lithium toxicity. Options #2 and #4 are incorrect because diets that are low in sodium, regardless of caloric intake, do not provide adequate nutritional balance for Lithium regulation.

7.46 ② Option #2 is correct. It is important that the multidisciplinary team discuss and collaborate with the client regarding discharge placements. The client will need support and assistance in making decisions about discharge and residential living arrangements. Option #1 may not be optimum because of possible co-dependence. Option #3 is incorrect because if the nurse visits independent of the client, that can diminish the sense of self-worth and decision-making. Option #4 is incorrect because reviewing rules with the client prematurely can inhibit the opportunity to explore feelings about this decision.

7.47 ② The client who is suspicious and delusional begins to demonstrate trusting behaviors when he/she shares their feelings with the nurse. Option #1 is incorrect because their delusional system is an indication of anxiety and delusions will increase with greater anxiety. Trust with the nurse is not related to an explanation of the client's delusions. Option #3 is incorrect because the nurse's response can be an indication of transference counter-transference issues and is not indicative of the client beginning to enter a trusting relationship. Option #4 may be secondary to Option #2. It is very beneficial that the client's anxiety level is becoming less intense, and this will facilitate the development of a trusting relationship.

7.48 ④ A client undergoing ECT needs to be instructed by the nurse concerning symptoms that could be experienced during and post ECT. A backache is not a usual effect. A thorough description of the pain in relation to severity, duration, location and what makes the pain better, needs to be assessed and reported to the physician. Options #1, #2, and #3 are expected effects of the procedure.

7.49 ② Options #2, #4, and #6 are correct. In
④ Option #1 the client is reluctant and still not
⑥ confident with self. In Option #3 the client is not comfortable enough to be self-aware of positive attributes. In Option #5 the client is not comfortable with nurse which means there is still not a degree of comfort with interaction.

7.50 ② The victim of interpersonal violence may have physical trauma and concealed injuries. This assessment is of utmost importance, so that the client's physiologic integrity is maintained. Options #1, #3, and #4 are done concurrently as the nurse is assessing for physical injury. Privacy and encouraging the client to verbalize feelings are important. Facilitating the client to identify and rally their family or significant others to assist them during the crisis is important in the care of the victim of interpersonal violence.

7.51 ③ A positive outcome of treatment of a sexually abused client is the verbalization that they are not responsible for the sexual abuse. The victim needs assistance to challenge the "belief of victims" which includes, "I am bad and deserve the abuse." Option #1 continues the myth of badness and that they deserved the abuse and actively consented to it. Option #2 is an outcome that would be positive, but usually is not an initial result of treatment. Option #4 is an expected outcome—though not a positive one.

7.52 ④ Option #4 is most therapeutic for reducing anxiety. Option #1 does not encourage personal growth. Option #2 does not deal with the anxiety. Option #3 addresses knowledge but not feelings.

7.53 ③ Option #3 is correct. Aripiprazole (Abilify) is an antipsychotic agent referred to as a dopamine system stabilizer. Since these antipsychotic agents cause sedation, sleeping during the night and decreasing daytime drowsiness can be done by administering the agent at bedtime. Option #1 is incorrect because it should be avoided, not limited. Option #2 is incorrect because Abilify may be administered with or without food since it is well absorbed either way. Option #4 is an incorrect statement.

7.54 ③ The therapeutic nurse-client relationship is a mutual learning and corrective emotional experience. The nurse utilizes self and specified clinical techniques in working with the client to facilitate insight and behavioral change. Options #1, #2, and #4 are incorrect because in a nurse-client relationship, the client's needs are of primary concern.

7.55 ① Option #1 is correct. Providing a room for the client's family would be the best plan to meet the client's emotional needs. Option #2 does not meet the client's emotional needs. Option #3 and Option #4 are secondary.

7.56 ② This statement reflects the client's understanding of the side effects of chemotherapy. Option #1 may or may not occur. Option #3 is not realistic. It may be possible at times, but the question requests a "realistic perception." Option #4 is inaccurate and may reflect blame and guilt.

7.57 ③ Fluoxetine HCL (Prozac) is an "energizing" antidepressant, and as clients begin to demonstrate a positive response, they have an increased energy level and would be able to become more participative in the milieu. Options #1 and #4 can be side effects of the medication. Option #2 is not indicative of Prozac which can actually inhibit sleep and is useful with clients who experience increasing sleeping and psychomotor retardation and lethargy.

7.58 ② The client with dementia has significant difficulty with communication. Therefore, simple and short sentences can enhance the client's ability to process the information. Option #1 is incorrect because reality orientation, not reinforcement of the client's altered thought process, is an important goal. Option #3 is incorrect because anti-anxiety (anxiolytic) agents are not appropriate in the care of a dementia client and can worsen their confusional state. Option #4 is important but secondary to Option #2.

7.59 ③ It is imperative that the nurse obtain the time of the client's last drink so that anticipation of when the client would most likely experience withdrawal symptoms will be known (usually occurring within 48-72 hours after the last drink). Options #1, #2, and #4 are important to note but do not take priority over Option #3.

7.60 ④ The client who experiences a dissociative disorder is protecting self from the intense levels of anxiety that are stressful and beyond coping abilities. This client needs a safe, non-threatening approach because client typically exhibits difficulty in establishing trusting relationships. Options #1, #2, and #3 are all reasonable nursing goals that must be developed within a multidisciplinary approach in collaboration with the client, but are secondary to Option #4.

CHAPTER 8

Physiological Adaptation

*When you're a nurse, you know that every day you will
touch a life or a life will touch yours.*
— AUTHOR UNKNOWN

✔ **Clarification of this test ...**

There have been no changes in percentages. This chapter still represents 11–17% of exam items. The minimum standards include providing direct care for clients with acute, chronic, or life-threatening conditions; including fluid and electrolyte imbalances, hemodynamics, illness management, and emergencies.

☞ Prioritize the delivery of care.

☞ Perform focused assessment.

☞ Recognize trends and changes in client condition and intervene as needed.

☞ Recognize signs and symptoms of complications and intervene appropriately when providing care.

☞ Evaluate the effectiveness of the treatment regimen for a client with an acute/chronic diagnosis.

☞ Identify pathophysiology related to an acute or chronic condition (e.g., signs).

☞ Manage the care of the client on telemetry.

☞ Manage the care of the client with a fluid and electrolyte imbalance.

☞ Perform wound and dressing change.

☞ Provide pulmonary hygiene (e.g., chest physiotherapy, incentive spirometry).

☞ Manage the care of a client with alteration in hemodynamics, tissue perfusion and hemostasis (e.g., cerebral, cardiac, peripheral).

☞ Maintain optimal temperature of client (e.g., cooling and/or warming blanket).

☞ Perform suctioning (e.g., oral nasopharyngeal, endotracheal, tracheal).

☞ Manage the care of a client with a pacing device (e.g., pacemaker, vagus nerve stimulator).

☞ Provide ostomy care and education (e.g., tracheal, enteral).

☞ Monitor and maintain arterial lines.

☞ Perform and manage care of client receiving peritoneal dialysis/hemodialysis.

☞ Perform emergency care procedures (e.g., CPR, respiratory support, automated external defibrillator).

☞ Implement and monitor phototherapy.

8.1 An older client was admitted to the emergency department presenting with atrial fibrillation? Three hours following the initiation of telemetry monitoring per healthcare provider's order, the central alarm sounds at the monitoring station, and the dysrhythmia has now changed to ventricular tachycardia. What is the first nursing action?

① Assess the client and check placement of leads.
② Call a Code Blue.
③ Notify the healthcare provider regarding the rhythm change.
④ Immediately administer lidocaine.

8.2 Which of these clients would be the priority to be assessed immediately following report?

① A client with a spinal cord injury who has a $PaCO_2$—36 mm Hg; ICP—15 mm Hg; and systolic arterial pressure (SAP)—120 mm Hg and is unable to move extremities.
② A client with a head injury with a MAP—90 mm Hg and ICP—8 mm Hg.
③ A client with a brain tumor who is complaining of a headache, with BP—170/58 mm Hg; HR—50 BPM; and motor, verbal, and eye opening responses to deep pain only.
④ A client who is 1 hour post-seizure and is resting on side with SaO_2—95%, but is lethargic.

8.3 Which clinical assessment findings would alert the nurse that an elderly client may be developing the complication of pneumonia?

① Change in functional and mental status
② Congestive and frequent cough
③ Temperature—102.4°F (39.1°C)
④ WBC—18,000 mm³

8.4 A client presents with the following ABG report: pH—7.47; pCO_2—34 mm Hg (24 mmol/L); HCO_3—24 mEq/ L. What is the priority of care for this client?

① Assist client to slow down breathing and assist with rebreathing device.
② Call the provider of care and report the arterial blood gas report of respiratory acidosis.
③ Place in the high-Fowler's and encourage breathing and coughing.
④ Place in prone position to prepare for respiratory therapy.

8.5 The UAP screams that the client with a diagnosis of atrial fibrillation who is being ambulated is suddenly feeling very dizzy. What action should the RN immediately assist the UAP to do with this client?

① Assess the client's blood pressure.
② Assess the client's apical pulse.
③ Encourage client to take deep breaths.
④ Help client to sit down.

8.6 Which of these plans are important for the nurse to implement when performing tracheostomy care? **Select all that apply.**

① Suction the tracheostomy tube every hour to maintain patency.
② Use cotton-tipped applicators and gauze pads to clean exposed outer cannula surfaces. Begin with hydrogen peroxide to clean the cannula and sterile saline to rinse it.
③ Use standard precautions when removing and cleaning the inner cannula.
④ Change and secure new tracheostomy ties after removing soiled ones.
⑤ If a knot is needed for the ties, tie a square knot that is visible on the side of the neck. One or two fingers should be able to be placed between the tie tape and the neck.

8.7 An older adult is admitted with a new onset of heart failure. A graduate nurse in orientation receives report for this client at 0700, including these lab reports. What is the priority of care for this client?

Serum Potassium—3.0 mEq/L (3.0 mmol/L)
Serum Glucose—110 mg/dL (6.11 mmol/L)
Creatinine—1.2 mg/dL (106 µmol/L)

① Consult with the preceptor regarding the care of a client with an elevated creatinine.
② Consult with the pharmacist to determine the procedure for administering glucagon.
③ Call and notify the provider of care regarding an order for furosemide.
④ When the healthcare provider (HCP) makes rounds, determine if there will be any revisions in the client's care due to these abnormal findings.

8.8 Which of these symptoms should be reported to the healthcare provider with these hemodynamic readings? Central Venous Pressure (CVP)—20 mm Hg; Pulmonary Artery Wedge Pressure (PAWP)—10 mm Hg; Cardiac Output (CO)—4-6 L/min. **Select all that apply.**

① Peripheral edema
② Hepatomegalyy
③ Poor skin turgor
④ Dry mucous membranes
⑤ Jugular vein distention

8.9 A nurse is providing care for an older client when the client becomes unresponsive and has the following cardiac dysrhythmia. After the nurse activates the emergency response system and determines there is no pulse, what should be the next action?

① Assess for response to noxious stimuli.
② Apply the defibrillator pads and administer a shock.
③ Begin giving 20 chest compressions.
④ Give two rescue breaths, and then start chest compressions.

8.10 Which one of these nursing actions indicates an understanding of how to successfully perform an IV access?

① Cleanse area at the site using friction in a circular motion from outward to middle with alcohol, iodine preparation or chlorhexidine. Allow to air dry for 1 to 5 min.
② Insert the catheter with bevel up at an angle of 15 to 20 degrees using steady motion (or as recommended by catheter manufacturer).
③ Advance the catheter through skin and into vein, but if flashback of blood is seen remove catheter from the site.
④ When using clean tourniquet, apply 8 to 10 inches above proposed insertion site to compress only venous blood.

8.11 A client is 3 days postoperative mitral valve replacement. Which recommendation should the nurse include in the nursing care plan to prevent postoperative complications?

① Maintain in supine position to prevent tension on the mediastinal suture line.
② Encourage deep breathing, but discourage coughing because of increased central venous pressure.
③ Decrease fluids to prevent fluid retention and development of congestive heart failure.
④ Encourage early activity to promote ventilation and improve quality of circulation.

8.12 Which of these clients should be assessed immediately after shift report?

① A client who is presenting with the tracheal deviating to the unaffected side several hours after having chest tube inserted.
② A client who is 1 hour post bronchoscopy and is presenting with a depressed gag reflex.
③ A client post thoracentesis after having 1000 mL of fluid aspirated and is now complaining of syncope 2 hours later when getting up too quickly.
④ A client with SARS who is presenting with sneezing and coughing.

8.13 A permanent demand pacemaker set at a rate of 72 is implanted in a client for persistent third degree block. Which nursing assessment indicates a pacemaker dysfunction?

① Pulse rate of 88 and irregular.
② Apical pulse rate regular at 68.
③ Blood pressure of 110/88, pulse at 78.
④ Tenderness at site of pacemaker implant.

8.14 Which assignment is most appropriate for a new RN of 8 months who is pulled from the surgical unit to the medical unit?

① A 40-year-old client with SARS and is on airborne precautions.
② A 50-year-old client following thoracic surgery and is on a ventilator.
③ A 60-year-old client who just returned from a bronchoscopy.
④ A 70-year-old client who needs teaching regarding the use of an incentive spirometer.

8.15 A client is 2 days postoperative aortic aneurysm resection. A complete blood count reveals a decreased red blood cell count. Which symptoms is the nursing assessment most likely to reveal?

① Fatigue, pallor, and exertional dyspnea.
② Nausea, vomiting, and diarrhea.
③ Vertigo, dizziness, and shortness of breath.
④ Malaise, flushing, and tachycardia.

8.16 A client has tested positive for tuberculosis and is started on isoniazid for 6 months. What information should the nurse plan to include in the client's teaching plan?

① The color of the urine will change.
② Subsequent TB tests will be negative after drug administration.
③ Other medications should be withheld during therapy.
④ Alcohol consumption is contraindicated.

8.17 Which finding would the nurse identify as interfering with the effective functioning of chest tubes?

① 15 cm. water suction on chest tube system.
② An air leak in water seal chamber.
③ Leaking blood around chest tube site.
④ Clots of blood in the chest tube.

8.18 A client is scheduled for a left lower lobe lobectomy. Which nursing observation most indicates the need for an anti-anxiety agent?

① Agitation and decreased level of consciousness.
② Lethargy and decreased respiratory rate.
③ Restlessness and increased heart rate.
④ Hostility and increased blood pressure.

8.19 Organize the following steps to suctioning in chronological order (with 1 being the first step in this procedure).

| ① Put on sterile glove. |
| ② Lubricate catheter with normal saline. |
| ③ Apply suction for 5-10 seconds. |
| ④ Explain procedure to client. |
| ⑤ Wash hands thoroughly. |

8.20 A client is admitted with dehydration secondary to diarrhea. A nursing history reveals the client has been on daily medications of digoxin 0.25 mg and furosemide 40 mg, which are to be continued according to admit orders. Which symptom is most important for the nurse to report to the next shift?

① Confusion and reports of yellow lights.
② Character and time of daily stools.
③ Intake and output for the last 24 hours.
④ Irritability toward friends and family.

8.21 A non-ventilated client with an ineffective breathing pattern related to severe dyspnea presents with cyanosis, tachycardia and hypotension. Which intervention has the highest priority?

① Encourage rest to conserve energy.
② Explain emergency procedures as they are happening.
③ Assess vital signs and respiratory status every 15 minutes.
④ Assess for bleeding tendencies and the potential for disseminated intravascular coagulation.

8.22 When changing the tubing on central lines, what is most important for the nurse to instruct the client to do?

① Sit in semi-Fowler's position, and take a deep breath prior to the procedure.
② Lie down, hold breath, and bear down when the line is opened.
③ Lie in the left lateral position, and hold breath during the procedure.
④ Sit in the Fowler's position, and exhale during the procedure.

8.23　Which nursing action is appropriate for a client with orthopnea, dyspnea, and bibasilar crackles?

① Elevate legs to promote venous return.
② Decrease the IV fluids, and notify the physician.
③ Orient the client to time, place, and situation.
④ Prevent complications of immobility.

8.24　A client is 3 hours postoperative thoracotomy. For the past 2 hours, there has been 200 mL per hour of bloody chest drainage. Which action should the nurse take?

① Increase the IV fluid rate.
② Administer oxygen at 5 liters/min. per face mask.
③ Elevate the head of the bed.
④ Advise the physician of the amount of drainage.

8.25　Which of these clients should the nurse intervene with immediately after shift report?

① A client with a newly implanted demand ventricular pacemaker, who has occasional periods of sinus rhythm, heart rate of 88-98 BPM.
② A client who has an order for verapamil with a history of atrial fibrillation.
③ A client diagnosed with atrial fibrillation and has a heart rate of 88 BPM at rest.
④ A client with an acute myocardial infarction (MI) and has a sinus rhythm, rate 74 BPM, with frequent premature ventricular contractions.

8.26　A client awakens during the night with dyspnea, severe anxiety, jugular vein distension (JVD), and frothy pink sputum. After the nurse begins oxygen at 4 liters per nasal cannula, which action should be done next?

① Place 2 pillows behind head, and elevate the legs.
② Notify physician about change in client's condition.
③ Increases IV fluids to liquefy the secretions.
④ Dim lights and provide privacy.

8.27　It is 0600 and a client is scheduled for a cardiac catheterization at 0800. Laboratory work completed 5 days ago showed: K 3.0 mEq/L (3.0 mmol/L), Na 148 mEq/L (148 mmol/L), glucose 178 mg/dL (9.88 mmol/L). He complains of muscle weakness and cramps. Which nursing action should be implemented at this time?

① Hold 0700 dose of spironolactone.
② Encourage eating bananas for breakfast.
③ Call the physician to suggest a stat K level.
④ Call for a twelve lead ECG.

8.28　A client is being treated for hypovolemia. Which observation would the nurse identify as the desired response to fluid replacement?

① Urine output 160 mL/8 hours
② Hgb—13g/dL; Hct— 49%
③ Arterial pH—7.34
④ CVP reading—8 mm Hg

8.29　The nurse is caring for an intubated, mechanically ventilated client. The nurse notes a "high pressure alarm" and finds the client coughing with secretions visible in the endotracheal tube. What are the priority nursing interventions?

① Silence the alarm and sedate the client for anxiety.
② Ambu the client and notify respiratory therapy.
③ Suction the client and monitor pulse oximetry.
④ Disable the alarm and order an arterial blood gas.

8.30　A client is admitted with arterial blood gasses of pH—7.57; pCO_2—29 mm Hg; HCO_3—22 mm Hg. In response, the provider of care's orders: O_2 via nasal cannula at 5L/min. What is the priority nursing action?

① Begin O_2 immediately.
② Determine the accuracy of the order.
③ Assess for pain.
④ Notify the laboratory to repeat the test prior to any action.

8.31 A client arrives at the emergency department with a penetrating chest wound and a rush of air through the trauma site. Organize the following interventions in chronological order (with 1 being the highest priority).

| ① Administer oxygen and begin set up for tube insertions. |
| ② Place air-occlusive dressing over chest wound. |
| ③ Monitor blood gases. |
| ④ Medicate for pain. |

| |
| |
| |
| |

8.32 A nurse caring for a client with a complete heart block would contact the physician regarding which order?

① Administer Lidocaine 50 mg IV push for PVCs in excess of 6 per minute.
② Administer atropine sulfate 0.05 mg IV for symptomatic bradycardia.
③ Anticipate scheduling client for a temporary pacemaker if pulse continues to decrease.
④ Mix 10 mL of 1:5000 solution of Isoproterenol in 500 mL D_5W for sustained bradycardia below 30.

8.33 A client develops severe crushing chest pain radiating to the left shoulder and arm. Which PRN medication should the nurse administer?

① Diazepam PO
② Meperidine IM
③ Morphine sulfate IV
④ Nitroglycerine SL

8.34 A client with sudden onset of deep vein thrombosis is started on a Heparin IV drip. Which additional order should the nurse question?

① Cold wet packs to the affected leg.
② Elevate foot of bed 6 inches.
③ Commode privileges without weight bearing.
④ Elastic stockings on unaffected leg.

8.35 A client presents with peripheral venous disease. The nurse will make which assessments with this client?

① Hair loss distal to the occlusion and a cool limb.
② Brawny color of extremity and sudden pain with exercise.
③ Peripheral edema from foot to calf and no pain.
④ Pale extremity when elevated and red when dependent.

8.36 Which assessment data indicates a client with a chest injury has sustained severe thoracic damage?

① Irregular S_1 and S_2
② Symmetrical respiratory excursion
③ Respiratory rate 30
④ Paradoxical chest movement

8.37 Which of these medications should be questioned for the client with this dysrhythmia?

① Atropine
② Isoproterenol
③ Dopamine
④ Digoxin

8.38 A client receiving a continuous IV heparin infusion has a partial thromboplastin time (PTT) 1-1/2 times greater than normal. What should the nurse do next?

① Discontinue the heparin infusion.
② Slow down the heparin infusion.
③ Check the prothrombin time (PT) results.
④ Continue to monitor the client.

8.39 A nurse is the first on the scene of a motor vehicle accident. The victim has sucking sounds with respirations at a chest wound site and tracheal deviation toward the uninjured side. What is the priority nursing action prior to the emergency personnel arriving?

① Loosely cover the wound, preferably with a sterile dressing.
② Place sand bag over the wound.
③ Sit the client up.
④ Place a firm, airtight, sterile dressing over the wound.

8.40 The nurse is caring for a client who is immediate postoperative for an abdominal aortic aneurysm repair. Vital signs include: blood pressure—100/70, pulse—120, respirations—24, urine output—75 mL over the past 3 hours. Which nursing action is a priority for this client?

① Weigh the client to determine postoperative fluid loss.
② Obtain an ECG to evaluate the cause of the tachycardia.
③ Decrease the rate of the IV fluids and start nasal oxygen.
④ Maintain on bed rest; evaluate for decrease in CVP readings.

8.41 Which nursing goal is appropriate for the client with deep vein thrombosis?

① To decrease further inflammatory response in the affected extremity and prevent emboli formation.
② To increase peripheral circulation and oxygenation of affected extremity.
③ To prepare client and family for anticipated vascular surgery on affected extremity.
④ To prevent hypoxia associated with the development of a pulmonary emboli.

8.42 What action should a nurse take if a pleur-evac attached to a chest tube breaks?

① Immediately clamp the chest tube.
② Notify the physician.
③ Place the end of the tube in sterile water.
④ Reposition the client in the Fowler's position.

8.43 The nurse is caring for a client who has been immobilized for 3 days following a perineal prostatectomy. The client begins to experience sudden shortness of breath, chest pain, and coughing with blood-tinged sputum. What would be immediate nursing actions?

① Elevate the head of the bed, begin oxygen, assess respiratory status.
② Assist the client to cough. If unsuccessful, then perform nasotracheal suctioning.
③ Position in supine position with legs elevated. Monitor CVP closely.
④ Administer morphine for chest pain. Obtain a 12 lead ECG to evaluate cardiac status.

8.44 Which of these interventions is most appropriate for the LPN to initiate for safe and effective suctioning for a client?

① The LPN hyper-oxygenates client only after suctioning.
② The LPN positions client in the prone position for the procedure.
③ The LPN uses clean technique during the procedure.
④ The LPN tests the equipment for proper functioning prior to the procedure.

8.45 The nurse should identify which client as being at highest risk for development of a pulmonary emboli?

① A 19-year-old four days postpartum with obstetrical history of a placenta previa.
② An obese 40-year-old man with multiple pelvic fractures from an auto accident two days ago.
③ A 65-year-old woman who is ten days post fractured hip repair and who is in physical therapy daily.
④ A 22-year-old leukemic client with a platelet count of 120,000/mm³ and hemoglobin of 9.0 g/dL.

8.46 Which clinical finding is most appropriate for the client who is taking a loop diuretic to report to the nurse practitioner?

① Tinnitus
② A weight loss of 2 lbs. (0.9 kg)
③ Blood pressure change from 160/98 to 141/90
④ An increase in urinary frequency

8.47 Which of these nursing actions is a priority for a client with this ECG strip on the monitor?

① Immediately begin CPR after establishing breathlessness.
② Administer amiodarone.
③ Prepare to cardiovert the client.
④ Have transcutaneous pacing ready at the bedside.

8.48 Two hours after a cardiac catheterization, the client begins to bleed from the femoral artery insertion site. Which nursing intervention is most appropriate?

① Assess pedal pulses and apply a sandbag.
② Apply manual pressure and notify the physician.
③ Place the client in Trendelenburg immediately.
④ Elevate the head of the bed 40 degrees and apply an ice pack.

8.49 When obtaining a specimen from a client for sputum culture and sensitivity (C&S), which instruction is best?

① After pursed lip breathing, cough into container.
② Upon awakening, cough deeply and expectorate into container.
③ Save all sputum for 3 days in covered container.
④ After respiratory treatment, expectorate into container.

8.50 Which assessment best indicates proper rehydration in a burn client with an IV order for 200 mL/hr?

① 400 mL of po intake over 3 hrs.
② Urine output of 100 mL per hr.
③ Heart rate of 105 per min.
④ Respiratory rate of 32 per min.

8.51 Which method is the most appropriate to assess or measure a client's jugular venous distension?

① Inspect the external jugular vein for distention with the client in the supine position.
② Observe for pulsations of the jugular vein that fluctuate with client's inspiration/exhalation.
③ Place the client in a Trendelenburg position for 5 minutes prior to assessment.
④ Recognize that a visible pulse at 2 cm above the sternal angle is recorded as distended.

8.52 Prior to sending a client for a cardiac catheterization, what is the priority nursing assessment finding that should be reported to the healthcare provider?

① Allergy to iodine and/or shellfish.
② Diminished palpable peripheral pulses.
③ Cool lower extremities bilaterally.
④ Anxiety over pending procedure.

8.53 Which nursing action would compromise safety when administering a tube feeding to a client with a tracheostomy?

① Place the client in supine position.
② Aspirate and return residual stomach contents.
③ Determine placement of tube.
④ Check bowel sounds.

8.54 Which method is the best for the nurse to evaluate the effectiveness of tracheal suctioning?

① Note subjective data such as, "My breathing is much improved now."
② Note objective findings such as decreased respiratory rate and pulse.
③ Consult with respiratory therapist to determine effectiveness.
④ Auscultate the chest for change or clearing in adventitious breath sounds.

8.55 While the nurse is providing care for a client who is on a volume cycled positive pressure ventilator, the low volume alarm sounds. What assessment should the nurse make?

① Client is biting on the tubing.
② Excessive fluid is in the ventilator tubing.
③ A leak in the client's endotracheal tube cuff
④ Client is lying on the tubing.

8.56 To assess the right middle lobe (RML) of the lung, the nurse would auscultate at which location?

① Posterior and anterior base of right side.
② Right anterior chest between the fourth and sixth intercostals.
③ Left of the sternum, midclavicular at the fifth intercostal.
④ Posterior chest wall, midaxillary right side.

8.57 During a cardiac assessment, the nurse assesses an S_4. What additional assessments indicate an understanding of the implications of this assessment?

① Occipital headache
② Jugular vein distention
③ Weight loss
④ Hepatosplenomegaly

8.58 A client becomes extubated while being turned, and becomes cyanotic with bradycardia and arrhythmias. Which action would be the highest priority while waiting for a physician to arrive?

① Immediately begin CPR.
② Increase the IV fluids.
③ Provide oxygen by ambuing and maintaining the airway.
④ Prepare the medications for resuscitation.

8.59 Place an X over the chamber that would be most important to assess for a client who has a chest tube connected to a water-seal chest tube drainage system and begins to present with the system below after the lung had expanded.

8.60 Identify the area where the nurse should place the stethoscope to auscultate the PMI during the physical assessment.

Answers & Rationales

8.1 ① Option #1 is correct. First assess the client and then the equipment for proper placement and connections. Lead placement needs to be assessed for accuracy of telemetry reading. If the dysrhythmia is truly a ventricular tachycardia, then follow the advanced directives outlined by client, including pulse assessment, medication administration, and/or initiating a code. Option #2 is incorrect since the accuracy of the dysrhythmia must be determined initially. Option #3 is incorrect. The assessment must be conducted first to determine if the information is accurate prior to notifying the healthcare provider. Option #4 is not the first nursing action until Option #1 has been implemented.

8.2 ③ Option #3 is the correct answer. This client needs to be assessed initially due to the headache, high systolic pressure and low diastolic with a widening in the pulse pressure, low heart rate and motor, verbal and eye opening only to deep pain which indicates there is some increase in the intracranial pressure. The client may need immediate intervention in comparison to the other clients. Option #1 is not a priority. The PaCO$_2$ should be maintained around 35 mm Hg and a normal oxygen level by adjusting the rate of the mechanical ventilation if client is being maintained on a ventilator. The bottom line for this question is that this client does not have hypercarbia which can lead to cerebral vasodilation, which increases the ICP. This client is not able to move extremities due to the spinal cord injury. This does not mandate immediate intervention. Option #2 is incorrect. The cerebral perfusion pressure (CPP) is calculated by subtracting ICP from the MAP which would be 82 mm Hg. This is right where the range begins. The CPP should be maintained above 70–80 mm Hg. Option #4 is not a priority over Option #3. This client is in the postictal phase which is the period of lethargy and limpness following the seizure, which is an expected behavior during this time.

8.3 ① Option #1 is correct. The elderly client presents often times with symptoms that are atypical and subacute. There is often alteration in the functional and mental status when developing an infection such as pneumonia. Another symptom the elderly client may present with is tachypnea, which is a consistent sign of pneumonia among elderly clients. Option #2 is incorrect; the cough may be absent or weak. In elderly clients with underlying congestive heart failure or emphysema, the auscultatory signs of pneumonia may be absent or masked. Option #3 is incorrect since the fever response may be blunted and pleurisy may be absent. Option #4 is incorrect since the WBC count may not be elevated initially when the client may just be starting to develop the complication of pneumonia.

8.4 ① Option #1 is correct since the client is experiencing respiratory alkalosis.

I CAN HINT: Always begin with the normal pH which is 7.35–7.45; then drop the 7 and decimal point to get the value range for the pCO$_2$ which is 35–45 mm Hg, and then the HCO$_3$ is 22–26 mEq/L (22-26 mmol/L). In the question, the pH is high and the pCO$_2$ is low, which means the client is breathing off too much CO$_2$. For an easy approach and more thorough detail of blood gas interpretation, refer to *Nursing Made Insanely Easy* by Manning & Rayfield. The goal for this client is to slow down the breathing and assist with rebreathing in order to hold on to more CO$_2$. Option #2 is incorrect. The client is not experiencing respiratory acidosis. If this were true, the pH would be < 7.35 and pCO$_2$ > 45 mm Hg. Option #3 does not address the concern with the respiratory alkalosis from hyperventilating. These nursing actions would be appropriate for a client in respiratory acidosis. Option #4 is incorrect, and does not address the clinical lab data outlined in the stem of the question.

8.5 ④ Option #4 is correct. The client may be experiencing a potential alteration in perfusion from the dysrhythmia. Safety is of paramount importance. While it is important to initiate an assessment, the immediate concern is fall prevention. Options #1, #2, and #3 are incorrect for this clinical situation.

I CAN HINT: Options #1 and #2 are both clinical assessments which is a hint they may not be the answer since the question requires immediate action. The keys are that the client *"is suddenly feeling very dizzy"* and *"what action should the RN immediately assist the UAP with?"*

8.6 ②⑤ Options #2 and #5 are correct. These are included in the standard of care for tracheostomy care. Option #1 is incorrect. The tracheostomy tube should not be suctioned routinely, as this may cause mucosal damage, bleeding, and bronchospasm. The tracheostomy should be suctioned as necessary. Option #3 is incorrect. Surgical aseptic technique should be used when removing and cleaning the inner cannula. Option #4 is incorrect. The new ties should be secured before removing the soiled ones to prevent accidental decannulation.

8.7 ③ Option #3 is correct since the serum potassium is low (normal range is 3.5–5.0 mEq/L or 3.5–5.0 mmol/L). Furosemide (Lasix) should not be administered with this low potassium level. The provider of care must be notified since the level is low. This low serum potassium may result in cardiac dysrhythmis, such as atrial fibrillation. Option #1 is incorrect since the creatinine level is within a normal range, and there is no need for additional management. Option #2 is incorrect since the serum glucose is within the normal range. (normal range is 70–110 mg/dL or 3.89–6 .11 mmol/L). There is no need to administer glucagon (Glucogen) since the client is not hypoglycemic. Option #4 is incorrect since the potassium level is the only one that is low. The other values are normal.

8.8 ①②⑤ Options #1, #2 and #5 are correct. The first part for successfully answering this question is to understand the normal hemodynamic values and to understand what the measurements indicate. The CVP reading evaluates the right side of the heart and the PAWP evaluates the left side of the heart. The normal values are as follows: CVP: 1–8 mm Hg, PAWP: 4–12 mm Hg, CO: 4–6 L/min. As you can see by reviewing the stem of the question, the CVP is elevated. Note that the CVP reading indicates preload complications. As a result of this preload complication, the client would present with peripheral edema, hepatomegaly, and jugular vein distention. If the PAWP was elevated, then the client would present with crackles in the lungs. If the CVP was decreased, then the client would present with poor skin turgor and dry mucous membranes.

I CAN HINT: Left sided heart failure = Lungs (watch the wedge); Right sided heart failure = Rest of the body (edema, hepatomegaly, jugular vein distention) (right = venous = CVP).

8.9 ② Option #2 is correct. Since the client is presenting with ventricular fibrillation, defibrillation should be initiated as soon as possible to convert the dysrhythmia to a normal rhythm.

I CAN HINT: A memory technique to assist you is to remember the action that is most important is to *"treat ventricular fibrillation with defibrillation."* Option #1 is incorrect. The nurse is concerned with a cardiovascular assessment, and is not conducting a neuro exam. While these other options in #3, and #4 are components of CPR, these should never delay the use of a defibrillator, necessary for conversion of this dysrhythmia. Option #4 is incorrect. Note: the NEW CPR guidelines do NOT start with two rescue breaths; the new guidelines begin with 20 chest compressions.

8.10 ② Option #2 is correct. This is an appropriate action for the nurse when accessing the IV site. Option #1 is incorrect. The circular motion should be from middle to outward and the time from drying should be 1 to 2 min. versus 1 to 5 min. Option #3 is incorrect because the flashback of blood should be seen and the catheter should not be removed. Option #4 is incorrect. The tourniquet should be applied 4 to 6 inches above proposed insertion site.

8.11 ④ Postoperative open-heart clients should be encouraged to be out of bed and ambulate as soon as possible. Option #1 is incorrect because the client is maintained in semi-Fowler's position. Option #2 is incorrect because coughing and deep breathing should be encouraged. Option #3 is incorrect as fluids are encouraged unless there is evidence of cardiac failure.

8.12 ① Option #1 is correct. The client is experiencing a tension pneumothorax. The tracheal deviation is a definitive sign of tension pneumothorax. It would be important for the nurse to assess for a decrease in the blood pressure, tachycardia, tachypnea, and decreasing SaO_2. These clinical findings would be indicative that the client is progressing toward respiratory failure. A tension pneumothorax occurs when air enters the pleural space during inspiration through a one-way valve and is not able to exit upon expiration. Pressure is placed on the heart and the lung from the trapped air. As a result, the increase in pressure compresses blood vessels and limits venous return, leading to a decrease in cardiac output. If not treated immediately, death can be a result. Option #2 is incorrect. A depressed gag reflex is an expected finding following this procedure due to the anesthesia received during the procedure. This is the reason the nurse must assess the gag reflex prior to administering any oral fluids. This return of the gag reflex usually takes approximately 2 hours. Option #3 is incorrect. This is not a priority over Option #1 which could lead to death. Option #3 is indeed a concern due to the risk for falls after having 1 L of fluid removed and attempting to get up quickly. This would

be the second client to see if the nurse had to organize the order for seeing these clients. Option #4 is a concern, but these are expected findings for SARS. This would not be a priority over Option #1.

I CAN HINT: The question you need to ask yourself is, "*Who would die first?*"

8.13 ② Anytime the pulse rate drops below the preset rate on the pacemaker, then the pacer is malfunctioning. The pulse should be maintained at a minimal rate set on the pacemaker. Options #1 and #3 do not indicate malfunction of the pacemaker. Option #4 may be an early sign of infection at the site.

8.14 ④ Option #4 is correct. The new RN should be competent at teaching the appropriate use of an incentive spirometer since the nurse is from a surgical unit. Postoperative care which includes prevention of alteration in gas exchange from shallow breathing, immobility, etc., and should be a routine skill for this new nurse of only 8 months. Refer to the book, *Nursing Made Insanely Easy*, by Rayfield and Manning, for the I CAN HINT and thinking strategy for delegation, "FLOAT." Functions of assessment; planning ability of the nurse who floats to the new unit for a day; Look for expected outcomes with the assignments; Omit specialized care; Acutiy, accountability and age must be considered; Tasks (what knowledge does the nurse need?). The bottom line is that one of the decision making strategies for delegation is to always consider the nurse's level of expertise in addition to the Scope of Practice. Option #1 is incorrect since clients with SARS would not routinely be admitted to a surgical unit due to infection control which means the new RN may not have any experience with this type of infection control precaution. Option #2 is incorrect. While the new RN may provide care during the post-op period, the care of the client on the ventilator involves more clinical decision making skills and expertise than the new RN may have developed after this brief period of time. Option #3 is incorrect since it would not be a priority over Option #4. If the new RN had not worked with a client immediately following a bronchoscopy, the nurse may not be knowledgeable about the Standard of Care which is to evaluate the gag reflex prior to administering any oral liquids.

8.15 ① These "constitutional symptoms" are characteristic of most types of anemia and are predominantly the result of tissue hypoxia secondary to inadequate red blood cells. Options #2, #3, and #4 are not as indicative of the loss of red blood cells.

8.16 ④ Alcohol consumption while on INH therapy has been reported to increase isoniazid-related hepatitis. Therefore, clients should be cautioned to restrict consumption of alcohol. Options #1, #2, and #3 are untrue.

8.17 ② An air leak would not allow negative pressure to be reestablished and would hinder complete resolution of the pneumothorax. Therefore, partial atelectasis could be noted. Option #1 is an appropriate order for chest tubes. Option #3 does not hinder the chest tube functioning. Option #4 would be an expected finding. It would be important for the nurse to ensure tube patency.

8.18 ③ The most indicative observation for anti-anxiety drugs is restlessness and increase in heart rate due to circulating catecholamines (fight or flight syndrome). Options #1 and #2 are more indicative of preoperative complications and should be reported before medications are given. Option #4 may be best treated by ventilating feelings.

8.19

| ④ Explain procedure to client. |
| ⑤ Wash hands thoroughly. |
| ① Put on sterile glove. |
| ② Lubricate catheter with normal saline. |
| ③ Apply suction for 5-10 seconds. |

8.20 ① This describes characteristic signs and symptoms of digoxin toxicity. Digoxin toxicity is a great concern in the presence of diarrhea or any circumstance that leads to alteration in fluid and electrolyte balance. This is especially true with the young or elderly. Options #2, #3, and #4 are appropriate for this client, but are not as high a priority as Option #1.

8.21 ③ Option #3: All are appropriate interventions to care for a client in acute respiratory distress. The priority of care for the non-ventilated client is to consistently assess airway and vital signs and to intervene if mechanical ventilatory support is needed.

8.22 ② This option is the safest procedure. Since the catheter goes into the thoracic cavity, it is subjected to changes in pressure which increase the risk of air emboli. Options #1, #3, and #4 are unsafe.

8.23 ② Orthopnea, dyspnea, and crackles are signs and symptoms of fluid excess. Decreasing the IV fluids is the priority. Option #1 would worsen the situation. Options #3 and #4 are not of priority to the situation.

8.24 ④ Chest drainage in excess of 100 mL/hr is not normal and the physician should be notified. Options #1 and #2 may be appropriate after the physician is notified. Option #3 may result in a decrease in blood pressure if client is bleeding.

8.25 ④ Option #4 is correct. Due to the frequent premature ventricular contractions, this client needs to be intervened with immediately after shift report due to the risk of progressing into a ventricular dysrhythmia which can be life threatening. Option #1 is not a priority to Option #4. This client is stable with no life threatening dysrhythmia. Options #2 and #3 are not a priority over #4.

8.26 ② The next priority is to notify the physician since the signs indicate pulmonary edema. Options #1 and #3 would increase fluids to the lungs. Option #4 is incorrect because the nurse should stay with the client for reassurance.

8.27 ③ The signs and symptoms are indicative of hypokalemia. A stat serum K level is needed to confirm the K level prior to going for cardiac catheterization. Option #1 is incorrect because Aldactone is potassium sparing and is an oral medication. Option #2 is not feasible prior to the cardiac catheterization since the client is NPO. Option #4 is unnecessary.

8.28 ④ The normal range for CVP is 1–8 mm Hg. A reading of 8 mm Hg would indicate a desired response from fluid replacement. Option #1 indicates a hypovolemic state. In Option #2, hematocrit is still high. Option #3 is acidosis which can result from various problems.

8.29 ③ Option #3 is correct. A high pressure alarm signals increased pressure in the airways. In the presence of visible secretions in the endotracheal tube, suctioning the client and monitoring pulse oximetry are priority to reducing airway pressure. Option #1 is never appropriate. Options #2 and #4 are inappropriate actions.

8.30 ② This blood gas indicates respiratory alkalosis and the intervention is to breathe into a paper bag or use a mask that causes the re-breathing of carbon dioxide. For this reason the accuracy of the order should be questioned. Option #1 is not indicated, Option #3 is appropriate, but not the priority. Option #4 would be costly and unnecessary, since there is no reason to question the validity of the lab report outlined in the question.

8.31

② Place air-occlusive dressing over chest wound to prevent further complications (pneumothorax, mediastinal shift).
① Administer oxygen and begin set up for tube insertions.
③ Monitor blood gases to determine early acid-base imbalances.
④ Medicate for pain with caution so as not to depress the respiratory center.

8.32 ① In complete heart block, the AV node blocks all impulses from the SA node so the atria and ventricles beat independently. Because Lidocaine suppresses ventricular irritability, it may diminish the existing ventricular response. All cardiac depressants are contraindicated in presence of complete heart block. Options #2, #3, and #4 are appropriate treatments.

8.33 ③ Morphine sulfate is given to reduce pain, anxiety, and cardiac workload. Option #1 does not reduce this type of pain. Option #2 is less common because it may induce vomiting and initiate a vagal response. Option #4 is incorrect because the nurse would administer it by IV to reduce pain and decrease overload. A client at home may have taken NTG SL.

8.34 ① Warm, moist heat is used to relieve the pain and treat the inflammation. Options #2, #3, and #4 are appropriate therapy.

8.35 ③ Venous disease results from obstruction such as thrombus, thrombophlebitis, or incompetent valves. Signs and symptoms include: little or no pain, brawn (reddish-brown skin color), cyanotic if dependent, stasis dermatitis, limb warm to touch, statis ulcers, and peripheral edema present which may be from foot to calf. Options #1, #2, and #4 would be assessed with arterial insufficiency. While in Option #2 part of it describes venous insufficiency, the sudden pain is a result of arterial complications.

8.36 ④ Paradoxical chest movement occurs with a flail chest. Immediate treatment of flail chest is directed toward improvement of ventilation and oxygenation as well as stabilization of the chest wall. Option #1 describes normal heart sounds. Option #2 is a normal finding. Option #3 occurs with increased anxiety.

8.37 ④ Option #4 is correct. The dysrhythmia is a third-degree or complete heart block. Notice the PR interval is getting longer. Digoxin is a cardiac glycoside that inhibits the sodium-potassium ATPase, resulting in an increase in cardiac contraction which may result in a decrease in the heart rate. If the client already has this potential complication occurring, then this would not be an appropriate drug for this client. Options #1, #2, and #3 may be included in the treatment plan for this dysrhythmia. Each of the actions of these drugs will actually cause the heart rate to increase.

I CAN HINT: Notice they spell "AID," Atropine, Isoproterenol, Dopamine. These will "AID" in increasing the HR for a client in a complete heart block.

8.38 ④ An expected result of Heparin therapy is prolonged PTT of 1.5–2.5 times the control, without signs of hemorrhage. Options #1 and #2 do not indicate a reason to discontinue or slow infusion since the PTT is appropriately prolonged. Option #3 is incorrect because the prothrombin time (PT) test is useful for assessing warfarin (Coumadin) therapy.

8.39 ① In an open pneumothorax, air enters pleural cavity through an open wound. Placing a sterile dressing loosely over the wound allows air to escape, but not re-enter the pleural space. Options #2 and #4 would prevent air from escaping. Option #3 is inappropriate since a chest tube has not yet been inserted.

8.40 ④ Client is at increased risk for development of hypovolemic shock. The vital signs and urine output correlate with the early signs of shock. CVP needs to be evaluated with previous readings. Option #1 is not a priority. Option #2 is incorrect because an ECG will not determine cause of tachycardia. Option #3 is incorrect because IV fluid will probably be increased.

8.41 ① It is important to prevent the complication of pulmonary emboli in clients at high risk. Option #2 relates to arterial disease. Option #3 is incorrect because surgery is not anticipated for this client. Option #4 is incorrect because preventing the problem is first priority.

8.42 ③ Option #3 is the safest for the client and will allow the nurse time to set up another pleurevac. Option #1 is unsafe and could result in a mediastinal shift. The majority of physicians will request the chest tubes not be clamped. Option #2 is not a priority. Option #4 is incorrect.

8.43 ① Based on the client's history, current immobility, and assessment factors, this client may be experiencing a pulmonary emboli. Priority nursing care is to prevent severe hypoxia and maintain ventilation. Option #2 is not appropriate. Option #3 is for hypotension. Option #4 is for a cardiac client who is experiencing severe chest pain.

8.44 ④ Option #4 is correct since it would be imperative for the LPN to test the equipment prior to using to verify the equipment is functioning properly. This is a standard of care that should be followed for all equipment. Option #1 is incorrect since the client should be hyper-oxygenated prior to being suctioned as well "versus only after suctioning." Option #2 is incorrect due to the incorrect position. Client should not be in the prone position, but in the Fowler's or semi-Fowler's position. Option #3 is incorrect. Surgical aseptic technique should be used when opening the suction catheter kits. Medical aseptic technique can be used to suction the mouth (oropharyngeal), whereas surgical aseptic technique must be used for all other types of suctioning.

8.45 ② Obesity, immobility, and pooling of blood in the pelvic cavity contribute to development of pulmonary emboli. Options #1 and #4 are high risk for shock and bleeding complications. Option #3 is incorrect because the client is not immobilized.

8.46 ① A potential adverse reaction is ototoxicity. Tinnitus may result from this problem. Options #2, #3, and #4 are expected outcomes from this medication.

8.47 ④ Option #4 is correct. Transcutaneous pads should be placed on the client with this third degree heart block; this is the treatment of choice. Notice in the strip that the p wave has totally disappeared which is indicative of a third degree heart block. Option #1 is incorrect since the HR would need to be assessed prior to initiating CPR. With the new CPR guidelines The American Heart Association has gone from the "ABCs" to the "CABs".

Chest compressions, Airway, and Breathing is the NEW 2010 AHA Guidelines. Chest compressions need to be of adequate rate and depth (*at least 100 per min*), allowing complete chest recoil after each compression, minimizing interruptions in compressions, and avoiding excessive ventilation. Option #2 is incorrect. Amiodarone would be contraindicated for this dysrhythmia since it would further decrease the sinus rate. Option #3 would be for a client with atrial fibrillation who does not respond to medication.

I CAN HINT: The key to successful outcomes with this question is to understand that a third degree heart block was on the strip and then how to handle this dysrhythmia. "PACE" will assist you in organizing this information. Transcutaneous pacing is the treatment of choice. There is an A and E in "PACE" to assist you in remembering atropine or epinephrine can be administered for a block to help increase the heart rate. The LAST thing we want to administer is a drug that will SLOW the heart rate down.

8.48 ② Option #2 is correct. The client is bleeding and the intervention is to stop it. Option #1 is incorrect. The assessment of the pulses is not going to stop the bleeding. Option #3 is incorrect. Option #4 is not appropriate for this situation.

8.49 ② Specimens should be obtained in the early morning because secretions develop during the night. Option #1 is incorrect because coughing deeply is indicated but not pursed lip breathing. Option #3 is appropriate for Acid-Fast Stain. Option #4 is incorrect because the earliest specimen is most desirable.

8.50 ② This indicates appropriate renal function. Option #1 doesn't evaluate renal sufficiency. Options #3 and #4 are too rapid which may indicate a hypovolemic state.

8.51 ② In measuring JVD, pulsations that fluctuate upon respirations are observed. Options #1 and #3 are incorrect because the client is positioned at a 45-degree angle, and the nurse inspects the internal jugular vein. Option #4 is incorrect because 2 cm or less is considered normal.

8.52 ① Allergies to iodine and/or seafood must be reported immediately prior to a cardiac catheterization to avoid anaphylactic shock during the procedure. The dye used has iodine in it, and so does seafood. Options #2 and #3 are appropriate following the procedure to evaluate potential arterial insufficiency. Option #4 could be a concern for the client prior to the procedure, however, between Options #1 and #4, the physiological complication that could occur from the dye would be a priority due to the risk of death.

I CAN HINT: Physiology first and then psychology!

8.53 ① To minimize risk for aspiration, the client should be maintained in semi-Fowler's position. Options #2, #3, and #4 are all appropriate interventions.

8.54 ④ To assess the effectiveness of suctioning, the nurse auscultates the client's chest to determine if the adventitious sounds are cleared and to ensure the airway is clear of secretions. Option #1 is subjective data and not as conclusive. Option #2 is correct but not as specific to suctioning as Option #4. Option #3 is inappropriate.

8.55 ③ Option #3 is correct. When the low alarm sounds, this usually indicates a leak. Options #1, #2, and #4 would result in a high volume alarm.

8.56 ② The RML is found right anterior between the fourth and sixth intercostal spaces. Options #1 and #4 are incorrect because the RML cannot be auscultated from the posterior. Option #3 is the point of maximum impulse or apical pulse.

8.57 ① S$_4$ is indicative of problems with hypertension. A client may present with an occipital headache upon arising in the morning, blurred vision, and an elevated blood pressure. Options #2 and #4 are related to right-sided heart failure. Option #3 is incorrect.

8.58 ③ Airway is the priority. The client's clinical changes have occurred due to hypoxia. Providing oxygen will maintain the client until the physician can reintubate. Option #1 is inappropriate since the client still has a pulse. Option #2 is incorrect since the hypoxia is not secondary to hypovolemia. Option #4 is not a priority.

8.59 The answer is the underwater seal chamber which is bubbling after the lung has expanded indicating an air leak. The nurse would expect there to be some bubbling initially since the tube is draining air, but once the lung has

reexpanded there should be no leaks in the system. The output in the drainage chamber is not an assessment that is a concern. If there had been more than 100 mL's in one hour, then further assessment would have been completed to determine if client was experiencing hypovolemia. The suction chamber should have continuous bubbling.

8.60

Notes

Optimism is the faith that leads to achievement. Nothing can be done without hope and confidence.
HELEN KELLER

CHAPTER 9

Reduction of Risk Potential

*A hero is an ordinary individual who finds
the strength to persevere and endure in spite
of overwhelming obstacles.*
— CHRISTOPHER REEVES

✔ **Clarification of this test …**

Note this percentage has remained 9–15% on the new NCLEX-RN®. These questions relate to focused assessments, care for the client undergoing treatments/procedures/surgery to reduce complications. These include diagnostic tests, lab values, therapeutic procedures, pre- and post-operative care, monitor/maintain equipment used for drainage, and obtain blood specimens peripherally or through a central line.

- ☛ Prioritize the delivery of care.
- ☛ Perform focused assessment/system-specific assessment.
- ☛ Perform diagnostic testing (i.e., electro cardiogram, O_2 sat, glucose monitoring).
- ☛ Verify appropriateness and/or accuracy of a treatment order.
- ☛ Assess and respond to changes in client vital signs.
- ☛ Evaluate responses to procedures and treatments.
- ☛ Recognize trends and changes in client condition and intervene as needed.
- ☛ Use precautions to prevent injury and/or complications associated with a procedure or diagnosis.
- ☛ Educate client about treatment and procedures.
- ☛ Recognize signs and symptoms of complications and intervene appropriately when providing care.
- ☛ Monitor the results of diagnostics testing and intervene as needed.
- ☛ Manage the care of a client within impaired ventilation/oxygenation.
- ☛ Obtain specimens other than blood for diagnostic testing (e.g., wound, stool, urine specimens).
- ☛ Obtain blood specimens peripherally or through central line.
- ☛ Insert, maintain, or remove a urinary catheter.
- ☛ Provide postoperative care.
- ☛ Provide client nutrition through continuous or intermittent tube feedings.
- ☛ Provide preoperative and postoperative education.
- ☛ Monitor and maintain devices and equipment used for drainage (e.g., surgical wound drains, chest-tube suction, negative pressure-wound therapy).
- ☛ Manage client during and following procedure with moderate sedation.
- ☛ Monitor and care for clients on a ventilator.
- ☛ Provide preoperative care.
- ☛ Insert, maintain or remove a gastric tube.
- ☛ Assist with invasive procedure (e.g., central lines, thoracentesis, bronchoscopy).

9.1 Which of these clients does the RN need to intervene with immediately due to the care the LPN is providing?

① The client is taken to the bathroom immediately following a lumbar puncture (spinal tap).
② The LPN encourages the client to wash hair prior to undergoing an electroencephalogram (EEG).
③ The LPN tries to keep client awake most of the night prior to undergoing an electroencephalogram (EEG).
④ The LPN inquires as to if the client has a history of claustrophobia and explains the tight space and noise that can be experienced with the scheduled Magnetic Resonance Imaging (MRI).

9.2 A client with a T6 spinal cord injury presents with a BP—170/72; HR—46 BPM; sudden severe headache and flushing on neck and face. What is the immediate nursing action for this client?

① Titrate the dopamine as prescribed.
② Elevate the legs if possible.
③ Apply compression stockings.
④ Elevate the head of the bed.

9.3 What clinical finding would be most important to report for a client with a spinal cord injury who is receiving dexamethasone?

① Blood pressure—130/82; HR—72 BPM
② Daily weight has increased 1 kg
③ Pale yellow secretions suctioned from endotracheal tube
④ Serum glucose—128 mg/dL (7.10 mmol/L)

9.4 An older client has been admitted to the Medical Unit following a cerebrovascular accident (CVA). The client presents with left-sided paralysis and has been experiencing dysphagia. Which of these actions by the UAP requires intervention by the charge nurse?

① The UAP puts the food on the unaffected side in the back of the client's mouth.
② The UAP brings the tray in the room on the unaffected side and places within visual range.
③ The UAP starts the feeding with some chicken broth to assist with swallowing.
④ The UAP positions the head and neck slightly forward.

9.5 Which of these clinical findings should be reported for a client with a diagnosis of parathyroid disease and presenting with a calcium level of 6.0 mg/dL (1.5 mmol/L)?

① Depressed patellar reflex.
② Paresthesia in the hand is produced when tapping over the median nerve at the wrist crease.
③ Foot extension of the big toe while fanning the other toes when stimulating the outside of the sole of the foot.
④ Carpopedal spasm after BP cuff is inflated above systolic pressure.

9.6 What plan of care is the priority for a client who is presenting with nausea, diarrhea, muscle weakness, and an abnormal ECG and is taking spironolactone lisinopril and glipizide?

① Report a serum potassium level of 5.2 mEq/L (5.2 mmol/L).
② Report a serum sodium level 146 mEq/L (146 mmol/L).
③ Instruct client about the importance of eating bananas.
④ Assess characteristics of the lips and mucous membranes.

9.7 Which of these clinical findings should be reported to the healthcare provider immediately for a client who is being managed and treated for acute low back pain?

① Discomfort that has lasted approximately 3½ weeks.
② When the leg is elevated, there is pain in the lower back.
③ L4 to L5 has diffuse, aching sensation.
④ A new onset of urinary incontinence.

9.8 What is the first nursing action for a client who has returned from having a bowel resection, and as the nurse is making rounds at the beginning of shift notices that client is becoming restless?

① Administer pain medication as ordered.
② Order stat labs for electrolytes and blood gasses.
③ Ask client's family if the client has a history of drug or alcohol abuse.
④ Assess vital signs and urine output.

9.9　A client with a history of Myasthenia Gravis is presenting with a HR of 112 bpm, R 24/min with accessory muscle use, anxiety and restlessness. Which of these are appropriate immediate nursing interventions? **Select all that apply.**

① Elevate the head of the bed.
② Administer furosemide 40 mg IV.
③ O$_2$ per healthcare provider (HCP) orders.
④ Teach the importance of wearing a medical identification bracelet.
⑤ Apply a lubricating eye drop.

9.10　What clinical findings require immediate action for a client diagnosed with peptic ulcer disease?

① HR—80 BPM and increased to 90 BPM, BP—138/70 decreased from 150/88.
② HR—88 BPM and decreased to 78 BPM, R—18/min and increased to 22/min, and BP—120/80 and increased to 140/88.
③ Complaints of heartburn and bloating during the middle of the night.
④ Abdominal distention increased with increase in the pain and vomiting.

9.11　The nurse is observing a client for complications following a craniotomy. The client begins complaining of thirst and fatigue. Which nursing observation is most important to report to the physician?

① Specific gravity of urine is increased; urine is foul smelling.
② Fluid intake over past 24 hours has been 3000 mL.
③ Urine output in excess of 4000 mL in 24 hours.
④ Presence of diarrhea and excoriation of anal area.

9.12　Before teaching a CVA client about self-care, which plan would be a priority?

① Have the client identify perception of health status.
② Identify the client's strengths and weaknesses.
③ Encourage client to discuss concerns with another CVA client.
④ Provide client with a written plan of therapy.

9.13　Which of these procedures is correct for wrapping a stump after an amputation?

① Make three figure-eight turns to adequately cover the ends of the stump.
② Wrap the ace bandage in a circular motion around the stump.
③ Unroll the bandage upward over the stump and to the front of the leg.
④ Wrap the stump so that it narrows toward the proximal end.

9.14　The client is admitted via the emergency room with a possible cervical spinal cord injury. What is the most important information for the nurse to obtain?

① History of accident and type of trauma.
② Neurological functioning.
③ Respiratory status and tissue perfusion.
④ Allergies and pre-existing medical conditions.

9.15　A child weighing 80 pounds (36.3 kg) is sent home in a hip spica cast. Which instruction is most important to include in the teaching plan designed to promote bowel functioning?

① Give a soap suds enema every day.
② Perform range of motion exercises to the upper extremities four times a day.
③ Give at least six to eight 8-ounce (237 mL) glasses of fluid a day.
④ Give a strong laxative every day.

9.16　What is the highest priority for a client 72 hours after having second-degree burns to 20% of his body in the lower abdominal area, back, and both legs?

① Airway
② Body image
③ Fluid and electrolytes
④ Pain

9.17　Which is the most important postoperative nursing action for the client following a scleral buckling procedure for detached retina?

① Remove reading material to decrease eye strain.
② Closely assess for presence of nausea and prevent vomiting.
③ Assess color of drainage from affected eye.
④ Maintain sterility for q 3 hr saline eye irrigations.

9.18 What would the nurse ask the client to do when evaluating the cranial nerve XI?

① Ask client to smell and identify different odors.
② Ask client to shrug the shoulders.
③ Ask client to read a Snellen chart.
④ Ask client to stick out tongue and move from side to side.

9.19 A client is admitted with a diagnosis of trigeminal neuralgia (Tic Douloureux) involving the maxillary branch of the affected nerve. The nurse would plan nursing care to assist the client with which problem?

① Intermittent blurred vision and tinnitus.
② Intense facial pain on affected side.
③ Attacks of severe dizziness and vertigo.
④ Impaired speech function due to muscle spasm.

9.20 During an evaluation, which assessment indicates an early sign of increased intracranial pressure?

① An alteration in the client's ability to answer questions and respond to verbal stimuli.
② Cushing's triad.
③ Decorticate posturing.
④ The presence of Doll's eyes.

9.21 The healthcare provider orders a wet-to-dry dressing for a client with a venous stasis ulcer. What is the correct method of implementing this order?

① Moisten the skin around the ulcer. Then apply a dry gauze dressing.
② Apply antibacterial ointment to the wound. Then apply a dry gauze dressing.
③ Apply a wet dressing and allow to dry. Then wet again to remove.
④ Apply a wet dressing. Allow to dry; then remove.

9.22 The nurse is caring for an elderly client with bilateral eye patches. Which nursing action would be most beneficial in preventing problems secondary to sensory deprivation?

① Maintain client sedation until eye patches are removed.
② Isolate client so others will not confuse him.
③ Maintain a calm, dark environment conducive to rest.
④ Speak to him frequently, and provide frequent touch.

9.23 Which statement made by the parents of a child with hydrocephalus indicates they understand how to care for a child with a ventriculoperitoneal shunt?

① "We will position our child on the operative side."
② "We will position our child in the semi-Fowler's position after surgery."
③ "We will report if our child starts vomiting."
④ "We will rely on the home health nurse to pump the shunt."

9.24 Which statement by the client best indicates an understanding of and preparedness for a scheduled magnetic resonance imaging (MRI)?

① "The dye used in the test will turn my urine green for about 24 hours."
② "I will be put to sleep for this procedure. I will return to my room in 2 hours."
③ "This procedure will take about 1-1/2 hours to complete. It will be noisy."
④ "The wires that will be attached to my head and chest will not cause me any pain."

9.25 When caring for a client with myasthenia gravis, what would be an important nursing consideration?

① Prevent accidents from falls as a result of vertigo.
② Maintain fluid and electrolyte replacement.
③ Control situations that could increase intracranial pressure and cerebral edema.
④ Assess muscle groups that are affected as they tend to be weaker toward the end of the day.

9.26 Which of these clients are a priority for the nurse to assess first after coming out of shift report?

① An infant with a tracheoesophageal fistula (TEF) who is presenting with substernal retractions, RR—60/min. at rest.
② An infant who is occasionally pulling at the right ear when awake.
③ A school-age child who is 2 hours postoperative for a tonsillectomy and adenoidectomy with HR—96 bpm and vomiting 30 mL of dark brown emesis.
④ A school-age child with cystic fibrosis (CF) who was admitted to the pediatric unit during the night shift and is presenting with large and foul-smelling stools.

9.27 What is the highest priority following a grand mal seizure?

① Remain with client and administer anticonvulsant medication.
② Document the events prior to the onset of the seizure.
③ Maintain a patent airway by turning client's head to the side and suctioning if necessary.
④ Protect client from injuring self by removing constricting clothes.

9.28 In planning the care of a client with an acute episode of Ménière's Syndrome, what should be included in the teaching plan?

① Adding salt to food.
② Avoiding sudden motion of the head.
③ Restricting fluids to 3–4 glasses daily.
④ Keeping cotton in affected ear.

9.29 Which instruction would the nurse include in a discharge teaching plan for the client with a diagnosis of glaucoma?

① Decrease intake of saturated fats and potassium.
② Eye pain and nausea should be reported to the physician.
③ Anticipate gradual increase in visual field.
④ Eye drops may be discontinued after two weeks.

9.30 Which clinical assessment finding should be documented in the nurses' notes indicating a complication of a deep vein thrombosis (DVT) for a client during the post-operative period?

① Client presents with a cool, painful, tingling pain.
② Client presents with weak peripheral pulses.
③ Client presents with pain in calf of leg when walking.
④ Client presents with a rapid onset of unilateral leg swelling with dependent edema.

9.31 Which statement made by a client with a left-sided hemiparesis from a CVA indicates an understanding of how to transfer out of the bed?

① "The wheel chair should be on the right side of the bed."
② "The wheel chair should be on the left side of the bed."
③ "I will use a cane."
④ "I will wait for the physical therapist to lift me out of the bed."

9.32 Which client would have the highest potential for skin breakdown?

① A client with functional incontinence.
② A client in Buck's traction.
③ A new postoperative hip replacement.
④ Two-hour postoperative knee replacement.

9.33 A client with a long leg cast on the right leg has a foot that is pale and cool to touch. An analgesic has offered no relief to severe leg pain after 45 minutes. What should be the first nursing action?

① Apply a heating pad to the right toes.
② Repeat the dose of analgesic stat.
③ Remove the cast immediately.
④ Notify the healthcare provider immediately.

9.34 Which of these clinical findings should the nurse monitor for with a client who has a nasogastric tube with suctioning? **Select all that apply.**

① Paresthesias
② Chvostek's sign
③ Flat T waves on ECG
④ Muscle cramps
⑤ Positive Trousseau sign

9.35 A client with a closed head injury has a nasogastric tube in place and begins to vomit. What is the highest priority?

① Check the nasogastric tube for appropriate placement.

② Reposition client in bed to the side lying position.

③ Notify physician.

④ Remove the tube immediately.

9.36 Which of these statements made by the client with Raynaud's phenomenon indicate a need for further teaching?

① "I will avoid all caffeine and nicotine."

② "I will take my calcium channel blocker to cure the Raynaud's phenomenon."

③ "I understand the symptoms can be precipitated by emotional upset."

④ "I will wear gloves when I go outside in the cold weather."

9.37 On the second day following a lumbar disc excision, the client complains of mild pain in both legs. The nurse's response is based on which understanding of leg pain in the early postoperative period?

① Should delay early ambulation.

② Can result from swelling which compresses the nerve.

③ Is common for months after surgery.

④ Indicates surgery was unsuccessful.

9.38 Which of these clients should be assessed immediately following shift report?

① A client with Trigeminal Neuralgia who is complaining of pain in the lips.

② A client with Bell's Palsy who is experiencing depression from a negative image.

③ A client with Guillain-Barré syndrome presenting with continuous drooling of saliva.

④ A client with dementia who is unable to remember the food that was served at dinner.

9.39 Which documentation indicates a clinical finding for a client exhibiting symptoms of myxedema?

① Increased pulse rate, from HR—68 bpm to HR—100 bpm

② Decreased temperature, from 98.9°F (37.2°C) to 97.2°F (36.2°C)

③ Fine tremors

④ Increased radioactive iodine uptake level

9.40 A client with Parkinson's disease has the nursing diagnosis, "*potential for injury related to tremors.*" What is most important for the nurse to instruct client about for promotion of safety?

① The use of crutches.

② Over-filling cup of hot liquids.

③ Care of contractures.

④ Methods to prevent decubitus formation.

9.41 Which nursing assessment is the most important regarding proper fitting of crutches?

① With the client standing, the top of the crutch should be approximately 2 inches (5.08 cm) below the axillary area.

② The bottom of the crutches should be positioned next to the heel of the foot.

③ The arms should be fully extended to the crutch hand grips.

④ The crutches should fit snugly under the arm for weight-bearing.

9.42 Following a left above-the-knee amputation, the nurse is teaching a client regarding positioning. Which response by the client indicates an understanding of the importance of the prone position postoperatively?

① "I need to lie on my stomach to keep from getting a flexion contracture at my left hip."

② "Lying flat keeps my blood flowing and prevents my stump from swelling."

③ "I need to lie on my stomach to prevent a pressure sore on my hips."

④ "I will always elevate my stump when I am in a chair to keep it from swelling."

9.43 Which of these statements made by the client require immediate evaluation for a client who recently had a paracentesis?

① "I am feeling as if I may pass out."
② "My shirt feels tight."
③ "I feel some discomfort at the incision site."
④ "I need to go to the bathroom."

9.44 Which nursing measure would be the most appropriate in preventing complications of immobility with an elderly client?

① Consistent use of bedrails.
② Physical restraints.
③ Encourage isometric muscle contraction.
④ Encourage as much assistance from the caregiver with activities of daily living as needed.

9.45 Which statement made by a client with hypothyroidism started on levothyroxine sodium indicates a need for further teaching?

① "This medicine might affect my diabetes."
② "I'll take this little pill every day before I have breakfast."
③ "I'll be able to quit taking this pill when I start feeling better."
④ "This medicine will affect the action of my heart pill, Lanoxin."

9.46 What is the most important to monitor when evaluating the desired response of calcium gluconate in treating acute hypoparathyroidism?

① Intake and output
② Confusion
③ Tetany
④ Bone deformities

9.47 Which of these plans indicate an understanding of the priority care?

① The licensed practical nurse (LPN) positions a client following a thoracentesis on the unaffected side.
② The unlicensed assistive personnel (UAP) limits fluids for a client who experienced a myelogram in the AM.

③ The RN explains to the client who is going for a bronchoscopy to expect the voice to become hoarse.
④ The RN notifies the healthcare provider (HCP) that a client expectorated a small amount of blood tinged sputum 2 hours post-bronchoscopy.

9.48 What would be most important for the nurse to caution the client to avoid with the diagnosis of hypothyroidism?

① Warm environmental temperatures.
② Narcotic sedatives.
③ Increased physical exercise.
④ High-bulk and low-calorie diet.

9.49 Which nursing measure would be least helpful in maintaining skin integrity?

① Measure lesion size using the two greatest perpendicular diameters and lesion depth or elevation, and document in record.
② Use an air-supported mattress or bed.
③ Educate client regarding how to safely take his iron supplement.
④ Encourage foods high in protein.

9.50 What is most important for the nurse to caution client about during the discharge teaching for a client who is newly diagnosed with multiple sclerosis and is preparing to go home?

① Ambulating every day.
② Staying away from being over-exposed to heat or cold.
③ Participating in stretching and strengthen exercises.
④ Participating in social activities.

9.51 The nurse is preparing to administer a scheduled dose of insulin Lispro as prescribed by provider of care to a client with Type 2 Diabetes Mellitus. The AM glucose level is 175 mg/dL (9.71 mmol/L). What is the priority nursing action?

① Ensure that a meal is at the bedside.
② Hold the medication.
③ Administer the medication IM.
④ Verify the order.

9.52 What is the priority plan for a client with hyperthyroidism?

① Extra blankets for warmth.
② Ophthalmic drops on a regular basis.
③ Increased sensory stimulation.
④ Frequent low calorie snacks.

9.53 Which observation by the nurse would indicate the client is beginning to accept blindness?

① Walking in hall without a walking cane
② Asking sister to fix her hair
③ Surveying her room, touching furniture
④ Not listening to TV or radio when alone

9.54 Which nursing intervention is inappropriate in helping a depressed client to sleep more hours per night?

① Teach deep breathing and relaxation techniques.
② Explore what client is thinking and feeling when unable to sleep.
③ Help client express feelings more clearly.
④ Administer a sedative-hypnotic medication at bedtime.

9.55 Which statement made by the client indicates a correct understanding of steroid therapy for Addison's Disease?

① "I'll take the medicine in the morning because if I take it at night, it might keep me awake."
② "I'll take the same amount from now on."
③ "I'll increase my potassium by eating more bananas."
④ "This medicine probably won't affect my blood pressure."

9.56 Which statement made by the client with Cushing's syndrome indicates a need for further teaching?

① "I realize I'll have to begin an exercise program slowly and gradually."
② "I'm going to have to keep a close eye on my blood pressure."
③ "I'm not really worried about getting pneumonia this winter."
④ "I'll be eating foods low in carbohydrates and salt."

9.57 Which of these tests should be performed prior to initiating a radial arterial puncture to evaluate ABGs?

① Compress the ulnar and radial arteries simultaneously while instructing client to form a fist. Instruct client to relax hand while releasing pressure on radial artery.
② Tap over the median nerve at the wrist crease.
③ After BP cuff is inflated above systolic pressure, evaluate for color return.
④ Compress the top of the finger, and evaluate the time for color to return to the finger tips.

9.58 What is the priority clinical finding that the nurse must monitor for a client who has pheochromocytoma?

① Blood pressure
② Skin temperature
③ Urine for occult blood
④ Weight

9.59 What would be the priority nursing care specific for an adult in Buck's traction?

① Checking site of pins for bleeding or infection.
② Applying topical or antibiotic ointment as ordered.
③ Assessing that the elastic bandages are not too loose or too tight.
④ Removing the bandages daily to lubricate the skin.

9.60 For an elderly client who has just had a prosthetic hip implant, which postoperative position should be maintained?

① The affected hip should be internally rotated and flexed.
② The affected hip should be adducted when turning the client.
③ In the supine position, the knees should be elevated 90 degrees.
④ When side-lying, the affected hip should be in a position of abduction.

Answers & Rationales

9.1 ① Option #1 is the correct answer. The LPN should not have the client up to the bathroom immediately following a lumbar puncture. The client should remain lying for several hours to ensure the site clots. The RN needs to intervene and assist client back to bed in addition to reviewing the Standard of Practice for clients following a lumbar puncture. Options #2 and #3 are the appropriate Standards of Practice for a client undergoing an EEG. Option #4 is incorrect. There is no need for intervention since the LPN is making the correct assessment for this procedure.

9.2 ④ Option #4 is correct. Clients who have lesions at the T6 or higher may experience the medical emergency of autonomic dysreflexia because the parasympathetic nervous system is unable to neutralize the sympathetic response. This condition may occur secondary to the stimulation of the sympathetic nervous system and inadequate compensatory response by the parasympathetic nervous system. Sympathetic stimulation is usually caused by a triggering stimulus in the lower part of the body. This stimulation may cause extreme hypertension, sudden severe headache, diaphoresis, restlessness, nausea, piloerection (goose bumps), and pallor below the level of the spinal cord's lesion dermatome. Stimulation of the parasympathetic nervous system causes bradycardia, flushing above the corresponding dermatome to the spinal cord lesion (flushed face and neck), and nasal stuffiness. The priority action is to sit the client up to decrease blood pressure secondary to postural hypotension. Notify the provider. Option #1 is incorrect. Dopamine will cause the blood pressure to increase further. Options #2 and #3 are incorrect for this client's clinical presentation.

9.3 ③ Option #3 is the correct answer. Dexamethasone (Decadron) may cause immunosuppression which places client at high risk for infection. The pale yellow secretions indicate an infection may be starting to occur. Option #1 is important to monitor the trends, but with only one BP report it is difficult to determine if this is a change in the blood pressure from the norm. This option as it reads would not be a priority to report. Option #2 must be continued to be monitored, but is currently not a priority over the symptoms of infection. Option #4 is slightly elevated, but is not a priority over Option #3.

9.4 ③ Option #3 is correct answer. Dysphagia is difficulty swallowing. Clients usually handle soft or semi-soft foods better than liquids. Chicken broth does not have any thickening and may result in aspiration. The nurse does need to intervene due to this potential risk of aspiration. Option #1 is a correct nursing action. Feeding the client slowly in small amounts and on the unaffected side will reduce the risk of aspiration. Option #2 does not require intervention since this action will assist with the hemianopsia and assist with client's visual range. Option #4 is an appropriate action and does not require intervention. This will assist client with chewing and swallowing since the head and neck are positioned correctly.

9.5 ④ Option #4 is correct. The normal range for calcium is 8.5 to 10 mg/dL (2.12 to 2.5 mmol/L). This client indeed had hypocalcemia. This is how the nurse would check the Trousseau sign. The Trousseau's sign of latent tetany is more sensitive than Chvostek's sign in hypocalcemia. This Trousseau's sign may be positive prior to gross manifestations of hypocalcemia, specifically tetany and hyperreflexia. When the BP cuff is inflated and held in place for 3 minutes, this results in the occlusion of the brachial artery, and the hypocalcemia and subsequent neuromuscular irritability may induce a muscle spasm of the hand and forearm of the client's hand. Another test to check for hypocalcemia is the Chvostek's sign. This sign is initiated by tapping over the parotid gland and if the lip twitches this is a positive sign. Another assessment for hypocalcemia would be checking for tingling of toes and fingers and around the mouth. Option #1 is incorrect. This clinical finding would indicate too much of a CNS depressant such as Magnesium Sulfate or a sign of hypernatremia. Option #2 is incorrect. This is the tinel's sign which is least sensitive, but most specific for carpal tunnel syndrome. Another test to check for carpal tunnel syndrome is the Phalen's sign test. The client will rest elbows on a flat surface such as a desk, with the elbows bent and the forearms up. Then the client will flex the wrists, letting the hands hang down for about 60 seconds. If client feels tingling, numbness, or pain in the fingers within 60 seconds, they may have carpal tunnel syndrome. Option #3 is incorrect. This is the Babinski reflex which is used to assess adequacy of the higher (central) nervous system. Option #3, the examiner begins by stimulating the heel and going forward to the base of the toes. A Babinski reflex is positive when the big toe moves toward the top surface of the foot and the other toes fan out after the sole of the foot has been firmly stroked. In an older child or adult, this sign would be abnormal and is a sign of a problem in the brain or spinal cord. This reflex, or sign, is normal in very young children. It is not normal after age two.

9.6 ① Spironolactone is a potassium-sparing diuretic, and when given with lisinopril, there is a potential problem with hyperkalemia. Option #1 is the answer due to the potassium level. (Normal: 3.5–5.0 mEq/L [3.5-5.0 mmol/L].) Option #2 is not the priority over option #1. In fact with the clinical presentation, the sodium would be low. (Normal: 135–145 mEq/L [135-145 mmol/L].) Option #3 is incorrect since these foods are high in potassium and could result in hyperkalemia. While option #4 is appropriate, it is not a priority to option #1.

I CAN HINT: Ace inhibitors, such as lisinopril (Zestril), inhibit angiotensin-converting enzyme (ACE), preventing conversion of angiotensin I to angiotensin II (reduced formation of angiotensin II decreases peripheral arterial resistance, thus decreasing aldosterone secretion). Spironolactone (Aldactone) promotes excretion of sodium and water, but retains potassium in the distal renal tubule. An easy way to remember Aldactone is think of "Alan at the commode holding on to a piggy bank which is a *postassium bank*" and think of him taking a "LEAK":

Low Na^+

Elevated T waves from ↑ K^+

Agranulocytosis with triamterene

K^+ must be monitored for hyperkalemia

9.7 ④ Option #4 is correct. This is a neurologic change and symptoms such as bladder or bowel changes or foot-drop should be reported to the healthcare provider immediately. Option #1 is incorrect, since when a client experiences acute low back pain, these symptoms may take 4 to 6 weeks to resolve. Options #2 and #3 are not findings that should be reported immediately. The client may present with both of these symptoms when there is a problem with acute low back pain.

I CAN HINT: The key to success with this question, as with many of the NCLEX® questions, it to remember that an "expected outcome" is most likely not going to be the priority to report or intervene with immediately! Options #2 and #3 are expected findings with acute low back pain.

9.8 ④ Post-operative restlessness should create a high degree of suspicion of hypoxemia (for instance—due to bleeding). Vital signs and urine output will give information regarding intravascular volume. Option #1 requires further assessment to rule out hypoxemia as the cause of the restlessness. Option #2 may be the second priority. Option #3 may indicate an erroneous assumption.

I CAN HINT: While studying the concept for "post-op" care for GI surgery, *Nursing Made Insanely Easy* will assist you in organizing these facts to facilitate organizing your clinical decision making skills for these type of test questions.

9.9 ① Options #1 and #3 are correct. Elevating the
③ head of the bed will assist with lung expansion.
Option #3 addresses the clinical symptoms of
hypoxia. Option #2 is incorrect. There is no
indication of fluid overload. Options #4 and #5
are not immediate needs.

I CAN HINT: The strategy is to focus on
the immediate concern with hypoxia and
then to address these in the options. The
principle for answering is using the guidelines
for the "ABC's". The basic need for oxygen
(airway) is indeed the priority as it is with the
management of the degenerative disorder in
addition to many other medical conditions.

9.10 ④ Option #4 is correct. This may indicate a
complication with perforation. This then
is followed by increasing pain with fever
and guarding of the abdomen. Peritonitis
can occur rapidly, so these clinical findings
are in need of immediate action. The nurse
should maintain the client NPO, keep on
bed rest, and notify the healthcare provider
immediately. Option #1 is incorrect. The HR
is not increased and BP not decreased enough
to indicate a complication with bleeding.
Option #2 is incorrect; there is no significant
changes to make this a priority over this risk for
perforation. Option #3 is a clinical presentation
for a duodenal ulcer that is characteristic by
high gastric acid secretion and rapid gastric
emptying. Since food buffers the effect of
the acid; then pain increases with an empty
stomach.

I CAN HINT: The key to answering this
question correctly is notice in the stem of the
question it reads "immediate action". Options
#1, #2, and #3 do not indicate an emergency.

9.11 ③ In diabetes insipidus, a potential complication
following a craniotomy, one of the first signs
is a significant increase in urine output and
pale colored urine. Option #1 is incorrect
because the specific gravity is decreased, and
foul smelling urine usually indicates infection.
Option #2 is incorrect because intake is
normal. Option #4 may be associated with
client receiving antibiotics, but is not a priority
over option #3.

9.12 ① Before teaching or client learning can occur,
the client must identify thoughts about his/
her current status including concerns, fears,
anxieties, etc. Option #2 is not a priority
because the nurse is processing instead of the
client. Option #3 is important, but is not a
priority over #1. Option #4 will be done at a
later time.

9.13 ① Option #1 is correct. Options #2, #3, and #4
are incorrect. Option #3 should be downward
over the stump and to the back of the leg.
Option #4 should be so that it narrows toward
the distal end.

9.14 ③ Respirations are a priority, especially with
cervical injuries. Options #1, #2, and #4 are all
important, but are all secondary to respirations.

9.15 ③ Adequate fluids will help maintain regular
bowel function. Options #1 and #4 are
unnecessary. Option #2, while beneficial, will
not promote bowel function.

9.16 ④ Second-degree burns create a lot of pain for the
client. Option #1 would be a priority within
the first few hours for upper extremity burns.
However, these are on the lower body. Option
#2 is a concern, but not a priority to pain.
Option #3 is a major concern initially after the
burns, but should be resolved in 72 hours.

9.17 ② It is important to prevent nausea and vomiting
as this would increase the intraocular pressure
and could cause damage to the area repaired.
Option #1 would not be effective. Option
#3 refers to an eye infection. This would
be important after the initial operative day.
Option #4 is incorrect because eye irrigations
are not common following this procedure.

9.18 ② Option #2 is correct for the CN XI (spinal
accessory). Option #1 is evaluation of the CN I
(olfactory). Option #3 is evaluation of the
CN II (optic). Option #4 is evaluation for the
CN XII (hypoglossal).

9.19 ② A characteristic of this condition is the intense facial pain experienced along the nerve tract. Nursing care should be directed toward preventing stimuli to the area and decreasing pain. Option #1 does not occur with this condition. Option #3 describes Ménière's disease. Option #4 may occur, but Option #2 is a priority.

9.20 ① Option #1 is an indication of an alteration in the level of consciousness which is the earliest sign of neurological changes. Options #2, #3 and #4 occur later after #1 has occurred. Option #2 includes increased systolic pressure, decreased pulse rate, and irregular respirations. IICP is well-established when this occurs.

9.21 ④ This method aids wound debridement. Option #1 would not be effective. Option #2 will prevent adherence of gauze to wound debris and limit debridement. Option #3, wetting again before removal, will defeat the purpose of wound debridement.

9.22 ④ The nurse should always speak when entering the room of a client with decreased vision. This makes the client aware of the nurse's presence. Options #1, #2, and #3 are incorrect because the client will become more confused with sensory deprivation.

9.23 ③ The parents need to understand the importance of monitoring and reporting signs of increased intracranial pressure. Vomiting is a sign of IICP. Signs of infection would also be important to report. Options #1 and #2 are incorrect positions. In Option #4, parents need to understand how to pump the shunt in order to maintain patency.

9.24 ③ This procedure takes approximately 1½ hours, and there is a lot of noise associated with the test. Option #1 is incorrect because there is no dye used for an MRI. Option #2 is incorrect because the client is not anesthetized for this procedure. Option #4 is inappropriate for this situation.

9.25 ④ The client has increased muscle fatigue and needs more assistance towards the end of the day. Option #1 is incorrect because the client does not experience vertigo. Option #2 is incorrect because though fluid and electrolytes are important, they are not a priority over Option #4 in this clinical situation. Option #3 is incorrect because increased intracranial pressure is not associated with myasthenia gravis.

9.26 ① Option #1 is correct. TEF is a medical condition in the neonate that the proximal end of the esophagus ends in a blind pouch, and the lower segment connects to the trachea. As a result of this pathophysiology, there may be an overflow of secretions into the larynx which can lead to laryngospasms. This leads to an obstruction to inspiration stimulating the contraction of the accessory muscles of the thorax to assist the diaphragm in breathing. As a result of this, substernal retractions are produced in addition to tachypnea. (Normal RR—30–50/min). When secretions are removed from the oropharynx, the laryngospasms resolve quickly. A brassy cough that can occur in the infant with TEF is a result of the constant laryngeal narrowing, usually secondary to edema. This is not indicative of the need to suction infant. This infant is the priority due to the immediate need to relieve the airway of the secretions. Option #2 is presenting with possible otitis media and does need to be assessed soon, but is not a priority over option #1 who has an airway complication. Option #3 includes expected clinical findings for a school-age child 2 hours-postoperative for a tonsillectomy and adenoidectomy. The HR is within normal range for this age. A small amount of blood that is partially digested, and is dark brown may be present with the emesis during the postoperative period. Option #4 is incorrect since this is an expected finding for a child with cystic fibrosis. Children with cystic fibrosis (CF) have poor digestion and absorption of foods, especially fats, which can result in frequent bowel movements that are bulky, large, and foul-smelling. These stools contain large amounts of fat which is referred to as steatorrhea.

I CAN HINT: Remember, "GFR" is a priority for assessing infants. "Grunting, Flaring and Retracting" are indicative of hypoxia. Another key to assist is to note that if the vital signs would have been provided in the option, then the heart rate and respiratory rate at rest would have been elevated if an infant is presenting with hypoxia. So remember, GFRTT (grunting, flaring, retracting, tachycardia, tachypnea) = HYPOXIA and IMMEDIATE ASSESSMENT!

9.27 ③ Option #3 is the safety with airway. Options #1 and #4, while correct, are not a priority to Option #3. Option #2 is incomplete. Documentation should also include during and after the seizure.

9.28 ② Avoiding sudden motion of the head will reduce incidence of vertigo, nausea, and vomiting. Option #1 is incorrect because salt should be restricted. Option #3 is incorrect because fluids should not be restricted. Option #4 is incorrect because cotton will not help the condition.

9.29 ② Eye pain and nausea may be indicative of increased intraocular pressure. Option #1 is for a client with hypertension and atherosclerosis. Option #3 is incorrect because the client may not experience any improvement in vision, but further deterioration may be prevented. Option #4 is incorrect because the eye drops may be continued indefinitely.

9.30 ④ Option #4 is correct. A deep vein thrombosis is a venous complication with marked leg swelling and dependent edema. Skin may become discolored with slightly painful ulcers. The area on the calf may be warm to touch. Peripheral pulses will be normal. Option #1 is incorrect since this would be more indicative of an arterial complication. With the arterial insufficiency the skin on the legs will be shiny and smooth. The extremity will have pallor on elevation. The peripheral pulses will be weak. The temperature will be cool to touch. A classic symptom of arterial insufficiency

is intermittent claudication. Option #2 is incorrect since this is indicative of an arterial complication as reviewed in the rationale for Option #1. Option #3 is incorrect since this represents intermittent claudication which is also an arterial versus a venous insufficiency. **I CAN HINT:** Three of the options indicate a complication with arterial insufficiency versus the one that is focused on the DVT.

9.31 ① When teaching paralyzed clients how to transfer themselves, it is important for them to understand that the strong side leads. Options #2, #3, and #4 are ineffective.

9.32 ① Option #1 would be the highest risk for skin breakdown due to the inability to get to the bathroom. Options #2, #3, and #4 are possibilities but are not priorities to Option #1.

9.33 ④ These are symptoms of compartmental syndrome which must be relieved as soon as possible. The only action within the scope of practice for the nurse is to document assessments and secure the healthcare provider's intervention immediately. Option #1 is an inappropriate response to the symptoms assessed. Option #2 is not typically ordered q 45 min., and it is only palliative. This action would be ignoring the fact that the client did not receive any pain relief from the previous dose. This ongoing pain is very indicative of compartmental syndrome. Option #3 is beyond the scope of practice, though bivalving is desirable.

9.34 ③ Options #3 and #4 are correct. Nasogastric
④ losses are isotonic, containing both sodium and potassium. Since these electrolytes are being pulled out, the clinical findings would be related to hypokalemia and hyponatremia. Other signs and symptoms of hypokalemia may include: fatigue, muscle weakness, nausea in addition to the flat T waves on the ECG monitor and muscle cramps. Hyponatremia may present with tachycardia, hypotension, hypoactive bowel sounds, anorexia, headache, muscle weakness, lethargy, confusion, seizures, coma. None of these are included in any of the options. Options #1, #2, and #5 are incorrect

since these are clinical findings consistent with hypocalcemia and do not occur with nasogastric tube suctioning. *Refer to rationale in 9.5 for description of Options #2 and #5.*

9.35 ② Option #2 is correct. It is done to decrease risk of aspiration. Options #1, #3, and #4 are incorrect. While the nurse may implement Option #1, it is not a priority to Option #2.

9.36 ② Option #2 is the answer. There is no cure for Raynaud's phenomenon. Treatment is based on symptoms, so there is a need for further teaching with this statement. Raynaud's phenomenon consists of intermittent episodic spasms of the arterioles typically in the fingers and toes. Spasms are not necessarily correlated with peripheral vascular problems. Symptoms are precipitated by emotional upset, exposure to cold, and nicotine and caffeine intake. Options #1, #3, and #4 are correct statements and indicate an understanding of this condition.

I CAN HINT: "STRESS" will assist you in remembering what to teach client about to prevent vasospasms.

  Stress management

  The hands, feet, nose and ears need to be protected when exposed to cold weather

  Refrigerated or freezer objects—client should wear gloves

  Environment needs to be warm

  Stress the importance of avoiding caffeine

  Stress the importance of avoiding tobacco products

9.37 ② The surgical inflammation can cause some temporary leg pain after disc excision. Option #1 is incorrect because early ambulation should be encouraged and sitting for long times is contraindicated. Option #3 may occur, but a prediction is not made at this time. Option #4 is inaccurate.

9.38 ③ Option #3 is correct. This clinical finding could result in a compromised airway. Option #1 is not a priority over #3. Option #2 is a concern, but is not a priority over #3. Option

#2 is a psychosocial need, and does not require immediate care. Option #4 is an expected finding for this client.

9.39 ② With myxedema, there is a slowing of all body functions. Options #1, #3, and #4 are associated with hyperthyroidism.

9.40 ② A full cup of hot liquids may be spilled due to hand tremors, and the client may be burned. Option #1 is inappropriate for this client. Options #3 and #4 are related to the potential for injury, but are related to rigidity—not tremors.

I CAN HINT: Always remember to go back to what the key concept the question is asking!

9.41 ① The crutches should be positioned about 2" under the axillary area to prevent nerve damage to the brachial plexus area which would result in arm paralysis or numbness. Options #2, #3, and #4 are incorrect positions.

9.42 ① The prone position provides maximum extension of the hip joint and prevents hip flexion contracture. If hip flexion contracture occurs, then it is very difficult to correctly fit or utilize prosthesis. Option #2 contains incorrect information. Option #3 is not a priority. Option #4 can result in contractures.

9.43 ① Option #1 is correct. After aspirating fluid from the client, the volume decrease may have resulted in a decrease in the blood pressure causing a decrease in cerebral perfusion. This can lead to syncope with the client complaining of a feeling of passing out. Option #2 is incorrect. After the procedure, the shirt should feel looser due to the aspiration of fluid. With this change, the abdominal girth should decrease; however, even if there was no change option #1 still is the priority due to the safety involved and risk for falls. Option #3 is expected and would not mandate immediate evaluation. The nurse would not ignore the statement, but this would not require immediate evaluation. Option #4 is not a priority since the client most likely voided prior to the procedure. This is simply a distracter and does not present a safety issue to the client.

I CAN HINT: Refer to *Nursing Made Insanely Easy* for a strategy for answering any question regarding any "CENTESIS"!

9.44 ③ This will prevent atrophy of the flexor and extensor muscle groups which will result in optimizing mobility. Options #1 and #2 are inappropriately restraining the client which will result in complications of immobility. Option #4 should say "encourage independence" versus "as much assistance."

9.45 ③ Thyroid hormone replacement is usually continued for life. A sudden discontinuing of the medication may cause a myxedema crisis. Option #1 is a correct statement because thyroid hormones may produce hyperglycemia due to the increased rate of carbohydrate breakdown. Option #2 is a correct statement because taking it before breakfast will prevent insomnia. Option #4 is a correct statement because thyroid hormones enhance toxic effects of digoxin preparations.

9.46 ③ Tetany is the major sign of hypoparathyroidism. Options #1 and #2 are important to monitor, but are not top priority. Option #4 is incorrect because bone deformities are most frequently observed with hyperparathyroidism.

9.47 ① Option #1 is correct. Remember, "Side up with puncture." Option #2 is incorrect. The client needs fluids to flush out the dye. Option #3 is incorrect. The voice should not be hoarse. Option #4 is incorrect since this is an expected finding, does not present a safety issue to the client; therefore, no need to notify the healthcare provider.

9.48 ② The client with hypothyroidism is very sensitive to narcotics, barbiturates, and anesthetics, and should avoid these with this diagnosis. If these are ordered, the nurse should question the order. Option #1 is incorrect because the client with hypothyroidism cannot

tolerate cold temperatures. Options #3 does not require caution. Option #4 would be more of a priority for a client with hypothyroidism due to the need to decrease constipation and promote weight loss. This is not something this client should avoid.

I CAN HINT: The key is to focus on the word "*caution client to avoid*" in the stem of the question.

9.49 ① This does not address the question. Options #2, #3, and #4 are very helpful in maintaining skin integrity.

9.50 ② Overexposure to heat or cold may cause damage related to the changes in sensation. Options #1 and #3 are incorrect because the client is encouraged to ambulate as tolerated and participate in an exercise program to include ROM, stretching, and strengthening exercises. Option #4 is incorrect because a client with multiple sclerosis is encouraged to continue usual activities as much as possible, including social activities.

I CAN HINT: The key is to focus on the word "*caution*" in the stem of the question.

9.51 ① Option #1 is correct. Lispro (Humalog) has an onset of less than 15 min. and peaks within 0.5 to 1 hr. It is imperative that food is at the bedside, so client does not experience any complications with hypoglycemia due to the rapid onset. Option #2 is incorrect. There is no need to hold this medication. Option #3 is incorrect; the standard of practice is to administer it subcutaneously. Option #4 is incorrect since there is nothing in the stem of the question that would cause the nurse to question if this was an appropriate order. If the AM glucose was low or the client was presenting with clinical assessments indicating hypoglycemia, then this would be an appropriate action.

I CAN HINT: Options #2 and #4 are similar. Cluster these together. Insulin is never administered IM. See, you CAN do this!

9.52 ② Clients with hyperthyroidism frequently exhibit exophthalmos which requires ophthalmic drops on a regular basis. Option #1 is incorrect because the client is usually sensitive to heat. Option #3 is incorrect because the care would include a calm, restful environment with low levels of sensory stimulation. Option #4 is incorrect since these clients need to increase their caloric intake.

9.53 ③ Acceptance of blindness would be exhibited by an exploration of their world. Option #1 demonstrates denial. Option #2 exhibits dependence. Option #4 could be a result of depression.

9.54 ④ Medication which produces dependence should be used only if other nursing measures and antidepressant medications have not worked, and the client is exhausted. Options #1, #2, and #3 are therapeutic interventions to help the client learn how to create an environment conducive to sleep.

9.55 ① If steroids are taken at night, they may cause sleeplessness. Option #2 is incorrect because the dosage has to be regulated according to stress. Option #3 is incorrect because the client with Addison's disease has hyperkalemia. Option #4 is incorrect because steroids can cause fluid retention which can increase the blood pressure.

9.56 ③ This statement does not indicate the client realizes that there is an increased susceptibility to infections. Option #1 is a correct statement. Option #2 is a correct statement because these clients may develop hypertension related to sodium and water retention. Option #4 is a correct statement since the diet should be low carbohydrate, low sodium, and high protein.

9.57 ① Option #1 is correct. This intervention evaluates the Allen's test. If the pinkness returns to the hand quickly, this indicates patency of the radial artery. This action may also be repeated for the ulnar artery in order to evaluate its patency. Option #2 is incorrect. This evaluates the Tinel's sign which is most specific for carpal tunnel syndrome. Option #3 is incorrect. This nursing action is not specific for this identified exam. It is simply a distracter. Option #4 is incorrect. This is evaluating capillary refill. This is an assessment for determining hypoxia; it is not specific to radial artery patency.

9.58 ① Hypertension is a major symptom associated with pheochromocytoma. While diaphoresis, glycosuria, and weight loss are also symptoms, an elevation in the blood pressure is the priority clinical finding that must be monitored (making Options #2 and #4 incorrect). Option #3 is not necessary, since hematuria is not associated with this medical condition.

9.59 ③ Option #3 is correct. Buck's traction is a skin traction and assessment is needed to make sure circulation is not being compromised. Option #1 is incorrect because Buck's traction is a type of skin traction. Therefore, there are no pins. This would be appropriate for a client in skeletal traction. Option #2 is incorrect because skin traction has no need for topical ointment. Option #4 is incorrect because the skin is not lubricated under the bandages.

9.60 ④ A position of abduction should be maintained. Flexion beyond 60 degrees and internal rotation should be avoided in the early postoperative period. Options #1, #2, and #3 are incorrect.

CHAPTER 10

Basic Care and Comfort

*Determine that the thing can and shall be
done and then ... find the way.*
    – ABRAHAM LINCOLN

✔ Clarification of this test ...

There have been no changes in percentages. This chapter still represents 6–12% of exam items. The minimum standards include: providing direct basic care and comfort, including elimination, mobility/immobility, performing skin assessment, and implement measures to maintain skin integrity and prevent skin breakdown; implement procedures necessary to safely admit, transfer, or discharge a client; measures to promote circulation, nutrition, non-pharmacological comfort interventions; promoting activities of daily living; complementary and alternative therapies; and promoting client ability to perform activities of daily living, rest, and sleep.

☛ Prioritize the delivery of care.

☛ Perform focused assessment.

☛ Perform skin assessment and implement measures to maintain skin integrity and prevent skin breakdown (e.g., turning, repositioning, pressure-relieving support surfaces).

☛ Provide non-pharmacological comfort measures (e.g., light dimming, warm blanket).

☛ Evaluate client intake and output and intervene as needed.

☛ Assess and manage client with an alteration in elimination (e.g., bowel, urinary).

☛ Implement measures to promote circulation (e.g., active or passive range of motion, positioning, and mobilization).

☛ Assist client to compensate for a physical or sensory impairment (e.g., assistive devices, positioning, compensatory techniques).

☛ Apply and maintain devices used to promote venous return (e.g., anti-embolic stockings, sequential compression devices).

☛ Assess client need for sleep/rest and intervene as needed.

☛ Manage the client's nutritional intake (e.g., diet, monitor height and weight).

☛ Insert, maintain, or remove a urinary catheter.

☛ Provide nutrition through continuous or intermittent tube feedings.

☛ Apply, maintain, or remove orthopedic devices (e.g., traction, splints, braces, casts).

☛ Insert, maintain, or remove a gastric tube.

☛ Perform post-mortem care.

☛ Recognize complementary therapies and identify contraindications (e.g., aromatherapy, acupressure, supplements).

10.1 While coordinating with rehabilitation, what would be the priority of care for a client who is post-op following a hip replacement?

① Instruct the client to lift the leg upward from a lying position.
② Encourage client to elevate the knee when sitting.
③ Keep abductor pillow in place while client is in the bed.
④ Review exercises with client on how to flex hip 90 degrees or more to prevent stiffness.

10.2 Which of these nursing actions indicate the nurse understands how to safely use a walker for an older-adult client who has been unsteady and requires assistance with ambulation after stretching a muscle in the right leg while exercising? **Select all that apply.**

① Advise to advance "affected" lower limb, then move unaffected limb forward.
② Discuss with client that wrists are even with the handgrips on the walker when arms are dangling downward.
③ Instruct client to wear nonskid slippers.
④ Review the importance of advancing the walker approximately 16 inches (40.64 cm).
⑤ Teach client the importance to advance walker with the "affected" lower limb.

10.3 An older client, who is being seen on the medical unit by the healthcare provider, complains of having difficulty sleeping at night. Which of these plans would be appropriate to include in the plan of care for this client? **Select all that apply.**

① Advise client to have a cup of warm tea 1 hour prior to going to bed.
② Avoid all caffeinated beverages.
③ Advise to drink a glass of water 20 minutes prior to going to bed.
④ Limit naps throughout the day.
⑤ Recommend the routine bath that is taken at home in the evening.

10.4 An older client with chronic pain from osteoarthritis asks the nurse what would be a recommended alternative therapy to use

along with the prescribed rehabilitation plan. What statement made by the nurse is the most appropriate response?

① "Discuss with your healthcare provider the possibility of starting acupuncture."
② "Discuss with your healthcare provider the need to change the NSAID client is currently taking."
③ "I am not able to discuss this question with you since it is not within my scope of practice."
④ "I recommend you add some music therapy to your daily routine to assist with pain control."

10.5 Which of these lab values would be a priority to report to the provider of care for a client who is receiving Lactulose for the diagnosis of encephalopathy, secondary to cirrhosis?

① Serum ammonia level 200 µg/dL (117.4 µmol/L)
② Serum potassium level 4.8 mEq/L (4.8 mmol/L)
③ pH—7.29; HCO_3—20 mEq/L (20 mmol/L)
④ AST—60 units/L; ALT—40 units/L

10.6 Place in chronological order the steps for placing a nasogastric tube in a client. All options must be used.

①Aspirate gently to collect gastric contents and test pH.
②Gradually insert the tube and when tubing reaches the mark, anchor the tube using tape.
③Measure the tubing from the tip of the nose, to the tip of the ear lobe, to the tip of the xiphoid, and mark it with adhesive tape.
④Explain procedure to client and assist client to high-Fowler's position if possible.
⑤Put on gloves and Lubricate the tip.

10.7 Which of the following statements, if made by a client with oliguric renal failure, would indicate a need for further teaching?

① "I will only eat processed foods in moderation."
② "I must limit the amount of salt I eat."
③ "I won't eat pickles and green olives anymore."
④ "I will use a salt substitute instead of table salt."

10.8 A client presents to the ED following a motor vehicle accident with a HR—108 bpm, RR—26/min, BP—94/62, hemoglobin (Hgb)—7 g/dL, and urine specific gravity 1.029. Which of these nursing actions require immediate intervention by the charge nurse?

① Places the client in the Fowler's position.
② Places the client in the supine position.
③ Places the client in the modified Trendelenburg position.
④ Hangs Lactated Ringer's solution.

10.9 What is the priority of care for a client with a score of 23 on the Braden scale?

① Initiate a plan for the prevention of pressure-ulcer development due to being in the high-risk category.
② Document and continue with current prevention plan for pressure ulcers since client is not in a high-risk category.
③ Continue to assess and monitor the measurement of the pressure ulcer.
④ Discuss treatment plan with nursing team to prevent any further skin breakdown.

10.10 Which of these documentations indicates the nurse understands how to accurately evaluate the client's stool for occult blood?

① Collected stool and placed in a clean container to examine for pathological organisms.
② Remained on regular diet prior to test being done.
③ Stool sample obtained from one area of the stool.
④ Guaiac tested positive for occult blood. Paper turned blue.

10.11 Which of these dietary selections should the nurse instruct the client to avoid when taking buspirone for an anxiety disorder?

① Chicken salad sandwich
② Grapefruit juice
③ Yeast rolls
④ Grilled cheese sandwich

10.12 Which of these interventions indicates safe practice for a client with chronic renal disease?

① Administers Milk of Magnesia for complications with gastroesophageal reflex disease.
② Administers lisinopril for BP 160/90.
③ Administers spironolactone for the increase in edema.
④ Encourages client to include green leafy vegetables in diet.

10.13 A client with chronic cancer pain has been receiving meperidine 100 mg PO q4h PRN for pain, without much relief. Which change in narcotic pain management would be the most valid suggestion to make to the healthcare provider?

① Decrease to twice a day.
② Decrease to every 6 hours PRN.
③ Give every 4 hours around the clock.
④ Give every 2 hours PRN.

10.14 Which of these food selections should the nurse question for a client in renal failure and presenting with spiked T waves on the ECG monitor?

① Dried apricots and orange juice
② Apples and rice
③ Scrambled eggs and slice of whole wheat toast
④ Fresh green beans and salad with cucumber

10.15 In a 7-month-old infant, which is the best way to detect fluid retention?

① Weigh the child daily.
② Test the urine for hematuria.
③ Measure abdominal girth weekly.
④ Count the number of wet diapers.

10.16 What would be a priority in establishing a bladder retraining program?

① Provide a flexible schedule for the client to decrease anxiety.
② Schedule toileting on a planned time schedule.
③ Teach client intermittent self-catheterization.
④ Perform the Crede maneuver tid.

10.17 How many milliliters (mL) should be documented indicating the total amount of fluid loss for an infant who had 12 soiled diapers weighing 5 grams at the end of a 10-hour shift? One dry diaper weighed 0.2 grams.

_____ mL

10.18 A client is admitted with frequent, loose stools. Prior to implementing orders to insert a Foley catheter, what should be the nursing priority?

① Apply fecal incontinence bag.
② Perform perineal care.
③ Administer an antidiarrheal agent.
④ Insert a rectal tube.

10.19 What would be the priority of care for a client who had a laparoscopic cholecystectomy 24 hours ago and is now calling the hospital to report right shoulder pain?

① Advise client that this discomfort is from how he was positioned during procedure.
② Discuss the importance of moving shoulder; performing ROM two times/day.
③ Eliminate any activity to the shoulder for next 24 hours.
④ Recommend client to sit upright in a chair and apply heat to the right shoulder 15 minutes every hour.

10.20 During report, the nurse indicates that the client's nasogastric tube (NG tube) quit draining over the last hour. Prior to that, it was draining 100 mL of fluid q 2 hr. Which plan would best assist this client?

① Place in a new NG tube.
② Reposition the tube to promote drainage.
③ Order a chest X-ray to determine placement.
④ Force 50 mL of normal saline down the tube.

10.21 During peritoneal dialysis, the nurse notes that the outflow is less than the inflow. Which nursing action is most appropriate?

① Reposition the dialysis catheter.
② Irrigate the catheter with 30 mL of normal saline.
③ Change the client's position.
④ Notify the healthcare provider immediately.

10.22 A client has a bovine graft inserted into the left arm for hemodialysis. During the immediate postoperative period, what should be the priority plan to prevent complications?

① Restart the IV above the level of the graft.
② Take blood pressures only on the right arm.
③ Elevate the left arm above the level of the heart.
④ Check the radial pulse on the left arm q4h.

10.23 A client is experiencing gastric upset after taking his phenazopyridine hydrochloride. Which nursing action is most appropriate?

① Tell client to seek treatment for probable pyelonephritis.
② Notify physician if urine turns red.
③ Discontinue medication if urine becomes cloudy.
④ Instruct client to take the drug with food.

10.24 Which nursing intervention is the priority for a client who is presenting with vomiting secondary to cholecystitis?

① Assess vital signs every 8 hours.
② Daily weight.
③ Incentive spirometer—daily.
④ Report a urine specific gravity that is 1.003.

10.25 A client has been transferred from a nursing home to the hospital with an indwelling urinary catheter. The urine is cloudy and foul-smelling. Which nursing measure would be most appropriate?

① Clean the urinary meatus every other day.
② Encourage the client to increase fluid intake.
③ Empty the drainage bag every 2–4 hours.
④ Irrigate the Foley catheter every 8 hours to maintain patency.

10.26 Which of these clinical assessments for a client who is post-prostatic resection (TURP) require further intervention by the nurse?

① Urine output is light red to red during the first postoperative day.
② Urine output has 2 blood clots during the first postoperative day.
③ Urine output is very dark red 2nd postoperative day.
④ Urine output is pale pink urine the 3rd postoperative day.

10.27 Which instruction should be included in the teaching plan of a client taking sulfasalazine?

① Restrict fluids to 1500 mL per day.
② Explain to client that the stool may turn to a clay color.
③ The medication should be continued even after symptoms subside.
④ If diarrhea occurs, the client should discontinue the medication.

10.28 What is the priority of care after the urinary catheter is removed?

① Encourage client to decrease fluid intake.
② Document size of catheter and client's tolerance of procedure.
③ Evaluate client for normal voiding.
④ Document client teaching.

10.29 The nurse is caring for a client with a perforated bowel secondary to a bowel obstruction. At the time the diagnosis is made, which nursing priority would be most important in the care plan?

① Maintain the client in a supine position.
② Notify the client's next of kin.
③ Prepare the client for emergency surgery.
④ Remove the nasogastric tube.

10.30 A client returns to his room following a ureterolithotomy with a left ureteral catheter in place. Which instruction concerning the catheter would be included in the nursing care plan?

① The catheter may be clamped for short periods of time.
② Teach the client that the urine from this catheter should be clear.

③ Gently advance catheter if there is no drainage for 2 hours.
④ The catheter should be irrigated every 2 hours to maintain patency.

10.31 A client with a peptic ulcer had a partial gastrectomy and vagotomy (Billroth I). In planning the discharge teaching, which instruction to the client should be included?

① Sit up for at least 30 minutes after eating to reduce peristalsis.
② Avoid fluids between meals to promote the transit of food from the stomach to the jejunum.
③ Increase the intake of high carbohydrate foods to prevent dumping syndrome.
④ Avoid eating large meals that are high in simple sugars and liquids.

10.32 Which statement made by a client scheduled to have a TURP would indicate a need for further teaching?

① "If I have this surgery, I will become impotent."
② "I will call the nurse if my bladder feels like it is full."
③ "A catheter will be in place to drain my bladder."
④ "At first my urine may be somewhat bloody."

10.33 Which of these nursing actions indicate the licensed practical nurse (LPN) and unlicensed assitstive personel (UAP understand how to safely position a client who had a lumbar laminectomy?

① Position client in the semi-Fowler's position.
② Position client in the Trendelenberg position.
③ Position client in the reverse Trendelenberg position.
④ Position a small pillow under the client's head, positioned in the supine position with knees slightly elevated.

10.34 The nurse would anticipate which assessment findings in a client who has developed a lower intestinal obstruction?

① Nausea, vomiting, abdominal distention
② Explosive, irritating diarrhea
③ Abdominal tenderness with rectal bleeding
④ Mid-epigastric discomfort, tarry stool

10.35 A client is beginning peritoneal dialysis. During the first infusion of dialysate, the client experiences mild abdominal discomfort. What should be the next nursing action?

① Stop the infusion.
② Decrease the total infusion volume.
③ Inform the client that the discomfort will subside after a few exchanges.
④ Notify the physician.

10.36 Which of these laboratory findings would be a priority concern for a client with the diagnosis of cystitis?

① Serum hematocrit 36%
② Serum WBC 6,000/mm³
③ Urine bacteria 105,000 colonies/mL
④ Urinalysis with 2–3 WBCs present

10.37 Which method would be the best to assess a client's understanding of colostomy care prior to discharge?

① Review teaching materials.
② Have client explain irrigation procedure.
③ Have client demonstrate colostomy care.
④ Observe colostomy film.

10.38 For a client receiving total parenteral nutrition (TPN), the nurse reviews the following lab values:

Glucose = 72 mg/dL (4 mmol/L)

Chloride = 98 mEq/L (98 mmol/L)

Sodium = 138 mEq/L (138 mmol/L)

Potassium = 3.0 mEq/L (3.0 mmol/L)

Based on this assessment, which nursing action is appropriate?

① Discontinue TPN administration.
② Notify healthcare provider and obtain order for potassium supplement.
③ Administer IV glucose immediately.
④ Check client vital signs immediately.

10.39 Which nursing action is most appropriate for a 2-month-old infant with reflux?

① Hold the next feeding.
② Teach the mother CPR.
③ Maintain normal feeding schedule.
④ Elevate the head of the bed.

10.40 A client is taking metoclopramide hydrochloride orally for nausea secondary to chemotherapy. In reference to the timing of the medication, when would the nurse instruct the client to take the medication?

① With each meal
② Thirty minutes before meals
③ One hour after each meal
④ At the same time each day

10.41 Which dietary modifications are important to include in a teaching plan for a client with cirrhosis of the liver?

① Decrease in calories and increase in protein.
② Decrease in carbohydrates and vitamin B.
③ Increase in carbohydrates and calories.
④ Increase in protein and fats.

10.42 A 3-month-old infant is scheduled for a barium swallow in the morning. Prior to the procedure, what should be the most appropriate nursing action?

① Offer the infant only clear liquids.
② Make the infant NPO for 3 hours.
③ Feed the infant regular formula.
④ Maintain NPO for 6 hours.

10.43 Which nursing action is most appropriate for a client receiving a tube feeding around the clock?

① Rinse the bag and change the formula every four hours.
② Rinse the bag and change the formula every shift.
③ Change the bag and formula every shift.
④ Rinse the bag and change the formula every two hours.

10.44 A nurse is obtaining a health history from a mother of a child with failure to thrive. Which assessment would provide the most pertinent data?

① Weight and height
② Urine output
③ Type of feedings
④ Mother-child interactions

10.45 What instructions would a nurse give a diabetic client who has been vomiting for 24 hours and is concerned about blood glucose levels?

① Take only half of the regular insulin dose.
② Attempt to maintain a regular diabetic diet.
③ Limit intake of sweets and sugar.
④ Drink liquids as often as possible.

10.46 Which of the following would be the best plan for prevention of constipation during the first trimester of pregnancy?

① Take mineral oil every morning.
② Increase bulk and fiber in the diet.
③ Take a mild laxative as needed.
④ Decrease fluid intake.

10.47 Which of these interventions indicate the nurse needs more information regarding how to safely ensure proper nasogastric tube placement?

① When confirming tube placement, place the tube's end in a container of water.
② Use a tongue blade and penlight to examine mouth and throat for signs of a coiled section of tubing.
③ Stop advancing tube when tape mark reaches the client's nostril.
④ Test pH (4 or < is expected).

10.48 Which of these nursing actions are most appropriate to delegate for a school-age child with Cystic Fibrosis?

① The unlicensed assistive personnel (UAP) would encourage fluids throughout the day.
② The licensed practical nurse (LPN) would give the child a diet including a lettuce salad with low fat dressing and limit to three crackers.
③ The licensed practical nurse (LPN) would administer the pancreatic enzymes on an empty stomach 40 min. following a meal.
④ The unlicensed assistive personnel (UAP) would discuss importance of child wearing a medic alert bracelet and review CPR with parents.

10.49 The nurse is preparing a teaching plan for feeding an infant postoperative repair of a cleft lip. In order to prevent complications, what is the priority to teach the mother?

① Feed the infant with a newborn nipple while holding him in the recumbent position.
② Clean the suture site with a cotton dipped swab soaked in Betadine.
③ Place the infant in prone position after feeding.
④ Feed the infant with a rubber-tipped syringe and bubble frequently.

10.50 Which assessment would be most important to report to the next shift for a client who received 6 units of regular insulin 3 hours ago?

① Kussmaul's respirations and diaphoresis
② Anorexia and lethargic
③ Diaphoresis and trembling
④ Headache and polyuria

10.51 A 3-year-old is admitted with nausea and vomiting. The nurse would offer which foods for initial PO intake?

① Ice cream
② Apple juice
③ Orange juice
④ Pudding

10.52 Organize these steps in chronological order for a client who is having a nasogastric tube removed.

①Assist client into semi-Fowler's position.
②Ask client to hold her breath.
③Assess bowel function by auscultation for peristalsis.
④Flush tube with 10 ml of normal saline.
⑤Withdraw the tube gently and steadily.

10.53 Which of these clinical observations would be most important for the UAP to report to the RN for a client with a C3 fracture?

① Unable to assist with ROM and move lower extremities.
② No bowel movement for 48 hours.
③ High pressure alarm going off on ventilator during respiratory therapy.
④ Client does not want to see any visitors today.

10.54 Which instructions should be given to an adult client in preparation for a plasma cholesterol screening?

① Eat a vegetarian diet for one week before the test.
② Limit alcohol intake to two glasses of wine the day before the test.
③ Abstain from dairy products for 48 hours before the test.
④ Only sips of water should be taken for 12 hours before the test.

10.55 What would be the priority of care for a client who has a blood sugar of 200 mg/dL (11.10 mmol/L) at 7:00 AM?

① Increase the PM dose of NPH insulin.
② Increase the AM dose of regular insulin.
③ Wake the client up at 3:00 AM and evaluate the blood sugar.
④ Decrease the PM dose of NPH insulin.

10.56 In working with an overweight adolescent with hypertension, what is the most helpful suggestion the nurse can make regarding long-term health promotion and maintenance?

① Avoid participating in organized sports.
② Join an adolescent weight-reduction support group.
③ Limit socialization with non-overweight friends.
④ Adhere to a 1000-calorie, low-fat diet.

10.57 A client has a nasogastric tube in place after extensive abdominal surgery and is complaining of nausea. The client's abdomen is distended, and there are no bowel sounds. What would be the first nursing action?

① Administer the PRN pain medication and antiemetic.
② Irrigate the nasogastric tube with normal saline.
③ Replace with a new nasogastric tube.
④ Check the placement and patency.

10.58 The nurse should plan on administering levothyroxine by mouth at which time of day?

① Prior to breakfast
② With lunch
③ At bedtime
④ Two hours after eating the main meal of the day

10.59 What is an appropriate plan of care for a client admitted in the acute stage of Hepatitis C? **Select all that apply.**

① Encourage intake of oatmeal, whole grains, strawberries, and apples.
② Instruct client to avoid alcohol.
③ Instruct client that after 3 months they may donate blood.
④ Encourage periods of rest initially followed by gradual increase in activity.
⑤ Administer acetaminophen for mild discomfort.

10.60 Which of these plans would be appropriate for a client requiring ostomy care? **Select all that apply.**

① Change pouch system daily.
② Eliminate popcorn, peanuts, and/or unpeeled vegetables for clients with an ileostomy.
③ Empty pouch when ¾ full.
④ Irrigate colostomy that is with the descending colon at approximately the same time daily.
⑤ Review the importance for the family to be included in the teaching plan and remain responsible for the home care.

Answers & Rationales

10.1 ③ Option # 3 is correct. This is the standard of care for the client in the post-op period following a hip replacement. Options # 1 and #2 can pop the prosthesis out of the socket. Option #4 is incorrect. This can also result in prosthesis displacement.

10.2 ①
② Option #1 is correct. This indicates safe practice.
⑤ Option #2 is correct. This does indicate an understanding of safe practice with walker care. Option #3 is incorrect. The standard of care should be to have the client wear safe shoes. Option #4 is incorrect. The walker should only be advanced approximately 12 inches (30.5 cm). Sixteen inches (40.6 cm) are too much and may result in a fall. Option #5 is correct practice and demonstrates an understanding of safe walker care.

10.3 ④
⑤ Options #4 and #5 are correct. Clients may be instructed with the following to assist in developing a bedtime routine. In addition to limiting naps throughout the day and continuing with routines from home, such as an evening bath, older clients can be encouraged to exercise regularly at least 2 hours prior to bedtime. Organize the sleep environment for comfort. Caffeine, alcohol, and nicotine should be limited at least 4 hr prior to bedtime. Fluids should be limited to 2 to 4 hours prior to bedtime. If client is anxious or stressed, engage in muscle relaxation. If someone is available for a back rub 15 min. prior to going to bed, this can also be very therapeutic. Warm milk and crackers can be soothing prior to going to bed. Options #1, #2, and #3 are incorrect for assisting with sleep.

10.4 ④ Option #4 is correct. Music therapy has been proved by research that it will assist in clients' daily living activities and provide a different and new focus. Option #1 is incorrect. This must be performed by a skilled practitioner. Option #2 does not include an alternative therapy. Option #3 is incorrect. The nurse is able to answer this question and provide recommendations to the client.

I CAN HINT: In reviewing these options, notice that options #1, #2, and #3 are focused on someone other than the client. The correct options focus on what the client can do. If you have no idea what the answer is, a great decision making strategy is to focus on the client.

10.5 ③ Option #3 is the correct answer. As you read the question, you want to ask yourself how does this medication work? If you only remember, that it works by binding with the protein which is then excreted through the stools then this will help you be successful! If the client experiences too many stools, then the complication of metabolic acidosis may occur. These labs, pH and HCO_3 indicate a complication with metabolic acidosis. Option #1 is an expected finding in liver disease. This is the reason the client is receiving the medication. The normal serum ammonia levels should be 20–70 mcg/dL (11.7–41.1 µmol/L). Option #4 is also an expected finding with a client who has a diagnosis of cirrhosis or hepatitis. The normal ranges for these are: AST—5–40 units/L; ALT—8–20 units/L. Option #2 is a normal value. Normal serum potassium level is 3.5–5.0 mEq/L (3.5–5.0 mmol/L).

10.6

④ Explain procedure to client and assist client to high-Fowler's position if possible.
③ Measure the tubing from the tip of the nose, to the tip of the ear lobe, to the tip of the xiphoid, and mark it with adhesive tape.
⑤ Put on gloves and Lubricate the tip.
② Gradually insert the tube and when tubing reaches the mark, anchor the tube using tape.
① Aspirate gently to collect gastric contents and test pH.

10.7 ④ Option #4 is correct. Many salt substitutes contain potassium and could lead to hyperkalemia in clients with renal failure. This must be clarified with the client. Options #1, #2, and #3 indicate an understanding by the client of the need to limit sodium intake.

10.8 ① Option #1 is correct. This client is presenting with a rapid heart rate, low blood pressure and low hemoglobin with an increase in the specific gravity. This client is dry and with the Hgb being <8 g/dL, the conclusion is the client has lost some blood or has an active bleed occurring. Now with this in mind, would you want them to sit the client in the Fowler's position? You are so correct! The answer is NO! This would cause the blood pressure to decrease even more. The nurse needs to intervene, so client does not get more hypotensive.

I CAN HINT: Notice that options #2 and #3 are both similar in the down position and option #4 is an isotonic fluid all of which would be administered for a client who was bleeding. A great clinical decision making testing strategy is to cluster similar options together. If you do not know the answer, this is an excellent strategy to assist you on your path to success!!! See, you do NOT have to know everything to pass. You must, however, be a great thinker! The question is asking which of these actions *"would require immediate intervention by the charge nurse."* When you see this, the nursing care is going to be either unsafe or not within the standard or scope of practice.

10.9 ② Option #2 is correct. The Braden scale is a tool for predicting pressure sore risk which includes six subscales: sensory perception, moisture, activity, mobility, nutrition, and friction and shear. Each of the subscales rates factors within the above schema from 1 (least favorable) to 4 (most favorable), for a total of 23 points. A score of 16–18 points or less is the cut off for adults in predicting risk. This client does not have one point off of the scale. The care would be to document findings and continue the prevention plan. It is obviously

working out with great outcomes. Option #1 is incorrect since the no. on the scale does not indicate the high risk category. Option #3 is incorrect since this scale does not measure the pressure ulcer status over time. The Braden scale evaluates the risk assessment for developing a pressure ulcer. The Pressure Ulcer Scale for Healing (PUSH Tool) is the tool that was developed by the National Pressure Ulcer Advisory Panel (NPUAP) as a quick, reliable tool to monitor the change in pressure ulcer status over time. Option #4 is incorrect since there is no need for a treatment plan.

I CAN HINT: The key to answering this question correctly is to know the numbers on the Braden scale. The total score is 6 to 23; a lower score indicates a higher risk for pressure ulcer development. This is the most reliable and most often used assessment scale for pressure ulcer risk; score of 16 -18 is cut-off for adults.

10.10 ④ Option #4 is correct. Options #1, #2, and #3 are incorrect. Option #1 should be in a sterile container. Option #2, client may be on a specific type of diet prior to test being done to minimize false results. Option #3 should be collected from various areas of stool.

10.11 ② Option #2 is correct. Grapefruit juice increases serum levels and effect; ingestion of large amounts of grapefruit juice is not recommended. Options #1, #3, and #4 are incorrect. There is no reason for these foods to be avoided.

10.12 ④ Option #4 is correct. These are high in folic acid that is important due to lack of erythropoietin. Option #1 is incorrect. This is unsafe, since magnesium can be elevated with this medical condition. Options #2 and #3 may be contraindicated due to risk of hyperkalemia.

I CAN HINT: The strategy is to understand the need for folic acid due to lack of erythropoietin. Then it is important to know the foods high in folic acid. While we are focusing on renal disease, keep in mind that we want to include these in the diet for young females who want to become pregnant. A client who is an alcoholic may also have a folic acid deficiency. The etiology for these other clients are not due to the lack of erythropoietin production, but from other physiological changes that result in the need for folic acid to be a priority.

10.13 ③ Research shows that around-the-clock (ATC) administration of analgesics is more effective in maintaining blood levels to alleviate the pain associated with cancer. Options #1 and #2 actually decrease the amount of pain medication. Option #4 might be too frequent an interval.

10.14 ① Option #1 is correct due to these foods being high in potassium. The spiked T waves and renal failure pointed to hyperkalemia. The foods that you need to organize in your mind are the ones that are high in potassium. The other options are not high in potassium.

I CAN HINT: A great way to remember the other foods high in potassium are the "OES": potatoes, tomatoes, avocadoes, bananoes, and orangetoes (just kidding! But bananas and oranges are high in potassium).

10.15 ① Option #1 is correct. Fluid retention is best detected by weighing daily and noting a gaining trend. Options #2 and #3 are incorrect and will not provide information regarding fluid retention. Option #4 can provide an estimation of the amount of urine output, but not about fluid retention.

10.16 ② This is a priority when establishing a program. Option #1 is incorrect. Option #3 may not always be necessary in all programs. Option #4 would only be appropriate for a client with overflow incontinence.

10.17 __57.6 mL__

Step One: Determine the amount of fluid loss.

(One gram of dry weight is equal to 1 mL of fluid loss)

12 diapers x 5 grams = 60 grams

Step Two: Determine the weight the dry diapers.

12 x 0.2 grams = 2.4 grams

Step Three: Determine total mL lost by infant.

60 grams – 2.4 grams = 57.6 grams

> I CAN HINT: Remember: 1 gram of dry weight is = to 1 mL of fluid. Remember to subtract the weight of each dry diaper prior to documenting fluid loss from the infant.

10.18 ② Careful perineal care should be performed prior to beginning the catheterization procedure to give added cleanliness to the area, especially when diarrhea is present. Option #1 is not necessary. Options #3 and #4 require a physician's order and are not appropriate.

10.19 ④ Option #4 is correct. During the diagnostic procedure, the abdomen is insufflated with CO_2 to assist the laparoscope to be inserted and assist in visualization. This CO_2 may result in shoulder discomfort. Option #1 is incorrect. Option #2 is not reported in research to demonstrate any evidence that this would alter this type of pain. Option #3 is incorrect. This action is unrelated to this type of pain from the procedure. I CAN HINT: The key to successfully answering this question is to understand that the pain is from the gas that was inflated in the abdominal area.

10.20 ② This will be the best plan to minimize trauma and be effective. Option #1 is not necessary in this situation. Option #3 is inappropriate. Option #4 is incorrect since fluid should never be forced down any tube.

10.21 ③ The outflow should always be greater than the inflow. After the dwell time, the dialysate should be diffusing out the extra fluid and waste products. By changing a client's position, you can affect the drainage. Options #1 and #2 are incorrect because peritoneal catheters are surgically placed and are usually not irrigated. Option #4 is done after Option #3 if there is not an increased amount of drainage. Sometimes problems with outflow are related to a full colon.

10.22 ② Blood pressures should always be taken on the arm opposite the one used for hemodialysis. Option #1 is incorrect because IVs should not be started in the grafted arm. Option #3 is not necessary after surgery. Option #4 would not necessarily prevent complications which is what the question is asking.

10.23 ④ Phenazopyridine (Pyridium) should be taken with food to minimize gastric distress. Option #1 is not a typical symptom of pyelonephritis. Option #2 is incorrect because this drug normally turns the urine red. Option #3 is incorrect because this drug does not make urine cloudy.

10.24 ② Option #2 is correct. The client would present with dehydration from the vomiting which could be monitored with a daily weight. Options #1 and #3 need to be assessed more frequently than the time in the options. Option #3 is incorrect since this would indicate urine is diluted which would not be true of fluid-volume deficit.

I CAN HINT: The strategy to answer this question is to link the pathophysiology of what occurs with vomiting to the priority interventions for the concept of Fluid-Volume Deficit. Any of the GI diseases that may cause vomiting and/or diarrhea could result in a potential complication of fluid-volume deficit. Daily weight is a great assessment to monitor the deficit of fluid.

10.25 ② Increasing fluids is an appropriate independent nursing action that facilitates the removal of concentrated urine. Options #1 and #3 are incorrect because they do not address the problem of the client's urine. Option #4 is incorrect and cannot be performed without a physician's order.

10.26 ③ Option #3 is correct. This would be a concern as the expected outcome for 48 hours following a TURP would be the urine should be pink in color, not dark red. Option #1 is incorrect. There is no need for further intervention since this is an expected finding for the first postoperative day. Option #2 is also an expected outcome and would not be a concern. Option #4 is incorrect. This is a desired outcome on day 3 and would not require further intervention.

I CAN HINT: The strategy for answering this question is to know the potential complications following a TURP, and to compare, contrast, and trend the clinical findings. In addition to the color of the drainage of urine, it would be important to monitor vital signs for tachycardia, tachypnea, and the amount of output compared to the intake. There are two strategies here that we want you to adapt as you continue your studying. First, always understand the characteristics of any fluid that drains from any tube. Note, the color, amount, consistency, etc. Second, always compare and contrast the vital signs to assess for any alterations in fluid volume status. This applies to many clinical situations.

10.27 ③ Sulfonamides need to be given with lots of fluids to prevent crystallization in the kidney tubules. The client should continue on the medication even after the symptoms subside. They may turn the urine an orange-red color temporarily. If the client has ulcerative colitis, medication would be continued even with diarrhea; HCP should be notified. Options #1, #2 and #4 contain incorrect information.

10.28 ③ Option #3 is a priority. Within 24 hours client should be voiding normally. Options #1, #2, and #4 are incorrect. Option #1 should be increased. Option #2 is not totally correct. The size of the catheter should have been documented when it was placed. Option #4 is important but is not a priority for this question.

10.29 ③ When the bowel perforates as a result of increased intraluminal pressure within the gut, intestinal juices are released into the peritoneum leading to peritonitis. Option #1 is incorrect because the client is kept in semi-Fowler's position. Option #2 is correct but is not a priority action. Option #4 is incorrect because it would be unwise to remove the nasogastric tube.

10.30 ② After surgery, a small amount of blood-tinged urine is normal. However, the client is taught that the urine should be clear. Options #1, #3, and #4 are incorrect because ureteral catheters are not to be clamped, advanced, or irrigated due to the small size of the ureter and the potential for trauma.

10.31 ④ The basic guidelines to teach a post-gastrectomy client are measures to prevent dumping syndrome. Option #1 is incorrect because the client is taught to lie down for 30 minutes after meals. Options #2 and #3 are incorrect because the client is taught to limit the intake of fluids, avoid highly spiced foods, and avoid high carbohydrate foods during meals.

10.32 ① Following TURP, the client will not have physiological impotency. Option #2 is correct because this could be an early indication of urinary retention. Options #3 and #4 are correct and indicate the client understands his postoperative management.

10.33 ④ Option #4 is correct. The procedure is a surgery on the lower back area. Alignment and stability are the priority in the care. Options #1, #2, and #3 do not provide the appropriate alignment and stability needed for this procedure.

10.34 ① There is distention above the level of obstruction and initially hyperactive bowel sounds. Options #2, #3, and #4 are incorrect

because there would be no stool as motility distal or below the obstruction would cease. Therefore, no diarrhea, rectal bleeding, or a tarry stool would be present.

10.35 ③ Option #3 is correct. Mild discomfort is expected with the first few exchanges until the peritoneal space has expanded to accommodate fluid. This will subside after several exchanges. Option #1 is unnecessary unless the client experiences acute pain. Option #2 is incorrect. This will interfere with the effectiveness of the dialysis. Option #4 is not necessary at this time.

10.36 ③ Option #3 is a priority due to count indicating infection. Option #1 is slightly low but is not a priority concern. In Option #2 the WBC is within normal limits. Option #4 is not a priority.

10.37 ③ A return demonstration is the most reliable method to evaluate the effectiveness of teaching. Options #1 and #4 are effective as initial presentation methods when teaching. Option #2 is not as effective as Option #3.

10.38 ② The normal plasma potassium level is 3.5–5.0 mEq/L (3.5–5.0 mmol/L). This client's potassium is low and needs replacement. Options #1, #3, and #4 do not address the problem.

10.39 ④ An infant with reflux should be maintained in an upright position. The head of the bed should be raised at a 30-degree angle. Option #1 may not be necessary, if positioning is effective. Option #2 is an action for the mother versus the infant. Option #3 is incorrect because the client's feedings should be changed to small volume, frequent feedings.

10.40 ② Since metaclopramide (Reglan) facilitates gastric emptying, it must be taken before meals. Options #1 and #3 do not promote optimum effects of the medication. Option #4 is incorrect because the time of administration should be changed to give with the client's meals.

10.41 ③ Option #3 is an appropriate diet for a client with cirrhosis of the liver. Options #1, #2, and #4 are inappropriate for this disorder.

10.42 ② An infant should be NPO 3 hours prior to the procedure. Options #1 and #3 are inappropriate. Option #4 is incorrect because it is not necessary for an infant to be NPO for 6 hours.

10.43 ① Research indicates there is an increased growth of organisms after four hours. Options #2 and #3 are inappropriate due to increased organism growth. Option #4 is not a necessary action to maintain asepsis.

10.44 ① This provides the most pertinent data in assessing actual growth. Option #2 is inappropriate for this situation. Options #3 and #4 are important assessments but are not a priority to Option #1.

10.45 ④ Diabetic ketoacidosis is frequently associated with dehydration. Fluids should be encouraged. Option #1 is incorrect because a diabetic should alter the dose according to serial glucose checks. Option #2 is incorrect because the client is not tolerating PO foods. Option #3 is incorrect because sweets can be used as calories in this situation.

10.46 ② This will assist in preventing constipation. Options #1 and #3 are incorrect for the pregnant woman. Option #4 will lead to more constipation.

10.47 ① Option #1 is the correct answer. This practice is unsafe. If the tube should be mispositioned in trachea, the client may aspirate water. Options #2, #3, and #4 are correct procedures and do not answer the question.

10.48 ① Option #1 is correct. The key to answering this question successfully is to have an understanding of Cystic Fibrosis and the scope of practice for the LPN and UAP. Cystic Fibrosis is a chromosomal abnormality characterized by a generalized dysfunction of the exocrine glands. The disease primarily affects the lungs, pancreas, and sweat glands. In the pulmonary system, the thick mucus provides an excellent medium for bacterial growth and secondary respiratory tract infections. Fluids are an excellent action to decrease the viscosity and assist with expectorating and this is within the scope of practice for the UAP. Option #2 is incorrect since the diet should be high-calorie; high-protein; fats as tolerated; increase salt intake. Option #3 is incorrect since the enzymes should be taken with meals. Option #4 is incorrect since this is not within the scope of practice for the UAP. The UAP does not teach.

10.49 ④ The rubber tip can be placed in from the side of the mouth to avoid the operative area and to prevent sucking on the tubing. Infants with cleft lip swallow excessive amounts of air so they require frequent bubbling. Options #1 and #3 are unsafe due to the risk for aspiration. Option #2 is incorrect because the site should be cleansed with saline or hydrogen peroxide.

10.50 ③ Regular insulin peaks in 2–4 hours. These are signs of hypoglycemia which may occur. Option #1 is incorrect because Kussmaul's respirations are signs of hyperglycemia. Options #2 and #4 are not indicative of hypoglycemia.

10.51 ② Clear liquids should be offered first. As child tolerates these fluids, then full liquids may be offered. Options #1, #3, and #4 are all part of a full liquid diet.

10.52

③Assess bowel function by auscultation for peristalsis.
①Assist client into semi-Fowler's position.
④Flush tube with 10 ml of normal saline. *Flushing will ensure that the tube doesn't contain stomach contents that could irritate tissues during tube removal.*
②Ask client to hold her breath. *This is to close epiglottis.*
⑤Withdraw the tube gently and steadily.

10.53 ② Option #2 could result in a complication with autonomic dysreflexia. This would be a medical emergency, so intervention is imperative to prevent this from occurring. Option #1 is an expected behavior with the diagnosis. Option #3 is expected during respiratory therapy. Option #4 is important, but is not going to result in a medical emergency.

10.54 ④ Only sips of water are permitted for 12 hours before plasma cholesterol screening for accurate results. Options #1 and #3 are incorrect because a normal diet should be eaten the week before the test. Option #2 is incorrect because alcohol intake will interfere with test results

10.55 ③ It is important to know what the 3:00 AM blood sugar is to determine if the hyperglycemia is from the somogyi effect. Options #1 and #4 will be adjusted after knowing if the AM blood sugar is the accurate reading or a rebound response to a low blood sugar at 3:00 AM. Option #2 is incorrect.

10.56 ② This is an excellent means of obtaining information and support while helping the client. Option #1 is incorrect because properly supervised physical activity is desirable, not to be avoided. Option #3 is incorrect because peer relationships are important, not to be avoided. Option #4 is not enough calories for an adolescent, and a diet too low in calories is hard to comply with and may set the adolescent up for failure.

10.57 ④ The first assessment in determining problems with nasogastric tubes is to determine tube placement and patency. Option #1 may be implemented after the placement and patency of the tube are determined. Option #2 would be completed only after option #4 was completed. Option #3 is inappropriate without further assessment.

10.58 ① Option #1 is correct since administering levothyroixine (Synthroid) prior to breakfast will reduce the possibility of insomnia, and the body avoids the need to fight the digestion of food with the digestion of the medication due to the 50–80% absorption rate associated with oral forms of this drug. Option #2 is contraindicated because the body will digest the food slowing the absorption rate of the medication. Option #3 is incorrect because insomnia is associated with this drug. Consequently, administration at bedtime will heighten the chances of sleep disruption. Option #4 is incorrect because the main meal of the day is subjective to the client.

10.59 ①
② Options #1, #2, and #4 are correct. Option #1
④ includes foods that increase the carbohydrate in the diet, which would be recommended for a client with hepatitis. Option #2 is correct since the diseased liver is unable to metabolize potential toxins like alcohol. Option #4 is correct because rest is important during the acute stages of the disease, so the metabolic demands on the liver are decreased and there is time for healing. As the client improves, they can increase their activity, but pace it with rest periods. Option #3 is incorrect because a client with a history of hepatitis should never give blood. Option #5 is incorrect. Acetaminophen is hepatoxic, so it should be contraindicated for this client.

10.60 ②
④ Option #2 is correct. High-fiber food can cause severe diarrhea for clients with an ileostomy. Clients with a colostomy should resume the regular diet gradually. Foods that were a problem preoperatively should be introduced cautiously. Option #4 is correct. Clients with descending-colon colostomies can irrigate to provide control over effluence. Clients should irrigate at approximately the same time daily. Clients should use warm water (cold or hot water may cause cramping). Clients should wash around the stoma with lukewarm water and a mild soap. Commercial skin barriers may be purchased for home use. Foods in diet that cause offensive odors can be eliminated. Option #1 is incorrect. The pouch system should be changed every 3 to 7 days. Option #3 is incorrect. The pouch should be emptied when it is one third to one half full. Option #5 is incorrect. Although the family definitely should be included in the teaching plan regarding ostomy care, the client is ultimately responsible for own care.

Notes

Any fact facing us is not as important as our attitude toward it, for that determines our success or failure.
NORMAN VINCENT PEALE

CHAPTER 11

Pharmacological and Parenteral Therapies

*Words of course are the most
powerful drugs used by mankind.*
— Unknown

✔ Clarification of this test ...

Note: this percentage has remained 12–18% with the new NCLEX-RN®. Clarification of this test includes performing and directing activities necessary for safe administration of medications (adverse effects, dosage calculation, expected effects/outcomes, contraindications and side effects, blood and blood products, pharmacological interactions, pain management, and TPN).

☛ Handle and maintain medication in a safe and controlled environment.

☛ Prepare and administer medications, using rights of medication administration.

☛ Prioritize the delivery of client care.

☛ Evaluate client response to medication (e.g., therapeutic effects, side effects, adverse reactions).

☛ Assess client need for pain management.

☛ Use approved abbreviations and standard terminology when documenting care.

☛ Evaluate appropriateness and accuracy of medication order for client.

☛ Review pertinent data prior to medication administration (e.g., contraindications, lab results, allergies, potential interactions).

☛ Administer pharmacological measures for pain management.

☛ Educate client about medications.

☛ Administer controlled substances within regulatory guidelines (e.g., witness, waste).

☛ Monitor intravenous infusion and maintain site (e.g., central, PICC, epidural, and venous access devices).

☛ Titrate dosage of medication based on assessment and ordered parameters (e.g., giving insulin according to blood glucose levels, titrating medication to maintain a specific blood pressure).

☛ Perform calculations needed for medication administration.

☛ Insert, maintain, and remove a peripheral intravenous line.

☛ Access venous devices, including tunneled, implanted, and central lines.

☛ Participate in medication reconciliation process.

☛ Assess client for drug/alcohol dependencies, withdrawal, or toxicities and intervene as appropriate.

☛ Administer parenteral nutrition and evaluate response (TPN).

☛ Administer blood products and evaluate client response.

☛ Perform irrigations (e.g, bladder, eye, ear).

11.1 What is the priority of care for a client with a new prescription order for enoxaparin IM daily?

① Leave the bubble in the syringe when administering enoxaparin.

② Identify the client prior to administering the medication.

③ Rub the site gently after administering.

④ Notify the provider of care and question the appropriateness of the order.

11.2 Prior to administration of raloxifene, which data would be most pertinent for the nurse to review?

① Results from Dual-energy Xray absorptiometry (DEXA) scan.

② Past medical history with attention to risks for blood clots.

③ Most recent hematocrit and hemoglobin.

④ Client's ability to remain upright for 30 minutes after administration.

11.3 Which of these interventions should be included in the plan of care for a client presenting to the emergency department with a diagnosis of Diabetic Ketoacidosis (DKA)? **Select all that apply.**

① Administer Novolin N insulin IV as prescribed.

② Obtain IV access for 0.9 Normal Saline bolus.

③ Monitor for potassium greater than 5.0 mEq/L (5.0 mmol/L).

④ Review ABG for pH—7.48; HCO_3— 29 mEq/L (29 mmol/L); pCO_2—44 mm Hg.

⑤ Review urinalysis results for ketones.

11.4 Which of these plans would be important for a client with a new order for Sumatriptan? **Select all that apply.**

① Review with client the importance of notifying the healthcare provider for continuous or severe chest pain.

② Review the importance of taking isocarboxazid with this medication.

③ With the initial dose, monitor the blood pressure 2-4 hours before and after.

④ In addition to the medication, encourage client to lie down in a quiet, dark room to assist in decreasing complications from the migraine.

⑤ Advise not to drive until medication effect has been established.

11.5 A client has an order for Humulin N 70/30 insulin 18 units every morning subcutaneously plus the following sliding scale for Humulin Regular U-100 insulin before meals and at bedtime subcutaneously?

Blood Glucose Level	
(mg/dL)	Regular Insulin
Less than 70 mg/dL (3.89 mmol/L)	Call MD
70-120 mg/dL (3.89-6.66 mmol/L)	0 units
121-175 mg/dL (6.72-9.71 mmol/L)	2 units
176-225 mg/dL (9.77-12.49 mmol/L)	4 units
226-275 mg/dL (12.54-15.26 mmol/L)	6 units
276-325 mg/dL (15.32-18.04 mmol/L)	8 units
325-375 mg/dL (18.04-20.82 mmol/L)	10 units
376-425 mg/dL (20.87-23.59 mmol/L)	12 units
Greater than 426 mg/dL (23.65 mmol/L)	Call MD

At 0800, the client's blood sugar is 384 mg/dL (21.31 mmol/L). Shade in the amount the nurse will administer.

11.6 Which is the best action by the nurse who has drawn 2 mg of Morphine Sulfate into a syringe, and the client refuses the medication?

① Label the syringe and send it back to the pharmacy.

② Waste the medication with another RN witness and document.

③ Explain to the client that the medication is drawn up and needs to be administered.

④ Label the medication with the date and time, and save it for the next scheduled dose.

11.7 The nurse is caring for an older adult client who is 3 hours post-op total hip replacement with a history of COPD, and receiving Hydromorphone via PCA pump. The morning assessment reveals HR—62 bpm; RR—7 per min, client cannot be aroused from sleep. Which is the priority action by the nurse?

① Position the client in high-Fowler's.
② Administer oxygen at 8 liters via simple face mask.
③ Call the healthcare provider.
④ Administer naloxone 1 mg slow IV push.

11.8 Which is the best indication that Hetastarch is effective for a client who has a serum lactate level of 54 mg/dL (6 mmol/L); temperature—103°F (39.4°C); and heart rate of 128 bpm?

① BP increase to 118/78.
② Urine output = 160 ml over the past 4 hours.
③ PT = 35 seconds, aPTT = 102 seconds, INR = 3.
④ Temperature = 98.5°F (36.9°C).

11.9 The RN is delegating tasks for the day. Which task should the RN assign to the LPN?

① Administer carbamazepine po to a client with a carbamazepine level = 2.1 mg/L and reassess medication level over time.
② Develop a nutritional plan for a client on long-term phenytoin therapy.
③ Track changes in ALT/AST and assess for bleeding in a client who takes phenobarbitol.
④ Implement second teaching session to reinforce proper gum care for a client taking phenytoin.

11.10 Which laboratory data is most important for the nurse to review before discharging a 17-year-old female with a new prescription for isotretinoin?

① BUN and Creatinine
② CBC with differential
③ Serum HCG
④ Wound culture

11.11 Which of the following medications requires the nurse to caution the client about exposure to the sun? **Select all that apply.**

① Trimethoprim and Sulfamethoxazole
② Tetracycline
③ Cephalexin
④ Azithromycin
⑤ St. John's Wort

11.12 What instruction from the nurse should be included in the teaching plan for a client who is taking pramlintide for type 1 diabetes mellitus?

① "Administer medication with the AM dose of insulin in the same syringe."
② "Freeze unused vials of pramlintide."
③ "Administer oral medications 1 to 2 hours after injection of pramlintide."
④ "Recognize that the solution is cloudy, and this is an expected finding."

11.13 During the administration of Amphotericin B, what is the priority of nursing care?

① Assess for a spiked T-wave and report to healthcare provider.
② Monitor for a low digoxin level.
③ Encourage a diet low in calories and protein.
④ Evaluate the IV site for phlebitis.

11.14 What is the priority of care before pushing a medication via a heparin lock?

① Change the angiocath every 48 hours.
② Change the dressing every 24 hours.
③ Check for a flashback prior to administering the medication.
④ Flush the heparin lock with 25 mL fluid prior to administering the medication.

11.15 A client is being treated with Lorazepam 5 mg IV q hour. Which nursing action is a priority after administration?

① Have naloxone at the bedside and ready for administration.
② Obtain a baseline pulse oximetry reading.
③ Do a complete neurological exam every shift.
④ Check respiratory status every 15 minutes.

11.16 Which action would be appropriate for a client receiving a continuous infusion of heparin with a PTT greater than 150 seconds?

① Slow the heparin drip.
② Stop the heparin and notify the healthcare provider.
③ Maintain the heparin at the current infusion rate.
④ Increase the infusion rate and notify the healthcare provider.

11.17 Which medication should the nurse question?

① Carvedilol for a client with COPD
② Enalapril for a client being discharged post MI
③ Hydrochlorothiazide for a client with stage 1 hypertension
④ Digoxin for an adult patient with a heart rate of 64

11.18 What should the nurse teach a client who is being discharged with sublingual nitroglycerin?

① Take the medication 5 minutes after the pain has started.
② Stop taking the medication if a burning sensation is present.
③ Take the medication on an empty stomach.
④ Avoid abrupt changes in posture when taking nitroglycerin.

11.19 While monitoring a client receiving pain relief from client-controlled analgesia (PCA), what should be the priority care for this client?

① Set the pump's hourly infusion rate to equal total mL/hour needed to control pain.
② Evaluate the client for orthostatic hypotension.
③ Monitor the respiratory rate for tachypnea.
④ Inform the client that all of his pain can be controlled by simply pushing a button.

11.20 Which statement made by the client indicates an understanding of the health promotion teaching regarding lithium?

① "I will increase my fluid intake."
② "I will decrease my fluid intake."
③ "I will increase my salt intake."
④ "I will decrease my salt intake."

11.21 What should be the most appropriate nursing action for a child after administering Dimetane-DC cough syrup and noting the child has become excitable and restless?

① Report the child's behavior to the healthcare provider.
② Decrease the dose by half in the future.
③ Have the child drink a glass of warm milk to dilute the medication.
④ Chart the client's response to the medication and alert the next shift.

11.22 An elderly client experiencing diarrhea for 4 days has been taking Kaopectate at home. Which nursing assessment indicates a complication of kaolin and pectin mixtures?

① Itching
② Fecal impaction
③ Nausea
④ Dysrhythmia

11.23 Which assessment finding indicates a side effect of meperidine and hydroxyzine hydrochloride for an elderly client?

① Tachypnea
② Lethargy
③ Hypertension
④ Disorientation

11.24 What is the priority of care for a post-partum client who has Ibuprofen 600 mg ordered Q 6 hours ATC (around the clock) and has been complaining of cramping and bleeding that has been heavy since delivery, 4 hours ago? Labs drawn on admission (pre-delivery) are as follows: WBC—14,000 mm³; HGB—10.8 g/dL; HCT—28.6%; Platelets—120,000/mm³?

① Start a pad count.
② Start a calorie count.
③ Substitute Aleve for Ibuprofen.
④ Hold the Ibuprofen; consult with the healthcare provider.

11.25 The nurse is preparing to start a blood transfusion of 250 mL packed cells to the client. Which would be most important for the nurse to consider during this process?

① Hang D₅W for flushing blood tubing.
② Start transfusion at 60 mL per hour.
③ Warm the blood in the microwave.
④ Start transfusion with a 19-gauge needle.

11.26 A nurse is closely monitoring the client in the Intensive Care Unit who is receiving amiodarone by intravenous drip. The nurse understands that the infusion must be stopped if any of the following EKG changes occur. **Select all that apply.**

① Sinus bradycardia
② Atrioventricular (AV) block
③ Ventricular tachycardia
④ Atrial fibrillation
⑤ Q-T prolongation
⑥ Premature atrial contractions

11.27 In addition to the digitalis levels, it is also necessary for the nurse to periodically evaluate which lab values?

① Creatinine levels
② Serum potassium
③ Urine potassium and sodium
④ Blood urea nitrogen and glucose

11.28 Which observation indicates the most common side effect of Trimethoprim-sulfamethoxazole?

① Hypotonia
② Loss of hearing
③ Hypotension
④ Urticaria

11.29 Before beginning a dopamine infusion on a client, what is the priority assessment?

① Urine output
② Weight
③ Patency of IV
④ Pulmonary artery pressures

11.30 The nurse is assessing a client who is scheduled to receive diltiazem. What is the priority of care after the nurse reviews the chart below?

Vital Signs		
Date	8/4/15	8/5/15
Time	8 AM	8 AM
Temp.	97.8°F (36.6°C)	98.2°F (36.8°C)
Heart Rate	86	58
Respirations	20	22
BP	124/88	118/72

① Administer the medication as prescribed.
② Administer and advise the UAP to monitor the blood pressure every 2 hours.
③ Hold the medication and notify the provider of care.
④ Discuss the undesirable effect of this medication with the client.

11.31 Which of these clients should be seen initially after shift report?

① A client with an order for interferon 2A, but the RN refuses to administer due to a history of egg allergy.
② A client who is receiving doxorubicin and complaining of nausea and vomiting.
③ A client with cancer who is receiving vincristine and is complaining of discomfort at IV site.
④ A client with cancer who is receiving bleomycin and is beginning to present with alopecia.

11.32 Which of these nursing actions from a nurse who is admitting an older client to the medical unit with a history of diabetes mellitus, asthma, and hypertension require further intervention by the charge nurse?

① The nurse requests the family members to be involved with the medication reconciliation.
② The nurse is reconciling any written medication that the client has been taking prior to admission.
③ The nurse is reconciling medication orders only written by the healthcare provider (HCP).
④ The nurse explains to the client and family that medication reconciliation is a Joint Commission National Patient Safety Goal.

11.33 An adult client is admitted to the outpatient clinic to receive 2 units of blood for a hemoglobin of 7.0 g/dL. Which of these actions is vital to administering the blood safely? **Select all that apply.**

  ① Follow protocol and check client identity with blood label by two nurses.

  ② Place client in a private room near the nurse's station in case of allergic reaction.

  ③ Administer the blood slowly at 15 gtts/minute for the first 15 minutes.

  ④ Check client BP, pulse, and temperature every 15 minutes during the first hour for possible indications of blood transfusion reaction.

  ⑤ Discontinue the blood immediately and keep the vein open with D_5W if there is a documented reaction.

11.34 What is the priority action before administering terbutaline to a client in labor who has a HR—144 bpm?

  ① Withhold the medication.

  ② Decrease the dose in half.

  ③ Administer the medication.

  ④ Wait 15 minutes; recheck the pulse rate.

11.35 The nurse is administering morning medications to assigned clients. Which of the following clients should the nurse with hold the medication and contact the healthcare provider?

  ① The client on furosemide that had a urine output of 60 mL/hour over the past 12 hours.

  ② The client on Digoxin who has a heart rate that is 98 and regular.

  ③ The client on Digoxin with a potassium of 3.8 mEq/L (3.8 mmol/L).

  ④ The client on an enalapril that is complaining of swollen lips.

11.36 Which of these clinical findings indicate effectiveness of treatment after the administration of Nitroprusside IV drip to a client in the Intensive Care Unit?

  ① Heart rate decreased to 88 from 120 beats per minute.

  ② Blood pressure decreased from 190/120 to 136/78 within minutes.

  ③ Chest pain decreased from sharp and stabbing level 10 to mild and level 5.

  ④ Relief of nausea and vomiting.

11.37 What is the most appropriate nursing action for a client with a new order from the provider of care for an intramuscular injection of neostigmine to a client with a history of asthma?

  ① Administer the medication.

  ② Check blood pressure and pulse.

  ③ Notify the healthcare provider, so the medication can be changed.

  ④ Ask the pharmacist if the medication can be given by mouth.

11.38 A client has been taking perphenazine by mouth for two days and now displays the following:

  • head turned to the side and arched at an angle

  • stiffness, and

  • muscle spasms in neck.

Which PRN medication should the nurse give?

  ① Promazine

  ② Biperiden

  ③ Theothixene

  ④ Haloperidol

11.39 When a client is taking tetracycline with St. John's Wort, what is the priority care?

  ① Recommend that client avoids beer.

  ② Report a change in the client's mood.

  ③ Advise client to stay out of the sun.

  ④ Review the importance of monitoring serum glucose.

11.40 Which statement by a client reflects a correct understanding of alprazolam?

  ① "I can take it whenever I feel upset."

  ② "I should not take this with anything but water."

  ③ "I need to quit drinking white wine."

  ④ "This medication will help me forget and go on."

11.41 The nurse administers meperidine 50 mg IM for pain as per physician's orders. Three hours later, the client again complains of pain, and the nurse administers a second injection of meperidine. Which statement describes the nurse's liability?

  ① The nurse administered the medication appropriately; there is no liability.

  ② The nurse violated the narcotic law in not having an order to administer the meperidine a second time.

③ The client was not injured. Therefore, the nurse is not liable.

④ The nurse should have waited at least 4 hours then there would be no liability.

11.42 Which instruction is a priority to give to a client with drug-induced Cushing's Syndrome?

① Increase calcium-rich foods to help prevent compression fractures.

② Restrict foods high in potassium.

③ Decrease drug dosage gradually.

④ Increase water intake.

11.43 Which response should the nurse recognize as the desired one to levodopa in the treatment of Parkinson's Disease?

① Dyskinesia

② Complete remission of symptoms

③ Less rigidity

④ Decrease in fine motor tremors

11.44 What should be the priority action for a client who is receiving vancomycin 500 mg IV and develops a flushed neck and face?

① Decrease the rate of the vancomycin.

② Discontinue the infusion.

③ Evaluate the client's temperature and vital signs.

④ Notify provider of care for an order for an antihistamine.

11.45 What is the best plan for the administration schedule for an adult taking a psychostimulant, such as methylphenidate?

① Breakfast and bedtime

② Early morning, late afternoon

③ Breakfast time—not after 2:00 PM

④ Late afternoon, dinnertime

11.46 What is the priority assessment before administering captopril?

① Apical pulse for 60 seconds

② Blood pressure

③ Urine output

④ Temperature

11.47 A psychiatric client with the diagnosis of schizophrenia tells the nurse that he is the King of England. What is the priority action for the nurse?

① Confront the client regarding this delusion and bring him back to reality.

② Reflect this statement back to the client to encourage therapeutic communication.

③ Respond with an open-ended response to get client to further discuss his thoughts.

④ Verify identify of the client prior to administering his medication.

11.48 Which of these prescriptions should the nurse clarify appropriateness with the provider of care for a client who had just undergone a craniotomy for sustained increased intracranial pressure (ICP)?

① Dexamethasone

② Morphine sulfate

③ Ondansetron

④ Phenytoin

11.49 A client who weighs 75 kilograms has an order for heparin, 5,000 units, subcutaneously (SC) every 12 hours. The vial contains 5,000 units/mL and the medication administration record (MAR) indicates that the client should receive 2 milliliters (2 mL). What is the priority nursing intervention?

① Question the order.

② Administer the 2 milliliters as ordered.

③ Perform a stool hemocult on the client prior to administration.

④ Check the lab values prior to administration.

11.50 Which of these statements made by the client indicate an understanding of misoprostol?

① "I will take a magnesium-based antacid with this medication."

② "I should not experience any NSAID-induced ulcers."

③ "I can expect to find some blood in my stool and emesis."

④ "I can still take this medication if I am pregnant."

11.51 The physician orders heparin 7,000 U S.C. q8h for a client with deep vein thrombosis. The heparin available is 20,000 units per 1 ml. How many milliliters of heparin should the nurse administer?

_____ milliliters

11.52 Which observations indicate the client is experiencing a side effect(s) of prednisone?

① Decreased sodium levels and increased urinary output
② Vomiting small amounts of bile-stained fluid
③ Bleeding gums with a decrease in clotting time
④ Ecchymosis and an increase in the retention of fluids

11.53 A client is brought to the ER by his family after severe, extensive burn injury. Which of these orders will the nurse question?

① Begin Lactated Ringers infusion stat.
② Give furosemide 80 mg IV push stat.
③ Give morphine sulfate 2 mg IV push stat.
④ Insert Foley catheter.

11.54 Which instruction will be included in a teaching plan for the client receiving a peripheral vasodilator?

① Take hot showers to promote the vasodilation effect.
② Small amounts of alcohol will enhance the medication.
③ Increase the sodium intake due to excessive loss.
④ Change body positions slowly to reduce syncope.

11.55 Which of the following nursing actions will be important in the safe administration of oxytocin?

① Assess respirations and urine output.
② Administer parenterally as the primary IV.
③ Have calcium gluconate available as an antidote.
④ Palpate uterus frequently.

11.56 Prior to the administration of hydralazine, the nurse will evaluate for which symptom?

① A decrease in the pulse pressure
② Pulse rate in excess of 110
③ A significant decrease in blood pressure
④ Presence of confusion and disorientation

11.57 Which response is the desired client response to hydroxyzine?

① Decrease in anxiety, and control of nausea and vomiting.
② Control of diarrhea by direct action on intestinal nerve endings.
③ Edema is decreased due to the increased excretion of water.
④ Inflammation in joint is decreased; pain is reduced.

11.58 What nursing action is most appropriate when inserting a vaginal suppository?

① Remove the suppository from the wrapper and lubricate it with Vaseline.
② Instruct client to place in tampon after inserting the vaginal medication.
③ With an applicator on the forefinger of your free hand, insert the suppository about 2 inches (5 cm) into the vagina.
④ Direct the applicator up initially and then down and forward.

11.59 Which of these statements made by the new graduate nurse indicates a need for further teaching about medication reconciliation?

① "It is the process of comparing a client's medication orders to all of the medications that the client has been taking."
② "It is a process that has been standardized across healthcare organizations with the implementation of electronic health records."
③ "It is done to avoid medication errors such as omissions, duplications, dosing errors, or drug interactions."
④ "It should be done at every transition of care in which new medications are ordered or existing orders are rewritten."

11.60 Which observation is a sign of impending toxicity from an aminoglycoside antibiotic such as gentamycin sulfate?

① Decrease in blood pressure
② Pulse rate drops from 140 to 90
③ Decrease in agitation
④ Hearing loss

Answers & Rationales

11.1 ④ Option #4 is correct. Enoxaparin should only be administered subcutaneously and never intramuscular. This is a violation of one of the rights of medication administration, "Right Route." Option #1 is incorrect even though the bubble should be left. With the order to administer IM which is not included in the standard of care, it is a priority to question the order. Option #2 is incorrect. While this is important, it is not a priority over Option #4 since the nurse should not get to the bedside with this inappropriate order. The order needs to be changed to a safe route first prior to even considering administering to the client. Option #3 is incorrect. No rubbing is the correct procedure, but before the nurse can consider the correct procedure the correct medication order remains the priority.

11.2 ② Option #2 is correct. Raloxifene (Evista) is an estrogen modifier and just like birth control pills (which also affect estrogen/progesterone) the risk for blood clots is high. If the client has a history of blood clots, this medication is contraindicated and must not be administered. Option #1 is incorrect. While the DEXA scan results would be nice, it is not a priority over Option #2. Option #3 is incorrect since the hct and hgb are not considerations with this medication. Option #4 is incorrect for this medication. It is with the bisphosphonates (all end in "*dronate*") that the client should remain upright.

11.3 ② Options #2, #3, and #5 are correct. 0.9 Normal
③ Saline (isotonic solution) bolus is necessary to
⑤ dilute the glucose in the intravascular space; this will stop cellular dehydration. In the presence of metabolic acidosis, the potassium increases and must be monitored. The nurse should review the lab data including urinalysis looking for ketones (indicating ketoses). Option #1 is incorrect because only regular insulin (Novolin R) can be given by the IV route and NPH (Novolin N) is an intermediate insulin with an onset of at least 1 hour. Option #4 indicates metabolic alkalosis. Clients who are experiencing DKA will present with metabolic acidosis.

11.4 ① Options #1, #4, and #5 are correct. Option #1,
④ coronary artery vasospasms/angina;
⑤ chest pressure (heavy arms or chest tightness must be reported. These are undesirable effects and must be further evaluated. Option #4 can be therapeutic for clients with migraines. Option #5 is a safety precaution for this medication until the effect has been established. Option #2 is incorrect. Sumatriptan (Imitrex) should not be administered within 2 weeks of stopping MAOIs since this may lead to MAOI toxicity. Option #3 is incorrect. The BP should be evaluated 1 hour before and after administration.

11.5 The correct dosage is 18 units for the regular morning dose plus 12 units for the sliding scale giving a total of 30 units in the syringe.

11.6 ② Option #2 is the correct option. All other options are not appropriate. A narcotic must be wasted immediately if the client refuses the medication, and this action must be witnessed by another RN and documented.

11.7 ④ Option #4 is correct. This client has opioid overdose. The age puts client at risk for toxicity and the vital signs coupled with the decreased level of consciousness (LOC) are key assessments for opioid overdose. Option #1 is incorrect. The high-Fowler's position is not only contraindicated for post total hip replacement, but it would not help the underlying issue of opioid overdose. Option #2 is incorrect. It would not be safe to place a client with COPD on this much oxygen via face mask. Option #3 is incorrect. The healthcare provider should be called after the naloxone (Narcan) is administered and the client is reassessed.

11.8 ① Option #1 is correct. Hetastarch is a plasma expander used to increase blood pressure (shift fluid into the intravascular space) for clients in hypovolemic shock. The increase in BP is the best indicator that this medication is working. Option #2 is incorrect. The urine output is still too low (40 mL/hr) to indicate effectiveness. Option #3 is incorrect. Hetastarch does have an anticoagulant affect, but these values do not indicate a therapeutic effect. Option #4 is incorrect. Hetastarch will not affect the temperature.

11.9 ④ Option #4 is correct. The key to this answer is that this is a second teaching session to reinforce gum care. An undesirable effect of phenytoin (Dilantin) is gingival hyperplasia and requires meticulous oral hygiene. If the teaching session was the first one, then it would need to be the RN initiating the teaching based on the scope of practice for the LPN and RN. Option #1 is incorrect. While the LPN can administer po medications, it would not be safe for the LPN to track the level over time. Option #2 is incorrect because LPNs do not develop nutritional plans. Planning should be done in collaboration with the RN.
Option #3 is incorrect because LPNs do not track lab changes that are connected with side effects (Phenobarbitol can adversely affect the liver, resulting in failure).

11.10 ③ Option #3 is correct. Isotretinoin (Accutane) is a known teratogenic agent, and the client must have a negative pregnancy test with each new refill of the prescription (every 30 days). The other options are incorrect for this medication.

11.11 ① Options #1, #2, and #5 are correct. These
② medications increase the risk for sunburn due
⑤ to the undesirable effect of photosensitivity. Options #3 and #4 would not need to have the same caution included.

11.12 ③ Option #3 is correct. Oral medications may be delayed in absorption. Options #1, #2, and #4 are incorrect for this medication. Insulin and pramlintide should not be in the same syringe. Option #2 is incorrect. This should never be frozen. Option #4 is incorrect. Do not administer if solution is cloudy. It may have difficulty concentrating. **I CAN HINT:** Symlin acts as a synthetic analogue of amylin, an endogenous pancreatic hormone that helps to control postprandial hyperglycemia. It slows gastric emptying, suppresses glucagon secretion and regulates food intake. "**DOSING**" will assist you in remembering some of the important facts for NCLEX® regarding this medication.

Dosing must be careful; it is available 0.6 mg/ml; dosing is in mcg, and insulin syringe for administration is in units.

Osteoporosis, thyroid disease, or alcoholism—use with caution

Solution is cloudy—do NOT mix

Insulin and pramlintide (Symlin) must be in SEPARATE syringes

Not to freeze

Give oral meds 1-2 hours after injection of pramlintide (Symlin).

11.13 ④ This anti-fungal medication is very irritating to the vein. The IV site must be evaluated frequently for phlebitis. Option #1 is incorrect, since the problem that can occur is hypokalemia which would present in a depressed T wave. Option #2 is incorrect, since the concern with this medication would be with digoxin toxicity. Option #3 should be small, frequent feeding of diet high in calories and protein.

11.14 ③ Checking for a flashback is a priority before administering any medication via a heparin lock. Another alternative would be to flush the lock, but 25 mL is too much fluid. Options #1, #2, and #4 are inappropriate.

11.15 ④ Benzodiazepines cause respiratory depression, especially by IV route. Option #1 Narcan is only for opioids. Option #2 would need to be accomplished BEFORE administration, Option #3 is correct; however, neuro exams need to be more often than once per shift.

11.16 ② The client is excessively anticoagulated. The heparin should be stopped immediately and the physician notified for further action. Option #1 is incorrect because the client is still receiving the drug, and it should be stopped. Options #3 and #4 are inappropriate actions.

11.17 ① Option #1 is correct. Carvedilol is a nonselective beta blocker medication. It will affect the beta fibers in the lungs causing bronchoconstriction. Option #2—Enalapril is an ACE inhibitor—appropriate post MI. HCTZ—Option #3—is often a first-line treatment for HTN. Option #4—Digoxin should be held if pulse <60.

11.18 ④ Nitroglycerin can cause hypotension. The client should avoid changing positions quickly to decrease the chances of falling. Option #1 is incorrect because the client should be taught to take medication with the onset of pain. Option #2 is incorrect because a burning or stinging sensation indicates the medication is working. Option #3 is incorrect because the client should be taught to place the medication under the tongue and let it melt, not swallow it.

11.19 ② Orthostatic hypotension and respiratory depression may occur from the PCA. Option #1 should read mg/hour. Option #3 is incorrect, and Option #4 may not relieve all the pain.

11.20 ① Increasing fluids is required to maintain a therapeutic lithium (Lithane) level. Option #2 can result in retention resulting in toxicity. Option #3 can lead to lithium excretion and reduce the drug effect. Option #4 can also result in retention resulting in toxicity. A 6-10 G salt intake is required to keep serum level in the therapeutic range.

11.21 ① While this type of response to antihistamines is not uncommon in young children, it is undesirable and must be reported to the healthcare provider, so a change in drug therapy can be initiated. Option #2 is not within the realm of the nurse's scope of practice. The healthcare provider, physician, nurse practitioner, or physician's assistant must order dose changes. Option #3 will not affect the medication. Option #4 is incorrect because the healthcare provider must be alerted, so a preventive action can be taken.

11.22 ② Kaolin and pectin may cause constipation which, although transient, may lead to fecal impaction, especially in the elderly. Options #1, #3, and #4 are not complications of Kaopectate.

11.23 ④ The elderly are prone to paradoxical reactions and can become agitated and disoriented. Options #1 and #3 are inappropriate. Option #2 is an expected finding.

11.24 ④ Option #4 is correct. Ibuprofen (Motrin) can cause or exacerbate GI bleed, GI ulceration/perforation, thrombocytopenia (low platelet count) and various forms of anemias (aplastic & hemolytic). When answering the question, begin with the labs that are included in the question. The hemoglobin/hematocrit and platelets are all decreased. The WBC count is elevated. Range for WBC include 5,000–10,000 mm^3; hgb—12 to 16 g/dL; hct 37–47% (or 3x hgb), and platelets—150,000–400,000/mm^3. The concern is with the signs of bleeding and the blood count. Option #1 would not be a priority over Option #4. While Option #1 needs to be evaluated, it will not fix the complication of bleeding. Option #2 is a distracter and does not address the bleeding. Option #3 is incorrect. These medications have the same undesirable effects, so Aleve will not solve the problem with bleeding.

11.25 ④ This is necessary to prevent hemolysis of the cells. Option #1 should read normal saline. Option #2 is too fast at the beginning. Option #3 should NEVER be done.

11.26 ① Answers 1, 2, and 5 are correct, as these
② changes are consistent with amiodarone
⑤ toxicity.

I CAN HINT: An easy way to remember this information is to recall the action of the medication. It prolongs the duration of action potential and effective refractory period; increases PR and QT intervals, decreases sinus rate, decreases peripheral vascular resistance. As a result, the clinical findings that would mandate the drug be stopped would include any dysrhythmia that may slow the rhythm too much. Options #3 and #4 are incorrect, as amiodarone is used to treat ventricular tachycardia and atrial fibrillation. Option #6 is incorrect since premature atrial contractions do not require treatment.

11.27 ② The serum potassium is very important to monitor while a client is undergoing digitalization (short period of increased doses of digitalis) because low levels can potentiate the effect of the digitalis. Options #1 and #3 assess renal function. Option #4 is incorrect because BUN assesses renal function while the glucose measurement is used in the monitoring of diabetes and other disorders of the pancreas, pituitary, or adrenal glands.

11.28 ④ Mild to moderate rashes are the most common side effects of Bactrim. Options #1, #2, and #3 are not side effects of Bactrim.

11.29 ③ A serious side effect of dopamine, if extravasation occurs, is sloughing of the surrounding skin and tissue. A patent IV is essential to prevent serious side effects. Option #2 contains correct information, but is not a priority over Option #3. Options #1 and #4 are not critical assessments at this time.

11.30 ③ The correct answer is option #3 since the HR has decreased from 86 to 58 bpm. This is a calcium channel blocker and the action is to cause a decrease in the contractility and decrease conductivity of the heart. As a result, the client may experience bradycardia. The blood pressure can also become too low, but this is not the situation with this client. The provider of care needs to know how client is responding. Option #1 would be unsafe nursing practice. Option #2 is ignoring the decrease in the HR in the above vital signs. Option #4 is important, but not a priority based on the vital signs.

11.31 ③ Option #3 is correct. Vincristine (Oncovin) is a vesicant and can be very damaging to the tissue. If client is complaining of discomfort at the site, the nurse needs to go and assess client immediately. Many times there will be a protocol for administration of antidotes and application of heat or cold prior to administering this drug. Option #1 is good practice since interferon is grown in eggs, and if there is an allergy there is a risk for the client to develop a hypersensitivity reaction. This is a good practice not to administer, and notify healthcare provider. Options #2 and #4 are expected outcomes, so would not be a priority over Option #3.

I CAN HINT: An easy way to remember the undesirable effect with vincristine (Oncovin) is to remember the "V". Vesicants damage the veins Very much if extra Vasation occurs. These drugs include Vincristine, Vinblastine, and Vinorelbine. When you see a question on these with a focus on discomfort at the IV site, you can safely know that this is a priority due to the damage that can occur.

11.32 ③ Option #3 is correct. A National Patient Safety Goal of The Joint Commission is to accurately and completely reconcile all medications across the continuum of care. The goal is to compare the medications the client is currently taking with those that have been ordered while client is hospitalized. During transition into a new facility, transitions across settings, services, providers, or levels of care, there is an increased risk for client to miss medications due to not being ordered. Option #3 needs further intervention since the nurse is only reconciling orders written by the healthcare provider and the over-the-counter meds must also be included in the reconciliation process. Option #1 is a correct statement because the client's family, along with the client, are an important part of this medication reconciliation; so there is no need for further intervention. Option #2 is a correct statement. There is no need for further intervention. Option #4 is a correct statement and does not require further intervention.

I CAN HINT: "RECONCILE" will assist you in organizing this information.

Regimen for all meds the client is taking

Evaluate and obtain all meds

Compare list of all meds

Over-the-counter meds

Note: herbs, vitamins, vaccinations, nutritional supplements, etc. due to drug interactions

Compare with what client is taking both prescription and nonprescriptions

Identify meds at time of admission, transfers, inpatient discharge

Lists of drugs

Evaluate and determine meds for post discharge

11.33 ① ③ ④ Options #1, #3, and #4 are all safe procedures for blood product administration. Option #2 is not necessary, and Option #5 is incorrect. The vein should be kept open with Normal Saline rather than with D_5W.

11.34 ① Maternal tachycardia is a side effect of Brethine. Other side effects include nervousness, tremors, headache, and possible pulmonary edema. Fetal side effects include tachycardia and hypoglycemia. Terbutaline (Brethine) is usually preferred over ritodrine (Yutopar) because of minimal effects on the blood pressure. Options #2 and #3 could be harmful. Option #4 is incorrect because the pulse is unlikely to decrease enough to give terbutaline (Brethine).

11.35 ④ Option #4 is correct. The client with the complaints of swollen lips may be experiencing the side effect of angioedema caused by ACE inhibitors in some clients. This swelling can be detrimental and spread to the throat, causing the client to experience difficulty breathing. Option #1 is incorrect because adequate hourly urine output is at least 30 -50 mL/hour, so this is a good urine output for a client on a diuretic. The client on Digoxin has a heart rate that is acceptable to administer digoxin, therefore option #2 is incorrect. Option #3 is incorrect because the potassium level is within normal limits.

I CAN HINT: enalapril (Vasotec) is an ace inhibitor. Refer to *Pharmacology Made Insanely Easy* for a strategy to remember this category of medication.

11.36 ② Option #2 is correct. Nitroprusside sodium (Nitropress) is the drug of choice for clients in a hypertensive crisis with a systolic BP over 180 and diastolic between 120-130. It is given IV and immediately lowers the blood pressure due to its potent vasodilating effect, immediate onset and short half-life. The heart rate would be decreased after administration, not increased; therefore, option #1 is incorrect. Options #3 and 4 are incorrect because this medication does nothing to correct chest pain or nausea and vomiting.

11.37 ③ Cholinergics such as neostigmine can cause bronchoconstriction in asthmatic clients which may precipitate an acute asthmatic attack. Thy healthcare provider will need to order an appropriate medication. Option #1 is unsafe due to adverse effects of bronchoconstriction. Option #2 is secondary to Option #3. Option #4 does not address the question that has a focus on the asthma and new medication order.

11.38 ② This medication is an anti-parkinsonian agent used to counteract the extrapyramidal side effect the client is experiencing. Options #1, #3 and #4 are antipsychotic medications which would not relieve the adverse effects.

11.39 ③ Both of these medications can cause photosensitivity. Options #1, #2, and #4 are incorrect.

11.40 ③ Sedative-type drugs should not be taken with alcoholic beverages. Option #1 is unsafe because maximum dose is 4 mg/day. Option #2 is incorrect because GI upset can be reduced if the medication is taken with food. Option #4 is an untrue statement. This drug is given for anxiety disorders or panic attacks.

11.41 ② The order does not state PRN. Therefore, the nurse only had an order for the first injection and not the second one. Options #1, #3, and #4 do not address the fact there was no order for the Demerol to be repeated.

11.42 ③ This is first priority because if steroids are withdrawn suddenly, the client may die of acute adrenal insufficiency. Option #1 is a problem associated with Cushing's Syndrome, but is not first priority. Option #2 should be increased due to hypokalemia. Option #4 is incorrect; water intake should be restricted.

11.43 ③ The drugs of choice to treat rigidity are the dopaminergics which include levodopa (L-Dopa). Option #1 is inaccurate and is an adverse side effect of L-Dopa. Option #2 is inaccurate. Option #4 is incorrect because anticholinergic drugs, such as benztropine mesylate (Cogentin) are beneficial for a client whose primary symptom is tremors.

11.44 ① Option #1 is correct. "Red Man Syndrome" occurs when the vancomycin is infused too quickly. Vancomycin should be infused in, over at least 60 minutes. Option #2 is incorrect. Option #3 is not the appropriate action for this clinical situation. Option #4 may help decrease the flushing, but Option #1 is the priority.

11.45 ③ The psychostimulant, methylphenidate (Ritalin) generates increased vigilance and attention in the medically ill, depressed client. However, with this comes hyperalertness, insomnia and tremors. Restricting the hours of scheduled administration can help to diminish the medication's side effects related to insomnia. Administering the last dose at least 6–8 hours before bedtime is preferred.

11.46 ② Captopril is an antihypertensive which necessitates blood pressure assessment prior to administration. Options #1 and #3 are important but not a priority. Option #4 is not necessary to assess prior to the medication administration.

11.47 ④ Option #4 is priority since client is having delusions. It is imperative for the client's identity to be confirmed prior to administering medications for the client's safety. Option #1 is partially true; however, it is not a priority to Option #4. Options #2 and #3 are incorrect for the client who is delusional. These options would be effective for therapeutic communication.

11.48 ② Option #2 is correct. This should be questioned since it is a narcotic and can mask the neurological assessment for this client. Options #1 and #4 may be administered to this client if indicated. Option #1 is a steroid and may be prescribed for inflammation and cerebral edema. Option #4 is an anticonvulsant and may be prescribed if client was to be at risk for seizures. Option #3 is an antiemetic and is used predominantly for nausea and vomiting following chemotherapy or surgery. It would not present a risk to this client. Due to the actions of the medications in options #1, #3 and #4, there would be no reason to clarify the appropriateness of the order.

I CAN HINT: Remember any drug that masks the neurological assessment would be inappropriate. "Droopy Deuteronomy" in the book *Pharmacology Made Insanely Easy*, outlines the effects from morphine … For a quick review it can result in **drowsiness**, **dizziness**, **decreased respirations**, **decreased GI peristalsis and urine output**, **decreased blood pressure**, and **drug dependence**. Just remember the "Six Ds"!

11.49 ① Option #1 is correct. If 2 milliliters are given, the client will receive 10,000 units of Heparin. The order reads for 5,000 units to be administered. This would be an overdose. Questioning the order is the safe action to take. Option #2 would be an unsafe dose. Options #3 and #4 should have been performed prior to approving the medication for administration. Even if they had not been performed, the priority still remains with Option #1 due to an unsafe order.

11.50 ② Option #2 is correct. Options #1, #3, and #4 are incorrect. Option #1 can lead to an increased risk in diarrhea. Option #3 should be reported to the provider of care. Option #4 is incorrect and should not be taken when pregnant. **I CAN HINT:** Misoprostol (Cytotec) acts as an endogenous prostaglandin in the GI tract to decrease acid secretion, increase the secretion of bicarbonate and protective mucus, and to produce vasodilation to maintain submucosal blood flow. These actions will help to prevent gatric ulcers.

11.51 <u>0.35</u> milliliters

$$\frac{20,000 \text{ U}}{1 \text{ mL}} \qquad \frac{7,000 \text{ U}}{X}$$

$$20,000 \text{ U/x} = 7,000 \text{ U/mL}$$

$$X = \frac{7,000 \text{ mL}}{20,000}$$

$$X = \underline{0.35} \text{ mL}$$

11.52 ④ Steroids such as prednisone have many side effects such as ecchymosis (large, bruised areas of the skin) and edema. Option #1 is incorrect because the sodium levels would be increased and the urine output decreased. Option #2 would indicate a problem with the gall bladder or liver. Option #3 is incorrect though bleeding gums may occur due to thrombocytopenia. The drugs will not cause a decreased clotting time.

9.53 ② Furosemide (Lasix) is a loop diuretic and would contribute to intravascular fluid volume deficit after burn injury. Option #1 is correct. Fluid resuscitation is a priority as severe burns cause fluid shift from the intravascular to the interstitial space. Option #3 is correct as IV morphine is the preferred drug and route for pain management after severe burn. Option #4 is correct as a way to monitor renal function and the effectiveness of fluid resuscitation.

11.54 ④ Vasodilators can cause postural hypotension which can lead to syncope when changing positions. Option #1 would not be encouraged because a rapid drop in blood pressure could lead to a severe hypotensive episode. Option #2 can potentiate the effects of CNS depressants. Option #3 is incorrect because sodium levels are not affected by vasodilators.

11.55 ④ Oxytocin stimulates the uterus to contract which necessitates the nurse to frequently assess the uterus. A prolonged tetanic contraction can lead to a ruptured uterus. Options #1 and #3 are pertinent to the care of a client receiving magnesium sulfate for pre-eclampsia. Option #2 is incorrect because oxytocin should be given via an infusion pump and never allowed to be the primary IV.

11.56 ③ Prior to administering an antihypertensive medication, it is important to assess the client for a decreased blood pressure. Option #1 is expected in a medication that has vasodilating effects like Apresoline. Option #2 would be consistent with a diagnosis of hypertension. Option #4 would indicate a decrease in oxygenation to the brain.

11.57 ① Hydroxyzine (Vistaril) is an antihistamine with CNS depressant, anticholinergic, and antispasmodic activities. Option #2 might refer to a medication like Imodium. Option #3 is often associated with the action of diuretics. Option #4 refers to an anti-inflammatory medication.

11.58 ③ Option #3 is correct. Option #1 is incorrect. It should be lubricated with a water-soluble lubricant. Option #2 should not be done because the tampon would absorb the medication and decrease the effectiveness. Option #4 should read to direct the applicator down initially (toward the spine), and then up and back (toward) the cervix.

11.59 ② Option #2 is correct. There is a lack of standardization in the process of medication reconciliation across healthcare organizations. This lack of standardization results in a variation in the historical information gathered, sources of information used, comprehensiveness of medication orders, and how information is communicated among healthcare providers. Options #1, #3 and #4 are accurate statements with regard to the process of medication reconciliation.

11.60 ④ Ototoxity (hearing loss) is a major adverse reaction from this drug. Other reactions include rash, urticaria, nephrotoxicity, nausea. and vomiting. Options #1, #2, and #3 are incorrect.

CHAPTER 12

Post-Test #1

We are what we repeatedly do.
Excellence, therefore, is not an act
but a habit.

— ARISTOTLE

✔ **Clarification of this test …**

The two post-tests are comprehensive, integrated exams and are comparable to the pretest. We suggest you complete the other chapters prior to taking the post-tests and practice test.

12.1 Which one of these clinical situations requires the charge nurse to intervene with the LPN who is providing care for these clients, and review the standard of care for the hospitalized client?

① Setting a bed exit alarm for a 48-year-old exhibiting memory problems.
② Positioning a 50-year-old client on the right side following a liver biopsy.
③ Allowing a 60-year-old surgical client to smoke outside the front door of the hospital.
④ Allowing an 85-year-old client with a steady gait to ambulate in the hallway unassisted.

12.2 A client is learning how to manage insulin dependent diabetes mellitus when experiencing sick days. Which instructions should be included in the client education to decrease the risk of developing complications? **Select all that apply.**

① The client should decrease the amount of insulin to half the ordered units on the days when sick.
② The client should test the serum glucose every 3 to 4 hours, and notify the healthcare provider for a serum glucose over 300 mg/dL (16.65 mmol/L).
③ The client should eat soft food such as soup, gelatin, or pudding 6 to 8 times a day if unable to eat typical food.
④ The client should notify the healthcare provider if unable to keep liquids down due to vomiting or diarrhea.
⑤ The client should test ketones in the urine only if unable to eat less than three meals per day while sick.

12.3 A client is admitted with a diagnosis of a head injury. Which clinical finding is most important for the nurse to report to the provider of care four hours after admission?

① Confused regarding person, place and time.
② Glasgow Coma Scale has increased from 7 to 12.
③ Heart rate—88 beats per minute; BP—122/78.
④ Left pupil constricts when bright light is shined into right pupil.

12.4 Which one of these assessments is most important to report to the healthcare provider for the wife of a rehab client who has sustained a C4 fracture spinal cord injury?

① The wife indicates to the nurse a feeling of a potential need for counseling to help cope with the current situation.
② The wife has elicited the support of family and friends in helping to provide care for husband after discharge.
③ The wife has lost 10 lbs. (4.5 kg) since the accident, and shares with the nurse feelings of hopelessness about the future have resulted in the inability to sleep at night.
④ The wife reports going to bed one hour earlier to get needed rest to assist in handling the current situation of the husband.

12.5 Which of these orders should the nurse question for a client receiving prednisone?

① Administer varicella zoster vaccine.
② Taper drug when discontinuing.
③ Notify provider of care of sore throat.
④ Monitor the sodium level.

12.6 After a client has a positive Chlamydia trachomatis culture, she and her husband return for counseling. Which question should the nurse ask during the assessment?

① "Do you have contacts to identify?"
② "What is your understanding regarding how Chlamydia is transmitted?"
③ "Do you have questions about the culture and its validity?"
④ "Do you have allergies to the medications?"

12.7 A preschooler is being same day discharged following a tonsillectomy. Which instruction is a priority to include in teaching the mother?

① Observe the child for frequent swallowing.
② Place the child in prone position.
③ Increase the child's fluid intake.
④ Notify the physician if white patches develop on the throat.

12.8 Which nursing activity is the most appropriate assignment for the nurse to delegate to the UAP?

① Ambulating a client who had a CVA two weeks ago.
② Bathing a client with COPD who is in acute distress.
③ Changing a central line dressing.
④ Bathing a client with diabetes who is on the ventilator.

12.9 What is the priority nursing action before administering an IM injection of meperidine to a client who has received thrombolytic therapy?

① Make certain all lab work has been completed.
② Verify the order with the provider of care.
③ Check the client's PTT.
④ Ascertain that all of the thrombolytic agent has infused.

12.10 What is the best response to a client with cardiomyopathy who asks how will he know if he is "over-doing it" when he gets home?

① "Fatigue is a good guide."
② "The healthcare provider will advise you on specific do's and don'ts."
③ "If you begin coughing up increased amounts of sputum, you have overdone it."
④ "It is best to let others do as much as possible for you."

12.11 Which comment made by a client who is hospitalized for treatment of uncontrollable aggressive impulses is most important to record to establish a baseline of data before beginning a behavior-modification plan?

① Client tells each nurse that she is his favorite.
② Client has been flirtatious with female members of the staff.
③ Client threatened to hit two clients within a 2-hour time span.
④ Client appears to be insincere and superficial in his interactions.

12.12 The healthcare provider (HCP) orders an analgesic to be administered to a woman in labor who is 9 cm dilated and having contractions every 3 minutes lasting for 50 seconds. Which nursing action is the most important?

① Identify client prior to administering medication.
② Calculate the amount of medicine to be administered.
③ Hold the medication and document in nursing notes.
④ Notify the physician regarding the status of the contractions.

12.13 A mother is admitted to the labor and delivery unit in a sickle cell crisis. Which nursing action is a priority?

① Administer oxygen.
② Turn to right side.
③ Provide adequate hydration.
④ Start antibiotics.

12.14 Which statement made by an older client indicates more health promotion regarding safely taking NSAIDs is needed?

① "I will take the NSAIDs on an empty stomach."
② "I will inform my dentist prior to surgery that I am taking NSAIDs."
③ "I will report tinnitus to my physician."
④ "I will inform my physician if my stool becomes dark and tarry."

12.15 Which of these plans indicate an understanding of the Standard of Care for an infant admitted with a new diagnosis of pertussis?

① The nurse wears a surgical mask when 3 feet from child.
② The nurse puts on gloves and a gown when entering the room.
③ The nurse uses only Standard Precautions during care.
④ The nurse assigns child to be in room with a child with tuberculosis.

12.16 The nurse is managing an oxytocin drip. Which clinical findings will require the nurse to stop the medication? **Select all that apply.**

① Fetal heart rate of 140.
② Contractions lasting 2 minutes.
③ Inadequate uterine relaxation.
④ Early decelerations on the fetal monitor.
⑤ Late decelerations with a decrease in variability.

12.17 Which comment made by a client indicates an understanding for safe care during the last trimester of pregnancy?

① "I will report any shortness of breath to my physician."
② "I will report any headaches or blurred vision to my physician."
③ "I will limit my fluid intake after 3 PM."
④ "I will limit my salt intake during this time."

12.18 What should the nurse look for in assessing pain in an 8-month-old infant?

① Decreased pulse rate
② Fluid intake increased
③ Respiratory rate decreased
④ Rubbing a body part and crying

12.19 How should the nurse position the ear of a 2-year-old while initiating ear drops?

① Pull the ear up and back.
② Pull the ear down and back.
③ Open the canal with an otoscope.
④ Position the client's head off the bed.

12.20 A child requires resuscitation secondary to a respiratory arrest. Which route is the most appropriate for the nurse to administer the epinephrine?

① IV
② Endotracheal
③ Intradermal
④ Subcutaneous

12.21 What should be the priority of care for a client admitted to the emergency room in severe emotional distress with Respirations—42/min and the blood gas pH—7.5 and pCO_2—34 mm Hg?

① Instruct the client to breathe into a paper bag.
② Start an IV of D_5W STAT.
③ Administer 0_2 immediately.
④ Place the client's head between the knees.

12.22 Which statement, made by the client during the admission interview, is most indicative that this client is in an abusive relationship?

① "My husband does not need to know that I am pregnant."
② "I will give my prescription to my husband to be filled."
③ "I got this bruise when I fell off the step ladder."
④ "My husband and father don't get along so I am not allowed to visit my family."

12.23 During a non-stress test (NST), the nurse observes a decrease in fetal heart rate with any fetal movement. Which nursing action is the most appropriate?

① Reposition the mother on her right side.
② Notify the physician for further evaluation.
③ Document results in the nursing notes.
④ Stop the oxytocin immediately.

12.24 An elderly client constantly screams out. The nursing staff is planning a behavior modification technique to deal with the screaming. Which initial nursing assessment is necessary in establishing a successful program?

① Monitor ability to complete activities of daily living (ADL).
② Assess levels of pain and correlate with response to analgesia.
③ Observe behavior at regular intervals to obtain baseline information related to the screaming.
④ Ask why the client is screaming and document it on the nursing assessment record.

12.25 A 4-year-old client is unable to go to sleep at night in the hospital. Which nursing interventions may best help promote sleep for the child?

① Turn out the room light and close the door.
② Tire the child during the evening with play exercises.
③ Identify the child's home bedtime rituals and follow them.
④ Encourage visitation by friends during the evening.

12.26 During a nursing history with a 16-year-old client, she states that she drinks "lots" of fluids and still feels thirsty. What additional information is particularly important for the nurse to obtain at this time?

① An overall pattern of weight loss or gain for past three months
② Use of narcotic medication and over-the-counter drugs
③ Medication and food allergies
④ Menstrual history and current menstrual status

12.27 At 7:00 AM, which assessment finding indicates rapid diuresis in a client who received 80 mg furosemide at 6:00 AM?

① Hypotension
② Bradycardia
③ Eupnea
④ Hypertension

12.28 A postoperative client is to receive caphalexin monohydrate 500 mg PO four times a day. When should the nurse schedule medication administration?

① Every 6 hours
② Prior to meals
③ Routine 9-1-5-9
④ After an antacid

12.29 The nurse observes a 10-year-old client who has leukemia with a new, large arm burn that appears oily. The client states it was burned on an iron and the client's mother put cooking fat on it, so it would not blister. What is the priority nursing action?

① Document the findings in the chart and suggest the mother to use an ointment next time.
② Call the provider of care immediately to advise the injury.
③ Teach the client that oil holds germs and infection is more likely.
④ Wash the burn with soap and water to remove the oil.

12.30 Which statement made by the parent of a 4-year-old with sickle cell anemia indicates a need for further teaching?

① "When she complains of pain, I give her baby aspirin."
② "I try to keep her away from people with infections."
③ "I sometimes have to give her meperidine for pain."
④ "I encourage her to drink a lot of water."

12.31 The nurse administers Oxycodone to a postoperative client. After 30 minutes, what should the nursing priority action be?

① Change the client's position in bed.
② Elevate the client's head and put a pillow under shoulders.
③ Observe the client for nonverbal behaviors indicating comfort.
④ Ambulate the client.

12.32 There is an order for starting regular insulin sliding scale.

Blood glucose levels:	Insulin order:
< 170 mg/dl (9.44 mmol/L)	No insulin
170-240 mg/dl (9.44-13.32 mmol/L)	10 units regular insulin S.C.
241–300 mg/dl (13.38-16.65 mmol/L)	20 units regular insulin S.C.
>300 mg/dl (16.65 mmol/L)	Notify provider of care for order.

The AM blood glucose level is 178 mg/dl (9.88 mmol/L). Point and click on the syringe, the appropriate amount that should be administered.

① 10
② 20
③ 30
④ 40

12.33 A client is intubated and is receiving oxygen by T-piece at 50% Fi0₂. The nurse notices that the client has an increase in secretions, becoming more anxious, and RR—42/min. What should be the first nursing action?

① Call the physician.
② Increase the Fi0₂.
③ Administer a sedative as ordered.
④ Assess lung sounds, suction PRN.

12.34 A healthcare provider has written an order for an HIV-positive infant to receive oral polio immunization. Which nursing actions are most appropriate?

① Wear gloves and a gown when administering the immunization.
② Administer the immunization as the infant is being discharged.
③ Call the physician and discuss the rationale for the immunization.
④ Administer the medication in the same manner as you would any other infant.

12.35 An adult client who is NPO with a nasogastric tube has orders to receive acetaminophen 650 mg PRN for a temperature greater than 101°F (38.3°C). Which measure should be included in the administration of this drug?

① The tablets should be swallowed carefully with sips of water.
② The medication should be withheld until the nasogastric tube is removed.
③ Placement of the nasogastric tube should be checked prior to giving medication.
④ Powdered medication should be used and mixed with water to form a solution.

12.36 An elderly client tells the nurse that he is worried about the wife's impending colostomy surgery. What is the most appropriate response to the husband?

① Review the wife's surgical procedure with the husband.
② Offer the client the option to take a class explaining the discharge care.
③ Encourage the husband to discuss how he feels and his fears about the surgery.
④ Explain the importance of the husband attending the teaching sessions offered by the interstomal therapist.

12.37 What is the nursing priority while planning care for an infant with congenital heart disease who becomes easily fatigued and vital signs increase during feedings?

① Give small, frequent feedings.
② Change diapers before feeding.
③ Increase the caloric content of the feedings.
④ Mix rice cereal in the formula.

12.38 A 4-month-old infant, who had a temperature of 100.3°F (37.9°C) following the last DTP (Diphtheria, Tetanus, and Pertussis) vaccine, is seen in the clinic for another immunization administration. Prior to administering the DTP, which nursing action is a priority?

① Withhold the immunization.
② Give half the dose this injection.
③ Consult with the physician on giving Pediatric DP (Diphtheria and Tetanus).
④ Instruct the parents to give acetaminophen following administration of the full dose of DTP.

12.39 During an examination with a mother in her last trimester, the nurse should identify which sign to indicate placenta previa?

① Painful vaginal bleeding
② Fetal bradycardia
③ Painless vaginal bleeding
④ Irritability of the uterus

12.40 Following the administration of an incorrect dose of medication, which statement best describes the incident on a variance report?

① Due to illegible physician order, 9 mg of gentamycin was given IV at 0200 instead of 7 mg IV.
② At 0200, gentamycin 9 mg was given IV instead of 7 mg IV as ordered.
③ At 0200, client received 2 mg more of gentamycin than was ordered.
④ Gentamycin 9 mg IV was given at 0200. Physician's order to decrease dose was not transcribed to the Kardex by previous shift RN.

12.41 What would be the priority nursing evaluation of the neurological status for a newly admitted client who has suffered a cerebral vascular accident?

① Equality of pulses in all four extremities.
② Orientation to person, place, and time.
③ Regularity of neuromuscular claudication.
④ Decrease in the pulse pressure and tachycardia.

12.42 Which laboratory test result suggests that the anorexic client is at risk for developing renal calculi?

① High serum calcium levels
② Low serum potassium
③ High serum osmolality
④ AST elevation

12.43 Following the initiation of an IV oxytocin drip, which is the most appropriate nursing action?

① Assess vital signs every 15 minutes.
② Check the frequency and duration of contractions.
③ Determine blood pressure every 4 hours.
④ Monitor urine output for polyuria.

12.44 What is most important to teach a client who is being discharged on home peritoneal dialysis?

① Drink only distilled water.
② Cap the Tenchkoff catheter when not in use.
③ Boil the dialysate one hour prior to a pass.
④ Clean the arteriovenous fistula site with hydrogen peroxide daily.

12.45 What is most important to include in the teaching plan regarding what to avoid for a client who is receiving a monoamine oxidase inhibitor (MAOI) medication for treatment of depression?

① Tropical vacations
② Aged cheeses and Chianti wine
③ Ice cream sundaes
④ Driving a car

12.46 Which action describes the best method for obtaining an infant's vital signs?

① Take an axillary temperature first because this is the most important measurement.
② Count respirations for 15 seconds and multiply the number by 4.
③ Count respirations for a minute prior to arousing the infant.
④ Use a stethoscope with a one and a half inch diaphragm for counting the apical pulse.

12.47 Which plan should be priority for a hypertensive client on captopril?

① Encourage client to take medicine with meals.
② Discuss the need for a potassium supplement.
③ If client misses a dose, take 2 doses at next scheduled time.
④ Instruct client to take this drug one hour before meals.

12.48 What is most important to include in the teaching plan regarding when to notify the healthcare provider for a client taking trifluoperazine?

① Nasal stuffiness
② Heat intolerance
③ Hand and arm tremors
④ Weight loss and diarrhea

12.49　Which statement made by the parents of a 9-year-old client with an ostomy indicates they are providing quality home care?

① "We change the bag at least once a week, and we carefully inspect the stoma at that time."
② "We change the bag every day so we can inspect the stoma and the skin."
③ "We encourage our daughter to watch TV while we change her ostomy bag."
④ "We only have to change the ostomy bag every ten days."

12.50　Which statement by the client best indicates an emotional readiness for surgery?

① "I know the physician isn't telling me everything, but at this point, I can't do anything about it."
② "I've never heard of this specialist before. Does he do much work here?"
③ "I'm glad the trapeze is on my bed so I can start working on my exercises as soon as I wake up."
④ "Can you please check my record to be sure it says I'm diabetic?"

12.51　To prepare an adolescent client for a lumbar puncture, which instruction should the nurse include in the teaching?

① General anesthetic will be used.
② Fluids will be restricted for 8 hours before the test.
③ The client will need to remain flat in bed for 8 hours after the test.
④ A compression bandage will be in place for 10 hours after the test.

12.52　What is the priority nursing care in assisting a client in diffusing escalating, aggressive/violent behavior?

① Utilizing an organized team to place the client in seclusion.
② Leaving the client alone in their room to identify feelings of anger.
③ Redirecting the client to a quiet activity to divert their attention and not disturb the other clients.
④ Assisting the client in identifying and expressing their feelings of increasing anxiety, frustration and anger.

12.53　Which medication can be given intravenously to reverse the effects of a narcotic overdose?

① Hydromorphine
② Disulfiram
③ Benztropine
④ Naloxone

12.54　Two days after the placement of a pleural chest tube, the chest tube is accidentally pulled out of the intrapleural space. What should be the nursing priority?

① Replace the tube, using sterile gloves.
② Apply a dressing immediately over the site, taping on 3 sides.
③ Instruct the client to cough to expand the lung.
④ Auscultate lung to determine if it is collapsed.

12.55　Metoprolol 12.5 mg is prescribed and available are 50 mg tables. Point to the correct dosage.

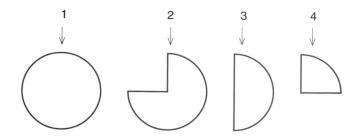

12.56　An older client uses a walker for ambulation support and is receiving a diuretic and must use the bathroom several times during the night. Which of these actions is a priority in promoting safety for this client?

① Maintain the side rails in the upward position.
② Leave the bedroom light on at all times.
③ Hold the diuretic medication.
④ Provide the client with a bedside commode.

12.57 In preparing the teaching plan for a prenatal client who is eight week's gestation with a positive VDRL, which instruction is most appropriate for the nurse to include?
① Refrain from taking any medications to prevent damage to the fetus.
② Take the penicillin for the prescribed time.
③ Refrain from sexual activity.
④ Maintain the confidentiality of sexual partners.

12.58 Which nursing action offers the most support to a child and family in the terminal stage of the child's illness?
① Encourage the family to avoid any reference to death so the child does not get upset.
② Limit the amount of visiting time so the child does not become over-exhausted.
③ Assure the ongoing participation of all disciplines in the child's care, even after discharge if needed.
④ Limit the amount of information and explanations given to parents who are already overloaded at this time.

12.59 What is a priority assessment for a geriatric client diagnosed with diabetes mellitus and is being discharged with a treatment plan that includes a 1500-caloric diabetic diet, insulin, and regular exercise by walking 30 minutes a day?
① Does the client have adequate vision and manual dexterity to administer own insulin?
② Does the client understand the impact diabetes will have on lifestyle?
③ Since the client is living alone, is there a need for Home Health Care to check on client daily?
④ Does the client understand how to perform daily urinary sugar and acetone determinations?

12.60 Which plan is a priority for a newly admitted client with meningitis due to Hemophilus influenza?
① Place in reverse isolation for at least 24 hours.
② Monitor vital signs and neurological checks every 4 to 6 hours.
③ Dim lights in the room and minimize environmental stimuli.
④ Encourage PO fluids to decrease the fever.

12.61 Prior to discharging a client after a mastectomy, the documentation in the chart should indicate that the client has been educated regarding which plan?
① Use a heating pad under the shoulder every other night.
② Wear a sling on the affected forearm for 4 weeks after surgery.
③ Attend the support group RESOLVE.
④ Avoid use of the affected arm for blood pressure evaluation or for any needle sticks.

12.62 The charge nurse notices that whenever a client is admitted with a history of sexual abuse, the 3–11 nurse, subtly and sometimes overtly, verbally attacks the client. Further investigation reveals that the 3–11 nurse was sexually abused as a child. What is the priority plan in making assignments?
① Assign the nurse to this client to promote therapeutic feedback to the client about the behavior from someone who has been "on the other side."
② Assign the nurse to the client and insist that the nurse begin therapy to work on unresolved feelings.
③ Assign someone else to the client because the nurse is not ready to cope with this and may be detrimental to the client.
④ Assign someone else to the client, but do not inform the nurse of your rationale for doing so.

12.63 Several clients are admitted to the medical unit at the same time. Each client has an order for an IV to be started. Which case should the manager assign as priority for an IV start?
① A client with abdominal pain.
② A client with vaso-occlusive cell crisis.
③ A client with mild dehydration.
④ A client with surgery scheduled in the morning.

12.64 What is the priority nursing action prior to removing a nasogastric tube and the nurse aspirates 350 mL of fluid?

① Return the 350 mL through the tube to the client's stomach.
② Remove the tube and have the client drink 350 mL of a clear liquid.
③ Chart the findings after removing the tube.
④ Notify the healthcare provider after removing the tube.

12.65 Which factor is most important for the rehabilitation nurse to assess during the admission of a new client?

① The client's expectations of family members.
② The client's understanding of available supportive services.
③ The client's personal goals for rehabilitation.
④ The client's past experiences in the hospital.

12.66 Two days after admission, a client's sputum culture is reported as positive for tuberculosis. While awaiting orders from the provider of care, what should be the priority nursing intervention?

① Initiate measures to transfer the client to a tuberculosis unit.
② Institute measures to initiate standard/airborne precautions in the hospital.
③ Arrange for all of the client's personal items to be decontaminated.
④ Notify the client's family that they have been exposed to a highly contagious disease.

12.67 Which plan is a priority for the nursing home client with organic brain syndrome?

① Encourage verbalization of feelings regarding the relationship with family who initiated his nursing home placement.
② Help client express favorite pastimes and enjoyable activities.
③ Orient client to present time and assist in being alert when family visits.
④ Direct conversations to assist client to reminisce and talk about important past events in his life.

12.68 A client with peptic ulcer disease (PUD) is seen in the clinic for pain associated with gout. Which medication order should be questioned by the nurse?

① colchicine
② allopurinol
③ probenecid
④ indomethacin

12.69 A client has an order for antacids for his peptic ulcer disease (PUD). Which statement by the client indicates an understanding of how to take antacids?

① "I will take them with food."
② "I will take them thirty minutes before and after meals."
③ "I will take them one hour after meals."
④ "I will take them with my other medications."

12.70 Which interventions will be most appropriate when obtaining urine from an indwelling catheter for culture and sensitivity?

① Unclamp the drainage spout from the urine bag, wipe it with alcohol, and collect the specimen in a sterile container.
② Clamp the catheter tubing, swab the injection port with alcohol, and aspirate urine into a syringe.
③ Remove the indwelling urinary catheter, insert a new one and obtain urine from the new sterile bag.
④ Don sterile gloves, disconnect the catheter from the drainage tubing, and drain the urine directly into a sterile container.

12.71 Which assistive care device should the nurse plan on having available for an elderly client who has a below-the-knee amputation?

① Crutches
② 4-point walker
③ A cane
④ Wheelchair

12.72 Prior to administering aspirin, the nurse will notify the healthcare provider if a client has which medical diagnosis?

① Peptic ulcer disease (PUD)
② CVA
③ Osteoarthritis
④ Rheumatoid arthritis

12.73 The nurse should identify which situation as an indication for the unlicensed assistive personnel (UAP) to participate in a clinical skills lab?

① Securing a Foley catheter bag on the side of the bed rail
② Elevating the head of the bed for a client receiving a tube feeding
③ Using gloves to empty urine from a graduated cylinder
④ Turning a client who is bedridden every two hours to prevent skin breakdown

12.74 A client with CVA begins to choke and cough on a piece of meat. Which action is the nursing priority?

① Provide blows to the back.
② Assist with expelling the meat immediately.
③ Avoid interfering with his attempt to expel the meat.
④ Administer 5 abdominal thrusts followed by a blind finger sweep.

12.75 A school-age child with a history of asthma arrives in the ER wheezing and reports a difficult time breathing for the last couple of hours. The client's albuterol aerosol x 4 has not helped. What should be the nursing priority based on protocol?

① Start an IV and prepare for administration of epinephrine.
② Walk the boy to x-ray stat for chest x-ray.
③ Administer a po fluid challenge stat.
④ Administer a breathing treatment with nebulizer and prepare for chest x-ray stat.

Category Analysis—Post-Test #1

1. Management of Care
2. Reduction of Risk Potential
3. Reduction of Risk Potential
4. Psychosocial
5. Management of Care
6. Health Promotion
7. Physiological Adaptation
8. Management of Care
9. Management of Care
10. Health Promotion
11. Psychosocial
12. Health Promotion
13. Health Promotion
14. Pharmacology
15. Safety and Infection Control
16. Pharmacology
17. Health Promotion
18. Reduction of Risk Potential
19. Pharmacology
20. Pharmacology
21. Physiological Adaptation
22. Psychosocial
23. Physiological Adaptation
24. Psychosocial
25. Health Promotion

26. Basic Care and Comfort
27. Pharmacology
28. Pharmacology
29. Safety and Infection Control
30. Health Promotion
31. Pharmacology
32. Pharmacology
33. Physiological Adaptation
34. Health Promotion
35. Pharmacology
36. Psychosocial
37. Basic Care and Comfort
38. Pharmacology
39. Health Promotion
40. Management of Care
41. Reduction of Risk Potential
42. Basic Care and Comfort
43. Pharmacology
44. Safety and Infection Control
45. Pharmacology
46. Basic Care and Comfort
47. Pharmacology
48. Pharmacology
49. Basic Care and Comfort
50. Psychosocial

51. Reduction of Risk Potential
52. Psychosocial
53. Pharmacology
54. Physiological Adaptation
55. Pharmacology
56. Reduction of Risk Potential
57. Safety and Infection Control
58. Psychosocial
59. Health Promotion
60. Reduction of Risk Potential
61. Management of Care
62. Management of Care
63. Management of Care
64. Basic Care and Comfort
65. Psychosocial
66. Safety and Infection Control
67. Psychosocial
68. Basic Care and Comfort
69. Basic Care and Comfort
70. Basic Care and Comfort
71. Reduction of Risk Potential
72. Pharmacology
73. Safety and Infection Control
74. Management of Care
75. Physiological Adaptation

Directions

1. Determine questions missed by checking answers.
2. Write the number of the questions missed across the top line marked "item missed."
3. Check category analysis page to determine category of question.
4. Put a check mark under item missed and beside content.
5. Count check marks in each row and write the number in totals column.
6. Use this information to:
   - identify areas for further study.
   - determine which content test to take next.

We recommend studying content where most items are missed—then taking that content test.

Number of the Questions Incorrectly Answered

Pretest	Items Missed																												Totals
Management of Care																													
Safety and Infection Control																													
Health Promotion and Maintenance																													
Psychosocial Integrity																													
Physiological Adaptation:Fluid Gas																													
Reduction of Risk Potential																													
Basic Care and Comfort																													
Pharmacology and Parenteral Therapies																													

C O N T E N T

Answers & Rationales

12.1 ③ Option #3 is correct. Allowing a post-op client to smoke is a violation of the standard of care for client's health and to the hospital policy. Option #1 is incorrect. The bed exit alarm would be appropriate for this client with memory problems who may be at risk for falls and does not require a review of the standard of care. Option #2 is incorrect. There is no need to intervene and review the standard of care when this is the correct position following a liver biopsy. This position provides pressure on the biopsy site which will decrease the risk of bleeding. Option #4 is incorrect. A client who ambulates steadily, even if client is 85-years-old, should be allowed to ambulate unless there is any contraindication due to medications, diagnostic tests, surgery, or if there is an order for immobility. There is no need to review the standard of care with the nurse since there is no indication of any risks.

12.2 ② ③ ④ Options #2, #3, #4 are correct. Option #2 is correct. The nurse must explain the "sick day rules" emphasizing that the client should take insulin agents as usual and test their blood sugar and urine ketones every 3 to 4 hours. In fact, insulin-requiring clients may need supplemental doses of regular insulin every 3 to 4 hours. The client should report elevated glucose levels (greater than 240 mg/dL (13.32 mmol/L) or as otherwise instructed) or urine ketones to the healthcare provider. Option #3 is correct. If the client is not able to eat normally, client should be instructed to substitute soft foods such a gelatin, soup, or pudding. Option #4 is correct. If vomiting, diarrhea, or fever persists, the client should have an intake of liquids every 1/2 hour to 1 hour to prevent dehydration. Fluid loss is dangerous: nausea, vomiting, and diarrhea should be reported to the healthcare provider. Clients with type 1 diabetes who cannot retain oral fluids may need hospitalization to avoid diabetic ketoacidosis and possibly a coma. Options #1 and #5 are not correct for the standard of care for the "sick day rules" for a diabetic client. The client should continue to take insulin or oral antidiabetic agents as ordered. The urine should be tested for ketones and reported to provider if they are abnormal (level should be negative to small). Clients need to learn the signs and symptoms of hypoglycemia (tachycardia, irritable, restless, diaphoresis, shakiness, weakness, headache, nausea, chills, confusion) and hyperglycemia (hot, dry skin, fruity breath).

12.3 ① Option #1 is correct. Confusion is one of the earliest symptoms of increased intracranial pressure. This may be an indication that the client is experiencing an increase in the cerebral edema or bleeding from the head injury. Option #2 indicates a positive outcome. The neurological status for this client is improving, so there is not a need to report this to the provider of care. The best possible Glasgow Coma Scale (GCS) is 15. The total scores of the GCS correlate with the degree or level of coma. Less than 8 is associated with a severe head injury and coma. A score of 9-12 indicates a moderate head injury. Greater than 13 reflects minor head trauma. Option #3 is not a correct answer since there is no indication of a change in these readings, and these values are considered to be normal. Option #4 is an expected finding. There is no need to report this finding.

12.4 ③ Option #3 is correct. This question is evaluating the ability for you to "*Recognize impact of illness on individual/family.*" This statement identifies several risk factors for this client that must be addressed. These include the weight loss, a feeling of hopelessness, and insomnia. There is a need for intervention on behalf of the wife. Option #1 indicates self awareness and does not require the nurse to report the finding to the healthcare provider. Option #2 is not correct since she has elicited support on her own which is very healthy. Option #4 is not correct. There is no need to report this when this is also a very healthy behavior.

12.5 ① Option #1 is correct. Prednisone (Deltasone) may result in immunosuppression of the body. A small number of people who get the vaccine may still get chickenpox. However, they usually have a milder case than persons who did not receive the vaccine. If taken with prednisone (Deltasone) the client may become infected with varicella. This order should be questioned in order to decrease this risk of an infection and provide safe client care. Options #2, #3, and #4 are appropriate for this medication and do not need to be questioned. It is important not to abruptly discontinue the prednisone (Deltasone). Option #3 is a statement that does not need to be questioned. This sore throat may indicate the client is experiencing an infection from being immunosuppressed and unable to fight off an infection, so the provider of care will need to be notified. Option #4 should be monitored. This does not need to be questioned. Clients taking this medication may experience an increase in the sodium level.

I CAN HINT: *An easy way to remember the lab changes that may occur when taking this med. is the little saying, "Some People Get Cold." Take the first letter of each of these words: S in "Some" is now sodium and the P in "People" is now potassium and the G in "Get" is now glucose and the C in "Cold" is now calcium. Remember to start with the arrow going up and then each one will be the opposite, so in other words the sodium is ↑, potassium is ↓, glucose is ↑, and calcium is ↓. This will help you remember this information FOREVER! See you CAN do this!*

12.6 ② The transmission of Chlamydia may or may not have been made clear to both partners so the nurse would have to assess this first. Chlamydia is a reported sexually-transmitted disease. Option #1 may be part of the follow-up. Option #3 is a possibility, but most cultures used today have few false positives. Option #4 would be done later in the nursing assessment.

12.7 ① It is a sign of hemorrhage. Options #2 and #3 are correct, but not priority to Option #1. Option #4 is incorrect because it is a sign of normal healing.

12.8 ① Option #1 is correct. The client is stable and the lowest acuity. Options #2, #3, and #4 would be inappropriate for the UAP, and not within the scope of practice.

12.9 ② Complications of thrombolytic therapy include bleeding which can occur with intramuscular injections. The nurse should confer with the provider of care about the appropriateness of the order. Options #1 and #4 are not necessary. Option #3 will be monitored, but is not a priority action in this instance.

12.10 ① Option #1 is correct. Fatigue is a useful guide in gauging activity tolerance in clients with decreased cardiac output. Option #2 is incorrect. The client is not asking for specific do's and don'ts, but rather a general guide to use for activity in general. This may indicate that the nurse is abdicating client-teaching responsibilities. Option #3 may indicate developing pulmonary edema, and the client should discontinue activity at this point. Option #4 is inaccurate and may cause the client to lose independence.

12.11 ③ This is the most concrete evidence of aggressive behavior. Options #1, #2, and #4 are less directly related to aggression.

12.12 ④ The information indicates the woman is in transition phase. Analgesics cause depressed respirations in the baby. Options #1 and #2 contain correct information but not for this situation. Option #3 does not address the immediate problem.

12.13 ③ Adequate hydration is a priority for any client in sickle cell crisis. Option #1 may be correct for the situation but is not a priority to Option #3. Options #2 and #4 are not priority actions for this client.

12.14 ① More health promotion is necessary since these medications should be taken with meals because they can cause GI distress. Option #2 is imperative since NSAIDs reduce platelet adhesiveness predisposing clients to bleeding, especially after surgery. Routinely, clients will stop the NSAIDs two weeks prior to surgery. There is no need for more teaching. Option #3 must be reported. It is an adverse reaction from these medications. There is no indication for more teaching. Option #4 indicates the client understands this is a problem. Dark and tarry stools indicate blood or bleeding from the GI tract.

12.15 ① Option #1 is correct. When providing care for infants with pertussis, infection control guidelines for droplet precautions should be implemented. These guidelines require a surgical mask within 3 feet of the client. Option #2 is not necessary for this medical condition. These personal protective equipment (PPE) would be appropriate for an infant who needed to be in contact precautions which would include: MRSA, Clostridium difficile, VRE, cellulites, etc. Option #3 would be included in addition to the droplet precautions for this infant. This is currently incorrect because it states that "ONLY" Standard Precautions should be used. This is incorrect since pertussis is transmitted as a droplet. Option #4 is incorrect since TB requires a different type of isolation precautions. It requires airborne precautions including a negative pressure room and an N95 mask.

I CAN HINT: It is important to know that if clients must be put in a room with another person that the isolation precautions should be the same. This is a great clinical decision making strategy that will help you in the future with these type of questions. The one exception is MRSA, VRE and Clostridium difficile. MRSA and VRE should not be put in the same room as a client with Clostridium difficile.

12.16 ②
③
⑤ Options #2, #3, and #5 are correct. Oxytocin (Pitocin) is used to induce labor or to help labor progress. It can be dangerous to the baby and can cause fetal distress as well as uterine rupture in extreme cases. Option #2 can result in a ruptured uterus if the drip continues. Option #3 is correct since this can also result in a risk for ruptured uterus and complications with the fetus from hypoxia and/or potential fetal/maternal death. Option #5 is correct. The infusion would need to be discontinued due to symptoms of hypoxia to the fetus as indicated by the late decelerations from uteroplacental insufficiency and the decrease in variability. Option #1 would be a normal finding. The normal FHR is 120–160. Option #4 may indicate head compression, but no complication with either fetal or maternal hypoxia that would mandate stopping the medication.

12.17 ② Signs of advanced pregnancy induced hypertension are headaches, blurred vision, and epigastric pain which are imperative to report to the provider of care. Option #1 is expected due to the enlarged uterus causing pressure on the lungs. Options #3 and #4 are not appropriate for this client.

12.18 ④ Since infants cannot talk, the nurse needs to be aware of nonverbal signs of pain such as rubbing his ear because of an earache. Option #1 would increase. Option #2 is non-specific regarding pain. Option #3 does not reflect pain.

12.19 ② The correct positioning of the child's ear while instilling ear drops is to pull the ear down and back. This will assist in accessing the auditory canal. Option #1 is correct for an adult client. Options #3 and #4 contain inaccurate information.

12.20 ② The quickest and most effective route would be via endotracheal tube. Remember NAVEL to assist in recalling the drugs that can be given via the endotracheal tube (Nitroglycerin, Atropine, Vasopressin, Epinephrine, and Lidocaine). Option #1 would be slower than #2, and the other distracters are incorrect.

12.21 ① Because of hyperventilation, the client is in respiratory alkalosis so having the client re-breathe their own CO_2 will reverse the blood gases. Option #2 does not address the problem. Option #3 is incorrect because the client is not hypoxic. Option #4 is for a client who feels faint.

12.22 ④ Option #4 is correct. This is indicative that the client is secluded from family which is a sign of abuse. Option #1 is the client's right to privacy. Option #2 is not indicative of abuse. Option #3 is not an indicative sign of abuse.

12.23 ② A decrease in the fetal heart rate (FHR) during the NST should be immediately evaluated by the physician. Options #1 and #3 do not resolve the immediate problem. Option #4 is incorrect because Oxytocin (Pitocin) is not used for the non-stress test.

12.24 ③ In designing an effective behavior modification program, an accurate baseline data about the target behavior in relation to frequency, amount, time, and precipitating factors must first be collected. Options #1 and #2 are incorrect because each Option assesses only one area of behavior that may be related to the target behavior of screaming and does not provide comprehensive data for developing a behavior management program. Option #4 will most likely give inaccurate information.

12.25 ③ Preschool-aged children require bedtime rituals which should be followed in the hospital if possible. Option #1 would increase child's fear. Options #2 and #4 would not promote sleep.

12.26 ① Excessive thirst and weight loss are two notable symptoms of diabetes mellitus. Options #2, #3, and #4 do not provide useful information related to the assessment information.

12.27 ① A decreasing pre-load caused by rapid diuresis can cause a significant change in cardiac output that can decrease systemic blood pressure. Options #2, #3, and #4 do not reflect diuresis.

12.28 ① A blood level must be achieved and maintained for antibiotics to be effective. Therefore, the medication is scheduled around the clock. Options #2 and #3 are inappropriate. Option #4 is unnecessary.

12.29 ④ Since clients with leukemia are immuno-suppressed, they are more susceptible to infections. Cooking fat applied to an open wound increases the possibility of infection. Burns should be immediately rinsed with tap water to reduce the heat in the burn. Options #1 and #3 do not address the immediate problem of cleansing the wound. Option #2 is not necessary at this time based on the information presented.

12.30 ① Aspirin can cause hemorrhage during a sickle cell crisis and definitely indicates a need for further teaching. Options #2 and #4 are important aspects in the case of a sickle cell client to prevent sickling crisis. Option #3 is an appropriate medication used to decrease the client's pain.

12.31 ③ In evaluating the effectiveness of pain medication, the nurse must first identify actual outcomes of the client's sense of well-being and comfort. Options #1 and #2 would be helpful in promoting comfort for the client. However, the priority is to determine pain medication effectiveness. Option #4 would be done after the client has some pain relief.

12.32 ① The correct answer is Option #1: 10.

12.33 ④ Additional assessment data helps define the problem. Suctioning can relieve distress and restore airway patency. Option #1 will delay nursing intervention to treat the problem. Option #2 will not be useful if the airway is not patent. Option #3 is inappropriate and could lead to further CO_2 retention.

12.34 ③ Polio is a live virus and should not be given to children who are immunocompromised. Options #1, #2, and #4 do not address the identified problem of the compromised immune system.

12.35 ③ Liquid acetaminophen may be administered via the nasogastric tube after tube placement has been checked. Option #1 is incorrect because the client is NPO so nothing can be taken orally. Option #2 is incorrect since medication should not be withheld. Option #4 is incorrect because Tylenol does not come in powdered form at this time.

12.36 ③ This is a common cause related to anxiety. Encouraging the husband to talk about his fears will assist in alleviating this anxiety. Other options are secondary.

12.37 ① Feeding small amounts more frequently will not cause as much fatigue and cardiovascular stress. Option #2 is important, but it does not relate to fatigue with feedings. Options #3 and #4 will not reduce the fatigue.

12.38 ④ Low-grade fever may occur after a DTP. An antipyretic is useful prior to and after immunizations. Option #1 is not indicated. Option #2 is incorrect because the child would still receive the Pertussis which would probably cause another febrile reaction. Option #3 would be correct if there was a concern with seizures.

12.39 ③ This is a sign of placenta previa. Option #1 could be a sign of abruptio placenta. Option #2 indicates fetal distress. Option #4 is not specific of any disorder.

12.40 ② This is a factual account of exactly what happened. A variance report should be factual and objective. Option #1 is incorrect because this statement blames the physician's handwriting. Option #3, while true, does not present all of the information. It simply states a conclusion which cannot be verified without further investigation. Option #4 does not present all the facts and places blame.

12.41 ② This is an integral part of the neurological evaluation. In addition, assessments of motor activity, eyes, and pupil equality are part of the neurological work-up. Option #1 is irrelevant for a neurological assessment. Option #3 is not a correct statement. Option #4 is incorrect since signs and symptoms of increased intracranial pressure would be an increase (widening) in the pulse pressure and a complication with bradycardia. The current clinical findings in Option #4 would indicate a complication of shock.

12.42 ① This indicates that osteoporosis is occurring and may lead to renal calculi. Option #2 does not respond to renal calculi. Options #3 and #4 are more likely to be seen in a client who is being treated for a chemical dependency.

12.43 ② Oxytocin is given to stimulate contraction of uterine muscle fibers. It is important to assess the contractions due to potential hypertonia and possible rupture of the uterus. Options #1 and #3 do not assess for the desired response to the medication. Option #4 is not the desired response as Pitocin does have a mild antidiuretic effect.

12.44 ② Capping the peritoneal catheter when not in use keeps the catheter sterile. Option #1 is unnecessary. Option #3 is unnecessary and probably harmful to the solution. Option #4 is incorrect because there is no arteriovenous fistula in peritoneal dialysis. This is hemodialysis access, and does not require daily cleaning with hydrogen peroxide.

12.45 ② MAO inhibitors, when combined with certain foods containing tyramine (especially aged and processed foods), cause a significant increase in blood pressure. Option #1 would be more appropriate when advising a client taking antipsychotic medications about the problem with photosensitivity. Option #3 is not relevant. Option #4 is more appropriate when advising a client taking antianxiety medications.

12.46 ③ Respirations should be counted for one full minute prior to arousing the infant with a temperature probe or stethoscope. After the infant is stimulated, the crying interferes with accurate evaluation. Option #4 is incorrect because observations should be done first.

12.47 ④ Food reduces absorption by 30–40%. Option #1 is incorrect due to the absorption reduction by food. Option #2 is incorrect because it may cause potassium toxicity. Option #3 may cause an overdose.

12.48 ③ These are major side effects of Stelazine. Extrapyramidal reactions should be reported immediately. Options #1, #2, and #4 represent possible side effects of antipsychotic medications, but do not require immediate intervention.

12.49 ① Ostomy bags should be changed at least once a week. This is a good time for the stoma to be closely inspected. Option #2 is incorrect because the bag should be changed only when the seal around the stoma is loose or leaking. Option #3 does not encourage client participation or foster independence. Option #4 is incorrect because the bag should be changed more often.

12.50 ③ This statement indicates acceptance and a readiness to participate in postoperative care. Option #1 indicates feelings of fear and helplessness. Option #2 indicates fear and lack of trust. Option #4 indicates fear that something will be missed.

12.51 ③ To prevent a post-lumbar puncture headache, the client should remain flat in bed for 8 hours after the test. Options #1 and #2 are not protocol for this test. Option #4 is inappropriate for procedure.

12.52 ④ As the client begins to escalate their anger, the nurse can be very helpful in using psychological/communication strategies. Option #1 is incorrect because it would be more useful to try Option #4 first. Option #2 can become potentially dangerous to the client and property. Option #3 might further escalate frustration and anger because of ability to focus and concentrate are diminished due to an elevated anxiety level.

12.53 ④ Narcan blocks the neuroreceptors affected by opiates to reverse the effects. Option #1 is a narcotic analgesic. Option #2 is used with alcoholic clients. Option #3 is an anti-Parkinson medication.

12.54 ② Option #2 is correct as this decreases the change of atmospheric air entering the pleura, but still allows for the escape of pleural air. Option #1, chest tube insertion is a medical procedure. The old tube is contaminated. Option #3 will not be useful. Deep breathing associated with coughing can increase the amount of atmospheric air entering the pleural space. Option #4 should be reevaluated after emergency measures are instituted.

12.55 ④ Option #4 is correct: 12.5 milligrams is ¼ of a 50 mg table.

12.56 ④ Option #4 is a priority for promoting safety for this client who must get up to void during the night. Option #1 would create a safety issue for this client. Option #2 does not address the nursing concept. Option #3 is not an alternative for the client.

12.57 ② It is vitally important to complete all the penicillin. Option #1 is a true statement concerning the pregnant client not taking over-the-counter medications unless directed by a physician but is not a priority for this client. Option #3 may be unrealistic. She needs to inform others and ideally, for the present time, refrain from sexual activity. Option #4 is incorrect because communicable diseases are reportable, and partners of contacts need to be notified so they may be treated.

12.58 ③ The care of a child who has been this ill involves many disciplines, and the family will continue to need support long after discharge. Option #1 is incorrect because they should be helped to openly deal with whatever issue the child raises. Option #2 is critical at this stage. Don't limit the time; help them use it fully. Option #4 is incorrect because one of the nurse's major functions is to keep the family well informed.

12.59 ① It is very important that the geriatric client have the visual and manual skills to administer their insulin. Options #2 and #3 are important to determine; but Option #1 is a priority. Urinary tests are not commonly used to monitor diabetes.

I CAN HINT: "MAKE" will assist you in evaluating if an elderly client is competent to administer insulin to self.

Manual dexterity

Adequate vision

Kogntive (Cognitive) ability

Evaluate signs and symptoms of hyper and hypoglycemia

12.60 ③ This will prevent complications with seizures which can occur. Option #1 is incorrect because clients with meningitis are placed in droplet precautions for at least 24 hours. Option #2 is incorrect because these assessments should be done more frequently. Option #4 is incorrect because many clients will be on fluid restriction due to potential increased intracranial pressure.

12.61 ④ No blood pressure or needle sticks are done on the affected arm because of potential circulatory impairment or infection. Option #1 is unnecessary. Option #2 is avoided. Gentle exercise started early in the postoperative course helps decrease muscle tension as well as repair muscle function more quickly. Option #3 is incorrect because the appropriate support group for a post-mastectomy client is Reach to Recovery.

12.62 ③ In the selection of client assignments, it is important for the charge nurse to consider the abilities of each staff member. When a nurse is having difficulty coping with certain types of clients, the nurse needs to be reassigned until there is an ability to deal with them in a therapeutic way. Options #1 and #2 are not appropriate for the situation. Option #4 is incorrect because it would be important for the charge nurse to address the client concerns to the 3–11 nurse.

12.63 ② The client with vaso-occlusive crisis is a priority for hydration due to the physiological clumping of the RBCs. With hydration, the circulation improves, decreases discomfort, and promotes adequate oxygenation. Option #1 is incorrect because an IV may not be indicated. Option #3 may not require an IV. Option #4 will have the IV for surgery started appropriately prior to surgery.

12.64 ① Option #1 is correct. The stomach contents should be returned to the stomach so that valuable electrolytes will not be lost. In Option #2, NG tubes are ordinarily utilized for stomach decompression or nausea. The nurse would not force 350 mL of fluid on a client that has just had the tube removed. In Option #3, this distracter does not address the question. Option #4 is an unnecessary action at this point.

12.65 ③ It is important for the nurse to understand what the client expects from the rehabilitation program for future success. Options #1, #2 and #4 are important to assess, but they are not as crucial for future success as the client's goals.

12.66 ② All clients with tuberculosis are placed in standard/airborne precautions in the hospital, and the nurse should begin preparations for this immediately. Option #1 is unnecessary at this time. When indicated, the provider of care will write appropriate transfer orders. Option #3 is incorrect because the personal items do not have to be decontaminated. Option #4 is secondary.

12.67 ④ The geriatric client should be encouraged to talk about life and important things in the past because of the recent memory loss. Option #1 is incorrect because he may not remember why or where he is. Option #2 is not as important as Option #4. Option #3 is incorrect because even with orientation, the client soon forgets.

12.68 ④ Indomethacin is an NSAID and is contraindicated in clients with peptic ulcer disease. It would also be contraindicated in clients with renal insufficiency. Options #1, #2, and #3 are potential orders for gout. Colchicine has an anti-inflammatory action limited to crystal-induced inflammation. Allopurinol inhibits the enzyme xanthine oxidase and blocks the formation of uric acid. Probenecid is an uriosuric drug which acts to inhibit renal tubular reabsorption of uric acid.

12.69 ③ When antacids are given 1 hour after eating, gastric acidity is minimized for another 1–2 hours, countering the food-induced stimulation of acid secretion. Options #1 and #2 are incorrect because if given with a meal, the antacid is wasted since food is an adequate buffer. Option #4 is incorrect because they interact with the medications and decrease the effectiveness.

12.70 ② Option #2 is the correct method that ensures a fresh, uncontaminated sample. Option #1 is incorrect. Urine obtained from the bag has been standing and will not give a reliable culture result. Option #3 is inappropriate and results in additional trauma to tissues. Option #4, urine collected from the bag, is not a reliable source for a culture.

12.71 ④ The client will be safest in a wheelchair. Option #1 is unsafe for an elderly client with a below-the-knee amputation. Options #2 and #3 are unmanageable without the assistance of a prosthesis.

12.72 ① Aspirin works by inhibiting prostaglandin production. As a result, a major side effect is gastric mucosal injury resulting in ulceration. Bleeding occasionally occurs from gastritis or ulceration. If PUD is already a problem, this client is predisposed to complications. Options #2, #3, and #4 would necessitate the use of aspirin.

12.73 ① This action would indicate a need for further clinical training. Securing a Foley catheter bag to the side of the bedrail can result in a reflux of urine back in the bladder. Options #2, #3, and #4 are appropriate actions.

12.74 ③ If the adult client is coughing forcefully, do not interfere with the client's attempt to expel the foreign body. Options #1, #2, and #4 are inappropriate.

12.75 ④ Option #4 is correct. This action will likely ease the breathing, so that other decisions can be made. Option #1 may not be the appropriate drug. Options #2 and #3 will likely add to the stress.

CHAPTER 13

Post-Test #2

What the mind can conceive and believe, and the heart desire, You CAN achieve.
— NORMAN VINCENT PEALE

✔ **Clarification of this test ...**

Just keep on working on your testing practice and study. Here are more questions to help you identify your study needs.

13.1 Which of these actions is most appropriate when the nurse is documenting in the electronic medical records on the computer in a semi-private room which is located at the client's bedside?

① No nursing action is necessary following documentation since this information is fully secured.
② Following each documentation, make certain the computer is facing away from the client.
③ Pull the curtain around the computer so client and family members are unable to review.
④ Following each documentation, the nurse should log off.

13.2 What is the priority nursing action for a client who is scheduled to have a hip replacement and has signed the consent, but while completing the pre-procedure checklist, the client says, "I don't really understand what they are planning to do! I don't think I want it done"?

① Reassure the client that this is a routine surgery, and there is nothing to worry about.
② Notify the surgeon that the client has questions and concerns about the procedure.
③ Answer the client's questions, and explain the procedure.
④ Inform the client that consent for the surgery has already been done.

13.3 What personal protective equipment is necessary for the nurse to apply when providing care and assisting the healthcare provider with a mother with HIV and who is in the Labor and Delivery Suites actively delivering her baby? **Select all that apply.**

① Gown
② Mask
③ Goggles
④ Gloves
⑤ Sterile gown

13.4 During a rehabilitation session, a client who is four weeks post cerebrovascular accident (CVA) gets angry and yells that nobody cares about how client is feeling and starts throwing objects in the room. What should be the priority nursing action?

① Stop the session and remove client from the room.
② Communicate with client in order to gain trust.
③ Speak to client strongly and ask client to stop the behavior.
④ Administer the PRN medication that is ordered.

13.5 Which plan should the nurse review during a health promotion offering for a group of older adults in the community?

① Older adults should receive the pneumococcal immunization annually.
② The influenza immunization should not be taken if there are any known egg allergies.
③ The herpes zoster immunization should be taken if client is over age 80.
④ The meningococcal (MCV4) immunization should be taken after age 66 and repeated every 5 years if client is high-risk.

13.6 Which of these home environmental assessments would present the highest risk for injury to a client with Parkinson's Disease?

① Throw rugs on carpet in a formal living room.
② Nightlight between bedroom and bathroom.
③ Eats meals and snacks in the kitchen at the bar and uses high bar stools.
④ Uses a cane for ambulation.

13.7 To promote safety, the nurse would implement which action in obtaining a blood specimen from a client with hepatitis B?

① Clean area with antiseptic solution.
② Wear a pair of clean gloves.
③ Apply pressure to site for 5 seconds.
④ Recap needle to avoid carrying exposed needle.

13.8 Which observation is most important during the first 48 hours after the admission of a client with severe anxiety?

① What is important to the client?
② How does the client view self?
③ In what situations does the client get anxious?
④ Who in the client's family has had mental problems?

13.9 An older adult client has an order for digoxin 0.25 mg PO in the morning. At 7:00 AM, the nurse reviews the following information:

• apical pulse, 68

• respirations, 16

• plasma digoxin level, 2.2 ng/mL (2.8 nmol/L)

Based on this assessment, which nursing action is appropriate?

① Give the medication on time.
② Withhold the medication, notify the physician.
③ Administer epinephrine 1:1000 stat.
④ Check the client's blood pressure.

13.10 A client is ordered cefoxitin 2 gm. IV piggyback in 100 mL 5% Dextrose in water. The primary IV is 5% Dextrose in Lactated Ringers infusing by gravity. Which safety measure should be included in the administration of this medication?

① The medication should be administered slowly at 20–25 mL/hr.
② The primary IV solution should be changed.
③ The piggyback infusion bag should be hung higher than the primary infusion.
④ An infusion pump must be obtained prior to administration.

13.11 When exploring ways to effectively manage the budget, the nurse will most likely find that she/he will have to set goals for the unit. What would be an appropriate goal for the unit?

① Decrease overhead by limiting supplies utilized to operate the unit.
② Stabilize the total work force by utilizing only part-time employees with limited working hours.
③ Develop an incentive program that will demonstrate cost-effective measures to maintain the overall budget.
④ Participate in open-forums to discuss the issues of budget management on a consistent basis.

13.12 Which symptoms should the nurse instruct a client who is being discharged on imipramine to report immediately to healthcare provider?

① Sore throat, fever, increased fatigue, vomiting, diarrhea
② Dry mouth, nasal stuffiness, weight gain
③ Rapid heartbeat, frequent headaches, yellowing of eyes or skin
④ Weakness, staggering gait, tremor, feeling of being drunk

13.13 The healthcare provider has just informed a client that an amputation of the leg is needed. The client is crying as the nurse enters the room. Which technique can the nurse utilize that would be most therapeutic?

① Sit with client quietly until crying stops; then inquire about feelings.
② Ask what is causing client to feel so badly.
③ Comfort by hugging and tell client not to worry.
④ Try to distract by talking about her family.

13.14 The client is admitted with cerebrovascular accident (CVA) and has facial paralysis. Nursing care should be planned to prevent which complication?

① Inability to talk
② Inability to swallow
③ Inability to open the affected eye
④ Corneal abrasion

13.15 During the newborn assessment, the nurse is evaluating the Babinski reflex. Locate where the nurse would stroke to elicit this response.

13.16 Which of these home health clients should the nurse visit and assess first?

① A student who reports experiencing severe anxiety with an exam.
② A client hearing a voice saying that it is time to accept the fact life is not worthy of living anymore.
③ A client who needs some adjustments on antipsychotic meds due to a few undesirable effects.
④ A client who refuses to come out of room and has not eaten in the last 24 hours since hearing about mother's death.

13.17 During a blood transfusion, a client presents with a hemolytic reaction. Which of these clinical findings should the nurse document in the chart? **Select all that apply.**

① Low back pain
② Urticaria
③ Chills
④ Bronchospasm
⑤ Flushing

13.18 A client is ordered to take metronidazole PO TID at home. Which client statement indicates a knowledge deficit and need for teaching?

① "I'll be sure to take this medication with meals."
② "I'll call my physician if my skin becomes itchy."
③ "I'll limit my alcohol intake to two drinks per day."
④ "I understand that my urine may become brown-colored and is normal."

13.19 Which assessment findings should be documented in the chart for a client who abuses cocaine?

① Bradycardia, miosis, hypertension
② Mydriasis, abdominal cramps, excessive salivation
③ Hypotension, bradycardia, abdominal cramps
④ Hypertension, tachycardia, tremor

13.20 Which technique should be used in the administration of heparin sodium?

① Gently massage the injection site.
② Do not aspirate after inserting the needle.
③ Use a 1-inch (2.54 cm), 18–20 gauge needle.
④ Administer the medication at the deltoid muscle.

13.21 A nursing unit is implementing a project involving changes in the way the unit is managed. The nursing manager on the unit continues to have problems with a team member that has been very disruptive regarding the implementation of the project. What is the best approach for the nurse manager in handling this situation?

① Call the unit supervisor and advise of the problems with the team member and ask how to handle the situation.
② Privately meet with the team member, review behavior, and determine if she/he is aware of the impact of her/his behavior has on the unit.
③ Involve the other members of the team in attempting to discourage the disruptive team member's behavior.
④ Counsel with the disruptive team member and ask why she/he is not happy working on this unit.

13.22 A client is experiencing a severe panic attack and has threatened to hurt another client on the unit. The nurse would expect to administer which PRN medication as ordered?

① Chlorpromazine
② Lithium carbonate
③ Haloperidol
④ Phenytoin

13.23 The nurse should teach the mother of a newborn which concept regarding umbilical cord care?

① Apply a sterile gauze dressing with petroleum jelly to cord.
② Position diaper over the umbilicus to maintain dryness.
③ Clean cord with alcohol several times a day and expose to air frequently.
④ Apply erythromycin ointment to cord several times a day to prevent infection.

13.24 What would be the priority nursing intervention for an extremely agitated client who is receiving rapid neuroleptization with haloperidol IM every 30 minutes while in the psychiatric emergency room?

① Monitor vital signs, especially blood pressure every 30 minutes.
② Remain at client's side for reassurance.
③ Tell client name and effect of medication.
④ Monitor anticholinergic effects of medication.

13.25 The nurse is caring for a client who is two days post-op abdominal surgery. Which assessment data, on the following intake and output sheet (I&O), would require further action by the nurse?

Source	7a-7p	7p-a
P.O.	0 ml	0 ml
IV	1500 ml	1500 ml
Urine	900 ml	1000 ml
Nasogastric tube	500 ml	50 ml

① P. O. intake
② Intravenous fluid balance
③ Urine output
④ Nasogastric suction drainage

13.26 What is the nurse's next action when a client states, "I am going to end it all, myself"?

① Ask the client, "Do you have a plan to kill yourself?"
② Tell the client, "Suicide is not the answer. Let's talk about what has brought you to this decision."
③ Call the healthcare provider and report what the client has said.
④ Ask the client, "Have you ever felt this way before?"

13.27 Which action by the nurse is most appropriate when a client requests that a nurse on a previous shift not care for him again?

① Document the issue on an incident report.
② Inform the nurse manager of the incident.
③ Explain to the client the nurse was having a bad day.
④ Address the client's concerns with the charge nurse.

13.28 Which assessment would be important to include in the history of a school-age child with glomerulonephritis?

① Strep throat 12 days ago
② Weight loss with diarrhea
③ Increase in fluid intake and voiding frequently
④ Decrease in energy with an increased need for sleep

13.29 Which vital sign recorded on a 2-month-old infant should be discussed with the pediatrician?

① Heart rate of 120 beats per minute (bpm).
② Rectal temperature of 101.5° F (38.6°C).
③ Respiratory rate of 40/min.
④ Blood pressure of 90/60.

13.30 What clinical assessment finding is a priority to report to the provider of care for a client who is taking Amphotericin B?

① Anorexia
② Muscle cramps
③ Spiked T waves
④ Skin hot and dry

13.31 What is the nurse's best response to a preschool child who asks if he is going to die?

① "Everyone dies sometime."
② "Don't be silly. You get stronger every day."
③ "You sound concerned. Tell me what made you ask that question."
④ "You are eating so much better and getting out of bed sometimes."

13.32 The infant had a myelomeningocele repair. The parents' acceptance is observed by the home care nurse when they:

① State the infant will outgrow this problem in time.
② Have the neighbor do bladder expression.
③ Measure the head circumference daily.
④ Discuss the expectation of child walking in one year.

13.33 Prior to administering the Measles, Mumps and Rubella (MMR) vaccine to a 15-month-old toddler, what would be most important for the nurse to assess?

① Sibling reaction to immunizations.
② Allergies to eggs or neomycin.
③ Allergies in family members to medications.
④ Diarrhea in this client a week ago without temperature.

13.34 When assessing orientation to person, place and time for an elderly hospitalized client, which principle should be understood by the nurse?

① Short-term memory is more efficient than long-term memory.
② The stress of an unfamiliar environment may cause confusion.
③ A decline in mental status is a normal part of aging.
④ Learning ability is reduced during aging.

13.35 Which nursing action is a priority for a child admitted with a positive stool culture for Salmonella?

① Change diet to clear liquids.
② Initiate intravenous fluids.
③ Place child in contact precautions.
④ Apply cloth diapers.

13.36 After a client is admitted with early signs of pre-eclampsia, which is the priority nursing action?

① Start an IV.
② Measure vital signs.
③ Administer magnesium sulfate.
④ Notify lab to draw the blood.

13.37 Which clinical finding would be most important to report for a neonate with hyperbilirubinemia who is being treated with phototherapy?

① Bronze discoloration of the skin.
② Decrease in the number of wet diapers.
③ Flat anterior fontanel.
④ Maculopapular skin rash.

13.38 Which initial side effects from a client undergoing chemotherapy require ongoing evaluation?

① Alopecia and purpura
② Anorexia and weight loss
③ Nausea and vomiting
④ Coughing and shortness of breath

13.39 For the immobile client, which nursing assessment indicates a need for intervention?

① Drainage from the Foley catheter is clear, with a pH of 6.5.
② The client's skin blanches over the scapular areas.
③ Bilateral chest excursion is present.
④ The client drinks three glasses of orange juice every day.

13.40 Which of these clinical findings would require immediate intervention for a client who is receiving narcotics as prescribed?

① Temperature from 99.8°F to 101°F (37.7°C to 38.3°C).
② Blood Pressure from 148/86 to 150/88.
③ Heart rate from 88 BPM to 56 BPM.
④ Respiratory Rate from 18 to 26 per minute.

13.41 What is the most appropriate action for the nurse to take after noting the sudden appearance of a fixed and dilated pupil in a neuro client?

① Reassess in five minutes.
② Check client's visual acuity.
③ Lower the head of the client's bed.
④ Call the healthcare provider.

13.42 In developing discharge plans with the family of the client in stage four Parkinson's disease, it is most important for the nurse to include which activities?

① Ambulate twice daily.
② ROM to all extremities four times a day.
③ Hobbies and games such as knitting and putting puzzles together.
④ Encourage and provide writing materials.

13.43 Which statement made by the client in sickle cell crisis indicates a need for further teaching?

① "My pain is from poor circulation due to sickling of the cells."
② "I will need to see a genetic counselor when I get married."
③ "I have a trip planned to snow-ski in three weeks."
④ "I need to stay away from strenuous activities."

13.44 Which statement made by a client who is prescribed Allopurinol indicates an appropriate understanding of how to safely take the medication?

① "I will take the medication 60 minutes prior to meals."
② "I will drink 2.5–3 liters of fluid per day."
③ "I will increase my intake of vitamin C."
④ "I will continue eating oatmeal and a slice of whole wheat toast for breakfast."

13.45 Which statement made by the client indicates a correct understanding of client-controlled epidural analgesia (PCA)?

① "If I start feeling drowsy, I should notify the nurse."
② "This button will give me enough to kill the pain whenever I want it."
③ "If I start itching, I need to call the nurse."
④ "This medicine will make me feel no pain."

13.46 What is the initial nursing priority for an infant admitted to the pediatric unit with possible Hemophilus influenzae meningitis?

① Encourage fluids to prevent dehydration.
② Restrain child appropriately to maintain integrity of IV site.
③ Place child in droplet precautions.
④ Encourage parents to hold and rock infant to promote comfort.

13.47 Which statement by a client indicates that the client is using the defense mechanism of conversion?

① "I love my family with all my heart, even though they don't love me."
② "I could not take my final exams because I was unable to write."
③ "I don't believe I have diabetes. I feel perfectly fine."
④ "If my wife was a better housekeeper, I wouldn't have such a problem."

13.48 Which statement indicates parental understanding about the cause of their newborn's diagnosis of cystic fibrosis?

① "The gene came from my husband's side of the family."
② "The gene came from my wife's side of the family."
③ "There is a 50 percent chance that our next child will have the disease."
④ "Both my husband and I carry a recessive trait for cystic fibrosis."

13.49 Prior to mixing different types of insulin, what should be the nursing priority?

① Rotate the vial at least 1 minute between both hands.
② Gently shake each vial for at least 1 minute.
③ Throw away all cloudy color insulin.
④ Take the vials out of the refrigerator for 30 minutes.

13.50 Which diversional activity is most appropriate for an adolescent client recovering from a sickle-cell crisis?

① Walking in the hall 20 minutes 2 times a day.
② Watching the cartoon channel all day.
③ Talking to best friend on the telephone.
④ Putting together large-pieced wooden puzzles.

13.51 Which nursing observation indicates an early complication of hypoxemia in a child with epiglottitis?

① Tachycardia
② Cyanosis
③ Circumoral pallor
④ Difficulty swallowing

13.52 Which action observed by the nurse indicates a client's ability to care for their colostomy?

① Irrigating the colostomy with 2000 mL of warm tap water.
② Changing the appliance twice a day.
③ Inserting the irrigating tube 6" into the stoma.
④ Fitting the appliance securely around the edge of the stoma.

13.53 Which nursing action is most appropriate when an infant is admitted for fever, poor feeding, irritability, and a bulging fontanel?

① Perform neuro checks every four hours.
② Place the client in droplet precautions.
③ Monitor client's urine output closely.
④ Encourage fluid intake.

13.54 Which nursing action is a priority for a newborn with a myelomeningocele?

① Elevate the head of the bed to decrease intra-cranial pressure.
② Immediately intubate the infant to decrease the potential for respiratory distress.
③ Position the infant supine to prevent damage to the sac.
④ Cover the sac with sterile, warm, moist compresses to maintain asepsis.

13.55 Which statement made by a client indicates a correct understanding of the side effects of phenazopyridine hydrochloride?

① "My medicine will make me urinate more frequently."
② "My medicine should be taken only at bedtime."
③ "My medicine will cause my urine to become orange."
④ "My medicine should be taken before meals."

13.56 Which recommendation by the nurse offers the greatest support to a newly diagnosed AIDS client and his family?

① Avoid all contact with anyone except immediate family.
② Speak to a representative from the local AIDS support group.
③ Stop all sexual activity immediately.
④ Begin chemotherapy as soon as possible.

13.57 Which question would best aid the nurse in assessing the orientation of a client on the psychiatric unit?

① "Who is the president of the United States?"
② "Do you remember my name?"
③ "What is your name?"
④ "What time is it?"

13.58 In performing a nursing audit, the nurse is evaluating the nursing documentation. Which should be present in the charting for a client receiving total parenteral nutrition (TPN)?

① Weight, blood glucose, I&O
② Amount of blood withdrawn for lab studies
③ Position during dressing change
④ CVP reading obtained during infusion to TPN

13.59 Which client statement indicates a need for more information regarding oral contraceptives?

① "I will need check-ups every six months."
② "I should take the pill the same time each day."

③ "If I forget a pill one day, I should take it when I remember. Then take the next pill as scheduled the next day."
④ "If I miss 2 pills, I will take them when I remember and continue the normal schedule."

13.60 Which assessment is most important regarding safety for a client receiving vincristine sulfate?

① Fatigue and nausea
② Polyphagia and polydipsia
③ Hypotension and alopecia
④ Paresthesia and difficulties in gait

13.61 During morning assignments, a nurse is assigned to several clients. Which would be first to receive morning care?

① A client with a recent appendectomy
② A client with infectious meningitis
③ An immuno-suppressed client
④ A client with COPD

13.62 Which of these statements made by a RN to a GN during orientation indicates an understanding of the symptoms for an elderly client presenting with the following: a temperature of 103.4°F (39.7°C), moderate dehydration, bilateral rales in lower lobes of lungs, and disorientation to time and place?

① "The client is experiencing temporary delirium secondary to the infectious process."
② "The client is probably displaying early symptoms of Alzheimer's Disease."
③ "Elderly clients often get confused as a normal part of the aging process."
④ "A referral to a nursing home for continuing care will be necessary for this client."

13.63 A client in the ER is displaying the following symptoms:

- Elevated vital signs
- Hallucinations
- Aggressive behavior.

The client's friend says the client has been using hallucinogenic drugs. What would be the most appropriate nursing action?

① Put the client in full restraints.
② Decrease environmental stimulation.
③ Call the security guards.
④ Administer a PRN dose of chlorpromazine.

13.64 The nurse is caring for a client who is taking Disulfiram. The nurse should caution the client to avoid the intake of which of the following?

① Aged cheeses
② Liquid cough medicines
③ Chicken or beef liver
④ Yogurt or sour cream

13.65 The nurse does not know the answer to a question asked by the client. What is the most appropriate response to assist in developing a trusting relationship?

① "Why don't you ask your physician this question?"
② "Here is some written information that will answer your question."
③ "I don't know the answer, but will find out and let you know in 30 minutes."
④ "Don't worry about this issue; it should never happen to you."

13.66 The nurse is caring for a client who is extremely flirtatious, charming, and willing to manipulate others. Which measure should the nurse take?

① Set limits with the client's behavior and share plan with the nursing staff on all three shifts.
② Ask another nurse to care for this particular client.
③ Document the client's behavior, so that the healthcare provider will order medication to control client's behavior.
④ Listen empathetically and help meet the client's needs.

13.67 One of the goals for the nurse and client with Post Traumatic Stress Disorder (PTSD) that was mutually agreed upon was an increase in participation in "out of the apartment" activities. Which recommendation would be the most therapeutic while achieving that goal?

① Take a day trip with a friend.
② Take an 11-minute bus ride alone.
③ Join a support group and participate in a victim assistance organization.
④ Take a 10-minute walk with spouse around the block.

13.68 Which client diagnosis would be the first to receive morning care?

① Staph pneumonia
② Broken leg with skeletal traction
③ Cancer taking chemotherapy
④ COPD

13.69 A charge nurse is developing the assignment for the evening shift. In a semi-private room, Client A has neutropenia. Client B has a tracheostomy with purulent drainage and a pending C&S. Which assignment is the most appropriate?

① Assign an experienced nurse to care for both clients in the same room.
② Assign two nurses—one nurse for Client A, and another nurse for Client B—in the same room.
③ Place Client A in a private room. Assign the same nurse to care for Client A and Client B.
④ Place Client A in a private room. Assign different nurses to care for Client A and Client B.

13.70 A 6-month-old infant is on Isomil and weighs fifteen pounds. Which nursing observation on a home visit would indicate a need for further teaching?

① The infant is sucking a pacifier.
② The infant is crawling on the floor.
③ The father speaks sternly to the infant for pulling books from the bookcase.
④ The father gives the baby a bottle with whole milk.

13.71 What would be the priority assessment for an 11-month-old baby is having trouble gaining weight after discharge from the hospital?

① Observe the child at mealtime.
② Inquire regarding the child's eating pattern.
③ Weigh the baby each month.
④ Try to feed the baby for the mother.

13.72 A client has been receiving morphine sulfate 15 mg IV push for several days as pain management for severe burns. Nursing assessment reveals a decrease in bowel sounds and slight abdominal distention. Which nursing action is the most appropriate?

① Recommend morphine dose be decreased.
② Withhold pain medication.
③ Administer medication by another route.
④ Explore alternative pain management techniques.

13.73 Which assessment would be a priority for evaluating the status of a pleurevac connected to a right middle lobe chest tube?

① Incentive spirometry
② Breath sounds
③ Chest tube drainage
④ Chest x-ray

13.74 Following hip replacement surgery, an elderly client is ordered to begin ambulation with a walker. In planning nursing care, which statement by the nurse will best help this client?

① "Sit in a low chair for ease in getting up to the walker."
② "Make sure rubber caps are present on all four legs of the walker."
③ "Begin weight-bearing on the affected hip as soon as possible."
④ "Practice tying your own shoes before using the walker."

13.75 An elderly client with mild osteoarthritis needs instruction on exercising. In planning nursing care, which instruction would best help this client?

① Swimming is the only helpful exercise for osteoarthritis.
② Warm-up exercises should be done prior to exercising.
③ Exercises should be done routinely even if joint pain occurs.
④ Isometric exercises are most helpful to prevent contractures.

Good job!!
One more Practice Exam in the book!
You are almost there! You CAN do it!!

Category Analysis—Post-Test #2

1. Management of Care
2. Management of Care
3. Safety and Infection Control
4. Psychosocial
5. Health Promotion
6. Reduction of Risk Potential
7. Safety and Infection Control
8. Psychosocial
9. Pharmacology
10. Pharmacology
11. Management of Care
12. Pharmacology
13. Psychosocial
14. Reduction of Risk Potential
15. Health Promotion
16. Psychosocial
17. Safety and Infection Control
18. Pharmacology
19. Safety and Infection Control
20. Pharmacology
21. Management of Care
22. Psychosocial
23. Health Promotion
24. Pharmacology
25. Physiological Adaptation

26. Psychosocial
27. Safety and Infection Control
28. Health Promotion
29. Health Promotion
30. Pharmacology
31. Psychosocial
32. Health Promotion
33. Health Promotion
34. Health Promotion
35. Safety and Infection Control
36. Health Promotion
37. Basic Care and Comfort
38. Basic Care and Comfort
39. Reduction of Risk Potential
40. Pharmacology
41. Reduction of Risk Potential
42. Reduction of Risk Potential
43. Physiological Adaptation
44. Pharmacology
45. Pharmacology
46. Reduction of Risk Potential
47. Psychosocial
48. Health Promotion
49. Basic Care and Comfort
50. Health Promotion

51. Health Promotion
52. Basic Care and Comfort
53. Health Promotion
54. Health Promotion
55. Pharmacology
56. Psychosocial
57. Psychosocial
58. Management of Care
59. Health Promotion
60. Pharmacology
61. Management of Care
62. Physiological Adaptation
63. Psychosocial
64. Pharmacology
65. Psychosocial
66. Psychosocial
67. Psychosocial
68. Safety and Infection Control
69. Safety and Infection Control
70. Health Promotion
71. Health Promotion
72. Basic Care and Comfort
73. Physiological Adaptation
74. Health Promotion
75. Health Promotion

Directions

1. Determine questions missed by checking answers.
2. Write the number of the questions missed across the top line marked "item missed."
3. Check category analysis page to determine category of question.
4. Put a check mark under item missed and beside content.
5. Count check marks in each row and write the number in totals column.
6. Use this information to:
   - identify areas for further study.
   - determine which content test to take next.

We recommend studying content where most items are missed—then taking that content test.

Number of the Questions Incorrectly Answered

Pretest	Items Missed																										Totals
C Management of Care																											
O Safety and Infection Control																											
N Health Promotion and Maintenance																											
Psychosocial Integrity																											
T Physiological Adaptation:Fluid Gas																											
E Reduction of Risk Potential																											
N Basic Care and Comfort																											
T Pharmacology and Parenteral Therapies																											

Answers & Rationales

13.1 ④ Option #4 is correct. The Health Insurance Portability and Accountability Act (HIPAA) requires client confidentiality. It is required that after each use of the computer and when exiting the room of the client, the nurse log off from the computer. It is important that the others do not see the information on the screen. Option #1 is an incorrect statement. Options #2 and #3 do not address the need to log off of the computer. Just because the computer is not facing the client or the curtain is around the computer does not assure someone will not review the information on the screen.

13.2 ② Option #2 is correct. It is the physician's responsibility to explain the procedure and to obtain the consent. The nurse can answer client's questions, but it is ultimately the surgeon's responsibility. Option #1 is minimizing the client's concerns, and Option #4 is incorrect. Consent can always be withdrawn.

13.3 ① Options #1, #2, #3, #4 are correct. This is
　　② based on the CDC standards of care for a
　　③ client in labor and delivery and who has been
　　④ diagnosed with HIV. These same precautions should be followed even with no diagnosis of HIV in order to protect the nurse. CDC has outlined the Standard Precautions based on the nursing care being provided. If there is a risk for the nurse to come in contact with the client's blood and/or body fluids during delivery, then the first four options must be applied. Option #5 is not necessary for this client. If the client was in protective isolation due to being immuno-compromised, then sterile gloves and gown would be appropriate at that time. The focus with this question is standard/universal precautions.

13.4 ① Option #1 is the correct answer. It is the standard of care to remove the combative client from a setting where the client may harm self and/or others. Option #2 is important, but if client is yelling, it would not be the top priority for this situation. Option #3 is setting limits, and is an appropriate second action, but not a priority over Option #1 which has a focus on client "SAFETY." Option #4 would be last if all else fails.

13.5 ② Option #2 is correct. The immunization would be contraindicated for clients with known egg allergies. Options #1, #3, and #4 are incorrect. Option #1 is incorrect. If the client was not previously vaccinated or has no evidence of disease then one dose should be given at age 65. Option #3 is incorrect. The guidelines recommend this immunization for all adults over 60 year. Option #4 is incorrect. The meningococcal (MCV4) immunization is recommended for adults greater than age 56. Revaccination may be recommended after 5 years for adults at high risk for infection.

13.6 ③ The bar stools present the highest risk factor for falls to this client. Option #1 is a concern but not a priority over Option #3. Options #2 and #4 may assist client versus being a risk factor.

13.7 ② Clean gloves should be worn at all times when handling any client's body fluids. Option #1 is correct but not a higher priority over Option #2. Option #3 is incorrect because venipuncture sites of clients with hepatitis B should be held for a longer period of time due to possibility of increased bleeding associated with an impaired liver. Option #4 is unsafe.

13.8 ③ This will provide necessary information in the baseline assessment of the client's anxiety. Options #1, #2, and #4 are helpful data which can be collected during treatment, but do not take priority during the first 48 hours.

13.9 ② Withhold the medication and notify the physician because the therapeutic plasma level of digoxin is 0.5–2.0 ng/ml. Option #3 is not necessary at this time. Option #4 is not a priority.

13.10 ③ When using a gravity drip, the piggyback fluid level should be higher than the primary infusion. Option #1 is incorrect because the antibiotic should be administered within one hour. Options #2 and #4 are not necessary for safe infusion.

13.11 ③ Developing an incentive program to maintain revenue will involve the whole unit. This will also give accountability and responsibility back to the staff on the unit. Option #1 may be counter-productive. Option #2 may decrease quality of care. Option #4 may be useful and secondary to Option #3.

13.12 ① These are possible side effects of Tofranil which can be resolved by changing the dosage or changing the medication. Option #2 describes side effects of antidepressants which the client can learn to manage at home without changing the medication. Options #3 and #4 describe side effects of a different category of medications.

13.13 ① "Being with" the client as acknowledgement and dealing with impending loss demonstrates the nurse's acceptance of the client's need to grieve. Allowing the client time to cry and then asking to describe feelings demonstrates the nurse is willing to listen and validate the client's feelings. Option #2 is not acknowledging the situation requiring an amputation. Option #3 might be somewhat premature and uncomfortable unless both participants in the relationship find touching acceptable. It is inappropriate to tell her not to worry. Option #4 is avoidance of the situation.

13.14 ④ The client will be unable to close his eye voluntarily. When the facial nerve (cranial nerve VII) is affected, the lacrimal gland will no longer supply secretions that protect the eye. Options #1, #2, and #3 may occur, but nursing care cannot prevent them.

13.15

13.16 ② Option #2 is correct. This client may consider suicide and SAFETY becomes an immediate concern. Option #1 is not correct. While it is important for intervention so the anxiety does not escalate to a state of panic, it would not be a priority over Option #2 who may be suicidal. Option #3 is not correct. This client needs intervention, but not a priority over #2. Option #4 is indeed important to assess, but client does not have energy to perform suicide. There is no increase in energy, no plan, etc. The client is very depressed and needs help, but Option #2 needs immediate assessment due to the voices being heard about not being worthy to live.

13.17 ① ③ ⑤ These are correct. Hemolytic transfusion reaction clinical findings include: low back pain, hypotension, tachycardia, tachypnea, apprehension, sense of impending doom, fever, chills, flushing, chest pain, dyspnea, and onset is immediate. Options #2 and #4 are allergic reactions. Allergic reactions include: urticaria, pruritus, facial flushing, severe shortness of breath, bronchospasm. **I CAN HINT:** The key word is "*hemolytic versus allergic*" in the stem of the question. An allergic reaction would result in a release of histamines. This would be the same clinical presentation that would occur if the client had an allergic reaction from penicillin, pollen, chocolate, etc.

13.18 ③ Metronidazole will produce a disulfiram-like (Antabuse) reaction if any form of alcohol is used. Options #1, #2, and #4 indicate an understanding of the concepts related to taking this medication.

13.19 ④ Cocaine elevates the blood pressure and pulse along with causing a fine tremor. Cardiac arrhythmias can occur, especially with the use of crack cocaine. Excessive salivation and bradycardia are not found with cocaine abuse.

13.20 ② Aspirating the syringe with a subcutaneous heparin solution can cause bruising. Option #1 is incorrect because the heparin injection site should not be rubbed. Option #3 is incorrect because the needle is too long. Option #4 is incorrect because the medication should be given subcutaneously.

13.21 ② It is important to determine what the problem is with the disruptive team member. The best way to do that is in private. Review with him/her the disruptive behavior and attempt to determine the source of the problem. If this does not solve the situation, then the supervisor should be notified. Option #2 better describes the solution than does Option #4. Other team members should not be brought into the situation

13.22 ③ Haldol is particularly effective in reducing assaultive behavior associated with severe anxiety. Option #1 is more likely to be used as a PRN when a client is experiencing agitation associated with schizophrenia. Option #2 is an antimanic drug. Option #4 is an anticonvulsant medication.

13.23 ③ This will encourage drying and assist in preventing infection. Option #1 is appropriate for circumcision care. Option #2 will keep the area moist. Diaper should be placed below the umbilicus. Option #4 is incorrect because the antibiotic ointment is not necessary.

13.24 ① While all of these nursing interventions are necessary during rapid neuroleptization, monitoring vital signs is of utmost importance to assure client safety and physiological integrity. Rapid neuroleptization is a pharmacological intervention used to rapidly diminish severe symptoms which accompany acute psychosis. The alpha-adrenergic blockade of peripheral vascular system lowers blood pressure and causes postural hypotension. Options #2 and #4 are secondary. Option #3 may be done later.

13.25 ④ Option #4 is correct. Sudden cessation or drastic decrease of nasogastric drainage indicates blockage or disruption of the drainage system. Normal gastric production is 1-1.5 L daily. 500 mL per twelve-hour shift is expected. Option #1 is incorrect because the client has a draining nasogastric tube. P.O. intake is not expected. Option #2 demonstrates that the I.V. fluid balance is appropriate. Option #3 is incorrect because the urine output is slightly more than intake and is not a cause of concern.

13.26 ① Option #1 is priority to identify if the client has a plan for suicide before proceeding to intervention. Options #2, #3, and #4 do not assess if the client has a plan which is priority if a client mentions suicide intent.

13.27 ④ As a client advocate, the nurse needs to intervene to assure the client's request is met. The issue needs to be discussed with the charge nurse, so that accurate communication occurs between the shifts and personnel involved. Option #1 is inappropriate. Option #2 should occur, but after the charge nurse is advised of the situation. Option #3 is making excuses and not addressing the issue.

13.28 ① There is a 10–14 day latent period between group A beta hemolytic streptococcal infection and the onset of signs of glomerulonephritis. Option #2 includes signs of hypovolemia. Option #3 includes signs of diabetes mellitus. Option #4 is not specific to a particular diagnosis.

13.29 ② Option #2 is correct because a temperature above 101.3°F (38.5°C) rectally in a child less than 3 months old is abnormal and can signify a serious infection. Options #1, #3 and #4 are normal in a 2-month-old infant.

13.30 ② Option #2 is correct since a complication that may occur with a client who is taking amphotericin may experience an undesirable effect of hypokalemia. Hypokalemia may present with muscle cramps or a flattened or inverted T wave. Other complications that may occur include weakness of the skeletal muscles, hyporeflexia, irritability, and decreased bowel sounds. Option #1 is incorrect. Option #3 would be appropriate for hyperkalemia. Option #4 is incorrect.

13.31 ③ Exploring what happened to cause the client to ask the question would assist the nurse in answering questions. Options #1, #2 and #4 do not explore the client's feelings.

13.32 ③ Parents' participation in care may be the first sign of acceptance. Measuring the head circumference is important due to the risk of hydrocephalus following surgery, but even simple care like bathing the child, could bring acceptance. Option #1 is incorrect because the child has a chronic problem. Option #2 indicates parents' lack of interest and inability to care for child. Option #4 shows a lack of understanding about myelomeningocele.

13.33 ② Allergies to MMR come from egg, fowl, and neomycin due to the growth of the live virus in egg embryo. Option #1 is incorrect because there is no absolute relationship between the siblings' allergic responses. Option #3 is not relevant to this vaccination. Option #4 is more significant for oral polio administration.

13.34 ② The stress of an unfamiliar situation or environment may lead to confusion among the elderly. Option #1 is incorrect because long-term memory is more efficient than short-term. Options #3 and #4 are not affected by aging. The elderly client may be slower at doing things.

13.35 ③ Contact precautions prevent the transmission of Salmonella to other individuals. Options #1, #2, and #4 may be appropriate but are not a priority over Option #3 which will prevent transmission.

13.36 ② It is imperative to do a baseline assessment in order to successfully evaluate the treatment. Options #1 and #4 are not priority actions. Option #3 is correct but not a priority to Option #2.

13.37 ② Option #2 is the correct answer. A potential risk with the treatment of hyperbilirubinemia with phototherapy is alteration in fluid and electrolytes from the numerous stools. One way to evaluate the hydration of a neonate is the number of wet diapers in addition to the weight and characteristics of the fontanels. Option #1 is incorrect since this is an expected finding for a neonate with hyperbilirubinemia. Option #3 is incorrect. If the neonate was dehydrated, the fontanels would be sunken. Option #4 is incorrect for this clinical situation.

13.38 ③ The most common initial side effects of chemotherapy are nausea and vomiting. Options #1 and #4 are typically later findings. Option #2 can be a result of Option #3.

13.39 ② Blanching or hyperemia that does not disappear in a short time is a warning sign of pressure ulcers. Option #1 is normal urine. Option #3 is a normal respiratory assessment finding. Option #4 is irrelevant.

13.40 ③ Narcotics can cause a decrease in heart rate. Option #1 is irrelevant. Option #2 is incorrect because hypotension will result. Option #4 is incorrect because respiratory depression will result.

13.41 ④ A fixed and dilated pupil represents a neurological emergency. Option #1 does not take action necessary for the immediate situation. Option #2 cannot accurately be evaluated with increased ICP. Option #3 would increase the intracranial pressure.

13.42 ② In stage four Parkinson's disease, the client is immobile. Option #1 is incorrect because the client would be unable to ambulate. Options #3 and #4 are incorrect because the client cannot perform activities which require small muscle dexterity.

13.43 ③ The mountains are low in oxygen concentration which, along with increased activity, would contribute to sickling of the cells. Options #1, #2, and #4 indicate a correct understanding.

13.44 ② Fluids are imperative to decrease the side effects of a gout attack or renal stones. Option #1 is incorrect because the drug should be taken following meals due to nausea and vomiting. Option #3 will increase the likelihood of renal calculi formation. Option #4 is high in purine which is a precursor to uric acid. This counteracts the purpose of administering the medication.

13.45 ③ A common side effect of narcotics used in epidural pain management is itching. Options #2 and #4 are incorrect. Option #1 is secondary.

13.46 ③ To prevent the spread of the infection, the client is placed in droplet precautions for at least 24 hours after implementation of antibiotic therapy. Option #1 is incorrect because the fluids are determined by client status. Fluids are usually limited to prevent cerebral edema. Option #2 is appropriate but is not a priority to Option #3. Option #4 would cause discomfort to the client's head.

13.47 ② The client has converted his anxiety over school performance into a physical symptom that interferes with his ability to perform. Option #1 may be reaction formation. Option #3 is denial. Option #4 is projection.

13.48 ④ Cystic fibrosis is inherited by an autosomal recessive trait. Both parents are carriers of the abnormal gene. There is a 25 percent chance of passing the gene on to any of their offspring. Options #1, #2, and #3 are inaccurate.

13.49 ① Rotating resuspends the modified insulin preparations and helps to warm the medication. Option #2 causes bubbles and foam which can alter the dose. Option #3 is incorrect because longer acting insulins are supposed to be cloudy. Option #4 is incorrect because insulin does not have to be refrigerated as long as it is at normal room temperature.

13.50 ③ This will conserve energy and still meet psychosocial needs of peer involvement. Option #1 will not conserve much needed energy. Option #2 is an isolating activity and is not age appropriate. Option #4 is appropriate for preschool children.

13.51 ① Option #1 is correct. The heart rate correlates with hypoxemia and is an early finding along with restlessness. Options #2 and #3 would be late signs. Option #4 is a sign of epiglottitis.

13.52 ④ The appliance should fit easily around the stoma and protect the skin. Option #1 is incorrect because no more than 1000 ml of irrigation fluid should ever be used. Option #2 is incorrect because the appliance should only be changed when it begins to leak or becomes dislodged. Option #3 is incorrect because the catheter should not be inserted over 4" into the stoma.

13.53 ② These are classic signs of meningitis, and the client should be isolated from other clients. Options #1 and #3 are appropriate but are not a priority over Option #2 when the client is first admitted. Option #4 is inappropriate for this situation.

13.54 ④ Prevention of infection is critical for this infant. The head of the infant's bed should remain flat unless otherwise ordered. Option #2 is irrelevant to this situation. Option #3 is of utmost importance, but to do this, the infant must be prone or on his side.

13.55 ③ The drug may change the urine to an orange color. Option #1 is not accurate because this drug is not a diuretic. It has a local anesthetic action on the urinary tract mucosa. Options #2 and #4 are incorrect because the drug should be taken after meals.

13.56 ② The establishment of a support system from the beginning is very important to any terminally ill client, especially with a disease like AIDS that is associated with a social stigma. Option #1 is incorrect because general isolation is not necessary. The client does need education regarding exposure to infectious agents. Option #3 is not necessary as long as precautions are taken to prevent spreading the disease. Option #4 is inappropriate to the situation.

13.57 ③ This is a specific question related to the orientation of the person. Option #1 is incorrect because some well-oriented people do not know the answer to this question depending upon their age, educational level, etc. Option #2 is irrelevant. Option #4 is incorrect because without consulting a watch or clock, most well-oriented people cannot answer this question.

13.58 ① Daily weights, blood glucose, and I&O evaluate the effectiveness of TPN. Option #2 is unnecessary. Option #3 may be charted but is secondary to #1. Option #4 is incorrect. The CVP should not be determined with TPN infusing.

13.59 ④ If 2 pills are missed, they should be taken. However, another form of contraception for the remainder of the month should be used. Options #1, #2, and #3 are correct and do not require more information.

13.60 ④ These assessments indicate a problem with peripheral neuropathy. These can result in difficulties with safety and will mandate a change in the plan of care. Option #1 does occur but is not a priority over Option #4. Option #2 includes signs of diabetes. Option #3 is not a priority over Option #4.

13.61 ③ WBCs are usually decreased in the immuno-suppressed client which predisposes to infection. AM care should be completed on this client first, especially before the client with meningitis. Option #1: the nurse may find it useful to provide time for a PRN for pain to work before beginning AM care on this client. Option #4: this client would need care done slowly so as not to fatigue client.

13.62 ① Delirium, accompanied by some disorientation, is often caused by a systemic infection such as pneumonia, especially in an older person who may be more vulnerable to illness. Options #2, #3, and #4 are premature assumptions and are not based on the data presented.

13.63 ② The symptoms may subside with time and decreased stimulation. Options #1 and #3 are not necessary at this time. Option #4 is inappropriate.

13.64 ② Many liquid cough medicines have an alcohol base which will interact with the Antabuse to produce nausea and vomiting. Options #1, #3, and #4 are foods which interact with MAO inhibitor medications.

13.65 ③ Option #3 is most appropriate in developing a trusting relationship. Option #1 is practicing nurse avoidance. Option #2 is only providing information. Option #4 provides false reassurance.

13.66 ① A manipulative client needs firm limits, and those limits must be known and followed by all the nursing staff. If not, client will be able to split the staff into opposing forces. Options #2, #3, and #4 are inappropriate nursing actions with this client.

13.67 ③ Support groups of people who have suffered similar acts of violence can be helpful and supportive in teaching clients how to deal with the traumatizing situation and the emotional aftermath. Options #1, #2, and #4 are all reasonable recommendations to begin utilizing in a systematic desensitization program after the crisis period is alleviated.

13.68 ③ In an immuno-suppressed client, the WBC's are usually decreased which predisposes the client to infections. It would be important to do this client's AM care first, especially before all clients with a probable infection as the clients in Options #1, #2, and #4.

13.69 ④ Infection in a neutropenic individual may cause morbidity and fatality if untreated. Place neutropenic client in a private room. Limit and screen visitors and hospital staff with potentially communicable illnesses. Options #1, #2, and #3 may be harmful to client A.

13.70 ④ A 6-month-old on a soy-based formula is probably allergic to cow milk products. Many children who are sensitive to cow's milk cannot tolerate it until the age of 2. Options #1, #2, and #3 are acceptable activities in caring for this age child.

13.71 ① Direct observation of a typical mealtime will give the most information. Option #2 may or may not secure an accurate picture. The weight should be obtained more often or on each visit as opposed to Option #3. Option #4 circumvents the routine patterns of behavior surrounding feeding times.

13.72 ④ Morphine is the drug of choice for burn pain management. When a side effect becomes apparent, exploration of alternative techniques such as visualization become important. Option #1 might be used, but with a possible impending ileus suspected, this option is not ideal. Options #2 and #3 are inappropriate.

13.73 ④ The chest x-ray will be able to visualize fluid and air in the pleural space. Options #1, #2, and #3 would be beneficial to evaluate but are not as inclusive as Option #4.

13.74 ② Intact rubber caps should be present on walker legs to prevent accidents. Options #1, #3, and #4 should be avoided for 4-6 weeks.

13.75 ② Warm-up or stretching exercises should always be done prior to and after exercising. Option #1 is only one helpful exercise. Option #3 is incorrect because painful joints should not be exercised. Option #4 does not involve joint movements.

Notes

Strength does not come from physical capacity. It comes from an indomitable will.
– GANDHI

CHAPTER 14

*The genius thing that we did
was, we didn't give up!*
– JAY-Z

Practice Exam

✔ **Clarification of this test ...**

The Practice Exam has been designed to be comparable to NCLEX® with items represented according to these categories:

> **Safe and Effective Care Environment**
  • Management of Care   17–23%
  • Safety and Infection Control   9–15%

> **Health Promotion and Maintenance**   6–12%

> **Psychosocial Integrity**   6–12%

> **Physiological Integrity**
  • Basic Care and Comfort   6–12%
  • Pharmacological and Parenteral Therapies   12–18%
  • Reduction of Risk Potential   9–15%
  • Physiological Adaption   11–17%

The majority of the items are decision-making questions. We believe if you master the top NCLEX® behaviors and concepts listed at the beginning of the chapters, you will HAVE IT MADE!

14.1 A client with a new onset of increased intracranial pressure (ICP) has an order to administer morphine for severe headache. What is the priority nursing care?

① Assess respiratory rate prior to administering.
② Have naloxone at the bedside.
③ Notify the primary healthcare provider and verify appropriateness for this order.
④ Recommend client to cough and deep breathe on a regular schedule.

14.2 After report, which of these clients should be the priority for the nurse to evaluate?

① An immobilized client with peripheral edema who suddenly becomes anxious and very short of breath (SOB).
② A client with pneumonia with a WBC count of 20,000 mm³ and presenting with lymphadenopathy, temperature of 102.8°F (39.3°C) and O₂ stat of 92%.
③ A client with bronchitis with an O₂ sat of 90% expectorating thick, pale-yellow secretions and temperature of 101.2°F (38.4°C).
④ A 68 year-old client who is ambulating and suddenly stops and complains of pain in the calf in the right leg.

14.3 After a client had a renal transplant, which nursing actions indicate an understanding of how to safely provide care for this client? **Select all that apply.**

① Apply goggles.
② Place client in a room with negative-pressure air flow.
③ Wear sterile gloves and gown/mask when in contact with client.
④ Do not allow fresh flowers in the room.
⑤ Double glove.

14.4 Which assessment finding is most important to report to the provider of care for a client who has been discharged from the hospital after being in the hospital for 3 days with a left leg deep vein thrombosis (DVT) and a pulmonary embolism and is taking enoxaparin 80 mg subcutaneous every 12 hours?

① The client is unable to remember daughter's name.
② The left calf is warm to touch and is larger than the right.
③ The client has an ecchymotic area on leg.
④ The client reports not being able to have a PTT drawn.

14.5 Which of these nursing actions should be included in the rehabilitation plan for a client with a left cerebral hemisphere CVA? **Select all that apply.**

① Complete sentences that the client is unable to complete.
② Only use a communication board for all communication to prevent stress.
③ Look at client directly during communicating.
④ Speak slowly.
⑤ Give instructions one step at a time.

14.6 During hospital rounds, a nursing supervisor smells smoke coming from a client's bathroom. She/he opens the bathroom door and finds the client unresponsive on the floor and the waste can on fire. Which is the most appropriate response?

① Drag the client from the bathroom and close the door.
② Activate the fire alarm located outside the client's room.

③ Move the waste can to the shower and turn the shower on.
④ Call for help from other staff members.

14.7 During a cardiac assessment, where should the nurse place the stethoscope to accurately evaluate the aortic heart sound?

① the second intercostal space right of the sternum
② the second intercostal space left of the sternum
③ the fifth intercostal space at the left mid-clavicular line
④ the third intercostal space right of the sternum

14.8 What is the most appropriate nursing action after a nurse observes another nurse contaminating a chest tube?

① Report the incident to the supervisor.
② Clean the catheter with Betadine and continue with procedure.
③ Ignore the incident.
④ Offer to assist and get another sterile chest tube.

14.9 The client is returning from surgery with a chest tube after a lobectomy. Select the equipment that should be at the bedside for this client. **Select all that apply.**

① Clamp
② Sterile gauze
③ Sterile gloves
④ IV cut-down tray
⑤ Suction equipment

14.10 While performing an electrocardiogram (ECG), which of the interventions is most appropriate to implement?

① Use alcohol or acetone pads on the client's fleshy areas and secure electrodes.
② Have the client lie in the Semi-Fowler's position for the procedure.
③ Encourage client to breathe deeply during procedure.
④ If client has excess hair on his chest, shave the area, rub area with alcohol, and dry it before placing the electrodes.

14.11 During suctioning of a client with an endotracheal tube, the heart rate decreases from 100 to 50 beats per minute. What is the priority nursing action?

① Continue suctioning client.
② Administer epinephrine to increase the HR.
③ Stop procedure and evaluate the breath sounds.
④ Discontinue the procedure and reconnect client to the ventilator.

14.12 What is the priority nursing action for a client at home who has diabetes mellitus and is presenting with diaphoresis, lethargy, but is still arousable?

① Administer Glucagon subcutaneous (SC).
② Check HbA1c.
③ Give an 8 oz. (237 mL) glass of milk.
④ Notify the healthcare provider.

14.13 In preparing for a traumatic wound debridement, what intervention is most appropriate?

① Pack the wound with Betadine soaks prior to debridement.
② Prior to procedure, clean wound with alcohol.
③ Irrigate wound in preparation for debridement with 10 psi.
④ Pack the wound with gauze pads soaked in normal saline solution until debridement.

14.14 The nurse indicates an appropriate understanding of prioritizing the workload when implementing which client's plan of care first?

① A 7-year-old in a sickle cell crisis
② An 8-year-old admitted for shunt revision
③ A 17-year-old with a fractured femur
④ A 20-year-old with pelvic inflammatory disease

14.15 Which of these should be included in the plan of care for a client who has chronic kidney disease? **Select all that apply.**

① Assess for a flat T wave on the ECG monitor.
② Discuss the importance of using salt substitutes.
③ Encourage taking an NSAID for discomfort.
④ Review the importance of taking Aluminum hydroxide gel with meals.
⑤ Review the importance of monitoring and reporting trends in weight gain.

14.16 Which of these plans is appropriate while monitoring the care of a client on a ventilator and troubleshooting ventilator alarms? **Select all that apply.**

① Suction for high alarms.
② Silence alarms while at bedside during night hours
③ Assess for leak or disconnection for low pressure alarms.
④ Manually ventilate if alarms sound without apparent cause.
⑤ Check for kinking or compression of endotracheal tube for high alarms.

14.17 A client in a long-term care facility with heart failure has an order to receive a daily dose of enalapril 10 mg and is scheduled for hemodialysis this morning. When should the nurse plan to administer this medication to the client?

① The morning of dialysis
② The day after dialysis
③ 2 hours into dialysis
④ Upon return from dialysis

14.18 Which of these assessments is a priority for the nurse to report to the physician 6 hours after a cast has been applied to the left leg?

① The pedal pulse is stronger on the left foot.
② The left foot is cool to touch.
③ There is an alteration in the sensation to the left foot.
④ The capillary refill to the toes is less than 2 seconds.

14.19   On the fourth postoperative day after GI surgery, the nurse assesses a client shaking, diaphoretic, with a temperature of 103.6°F (39.8°C). What should be the priority assessment after the healthcare provider (HCP) is called for antibiotic orders?

    ① Client's weight
    ② Vital signs
    ③ Blood and urine cultures
    ④ Neurological evaluation

14.20   After evaluating the circulation in an arm in a cast, which assessment requires healthcare provider notification?

    ① Apical pulse of 88
    ② Tingling, cold fingers
    ③ Lack of cooperativeness by the client
    ④ Warm fingers with an alteration in capillary refill

14.21   While evaluating a quality indicator of client room placement, which of the following client transfers from the medical/surgical units to the maternity unit indicates the nurses know how to safely manage room placement for clients?

    ① A client with rubella
    ② A client with chronic hepatitis B
    ③ A client with RSV
    ④ A client with systemic lupus erythematosus

14.22   A client is to undergo an emergency appendectomy. Which assessment should be a priority before the anesthesia is administered?

    ① Location, intensity, and duration of the pain
    ② Last time client ate any solid food
    ③ Evaluation of vital signs
    ④ History of previous surgeries

14.23   What should be the priority nursing evaluation for a 30-hour-old newborn who begins to exhibit a high pitched cry, irritability, diarrhea, sneezing, and frequent tremors?

    ① History of maternal drug abuse
    ② Newborn sepsis
    ③ Cardiac arrhythmias
    ④ Maternal sepsis

14.24   Which nursing plan is the highest priority for a client after a grand mal seizure?

    ① Elevate the head of the bed.
    ② Place an oxygen mask on the client.
    ③ Report the characteristics and the length of the seizure.
    ④ Administer Valium IV push.

14.25   Select the correct procedures when following standard precautions. **Select all that apply.**

    ① Wear gloves when coming in contact with any body fluid.
    ② Place the client in a private room that has negative air pressure in relation to surrounding area.
    ③ Discard used needles immediately in the trash can.
    ④ Wear gloves when entering the room.
    ⑤ Avoid contact with client if nurse has an exudative lesion.

14.26   Which technique is appropriate to promote chest physiotherapy in an active 4-year-old child with Cystic Fibrosis?

    ① Perform percussion while having child sitting playing video games.
    ② Facilitate bronchial drainage by allowing child to hang upside down on monkey bars.
    ③ Encourage child to participate by beginning first with a healthy snack.
    ④ Provide a heavy blanket to provide warmth, comfort and to protect the skin.

14.27   A radium implant is found in the bed of a client who is being treated for cervical cancer. What is the most appropriate plan for the nurse to include in the care for this client?

    ① Reposition the implant immediately in the cervix with the physician's assistance.
    ② Remove it from the bed and discard in the unit's biohazardous materials container.
    ③ Remove it from the bed using tongs, discard in the biohazardous materials container in the room, and notify Radiology.
    ④ Remove it from the room after notifying the physician.

14.28 The nurse has administered sublingual nitroglycerin to a client complaining of chest pain. Which observation is most important for the nurse to report to the next shift?

① The client indicates a need to urinate frequently.
② Blood pressure has decreased from 140/80 to 98/62.
③ Respiratory rate has increased from 16 to 24.
④ The client indicates the chest pain has subsided.

14.29 A client was admitted for regulation of insulin. Client takes 15 units of Humulin N insulin at 8:00 AM every day. At 4:00 PM, which nursing observation indicates a complication due to the insulin?

① Acetone odor to breath, polyuria, and flushed skin
② Irritability, tachycardia, and diaphoresis
③ Headache, nervousness, and polydipsia
④ Tenseness, tachycardia, and anorexia

14.30 After abdominal surgery, a client is admitted from the recovery room with intravenous fluid infusing wide open. He receives 850 mL in less than 60 minutes. Which observation would indicate a problem?

① CVP reading of 8 mm Hg and bradycardia
② Tachycardia and hypotension
③ Dyspnea and oliguria
④ Rales and tachycardia

14.31 During the initial assessment of a client with myxedema, the nurse would carefully observe for which symptoms?

① Tachycardia, fatigue, and intolerance to heat
② Polyphagia, nervousness, and dry hair
③ Lethargy, weight gain, and intolerance to cold
④ Tachycardia, hypertension, and tachypnea

14.32 An elderly client is admitted with a possible fractured right hip. During the initial nursing assessment, which of the following observations of the right leg would validate or support this diagnosis?

① The leg appears shortened, is abducted, and externally rotated.
② Plantar flexion is observed with sciatic pain occurring down the leg.
③ From the hip, the leg appears longer and is externally rotated.
④ There is evidence of paresis with decreased sensation and limited mobility.

14.33 Which of the following instructions given to the client taking warfarin sodium indicates the nurse is negligent?

① Notify provider of care if stool becomes tarry.
② Eat a diet high in green leafy vegetables.
③ Return to the clinic for periodic blood tests.
④ Discontinue taking Ginseng while taking Coumadin.

14.34 A client develops acute renal failure and is on continuous peritoneal dialysis. Which assessment finding indicates the most common complication associated with this procedure?

① Hypotension
② Hypertension
③ Pruitis
④ Bradycardia

14.35 Which of these tasks is most appropriate for the nurse to delegate to an experienced UAP?

① Observe a newly diagnosed client with diabetes mellitus practice injection techniques using an orange.
② Obtain a clean catch urine specimen from a client suspected of having a urinary tract infection.
③ Obtain a 24-hour diet recall from a client recently admitted with anorexia nervosa.
④ Observe the amount and characteristics of the returns from a continuous bladder irrigation for a client after a transuretheral prostate resection.

14.36 Which reflex would be abnormal to observe in a 6-month-old child?

① Presence of a positive Babinski reflex.
② Extrusion reflex occurs when feeding.
③ Able to voluntarily grasp objects.
④ Rolls from abdomen to back at will.

14.37 A client is admitted to the emergency room with a gunshot wound in the chest and in severe respiratory distress. Which nursing action has the highest priority when managing the emergency?

① Establish and maintain an open airway.
② Start cardiopulmonary resuscitation.
③ Initiate oxygen therapy.
④ Obtain an arterial blood gas.

14.38 A toddler admitted with an elevated blood lead level is to be treated with intramuscular injections of calcium disodium edentate and dimercaprol. Which nursing action would have the highest priority?

① Keep a tongue blade at the bedside.
② Encourage the child to participate in play therapy.
③ Apply cool soaks to the injection site.
④ Rotate the injection site.

14.39 Which assessment finding indicates gentamycin toxicity?

① Decreased hearing
② Blurred vision
③ Nausea and vomiting
④ Macular rash

14.40 Which assessment documents an allergic blood transfusion reaction?

① Hypotension
② Chills
③ Respiratory wheezing
④ Lower back discomfort

14.41 Prior to administering atenolol and digoxin, which assessment is most important to report and document?

① Bradycardia
② Tachycardia
③ Hypertension
④ Serum potassium—3.8 mEq/L (3.8 mmol/L)

14.42 What should be the priority assessment for a client who is admitted to the outpatient oncology unit for routine chemotherapy transfusion with the current lab reports: WBC—2,500 mm³; RBC—5,100 mm³; and calcium 5 mg/dL (1.25 mmol/L)?

① Fatigue related to decrease in red cells.
② Infection related to low white cell count.
③ Anxiety secondary to hypoparathyroid disease.
④ Fluid volume deficit due to decreased fluid intake materials.

14.43 A urinalysis has been done on a client who has been complaining of dysuria, urinary frequency, and discomfort in the suprapubic area. After evaluation of the results, the nurse would order a repeat urinalysis based on:

① Negative glucose
② RBCs present
③ No WBCs or RBCs reported
④ Specific gravity 1.018

14.44 What is the priority care for a client in Buck's traction?

① Turn the client every two hours to the unaffected side.
② Maintain client in a supine position.
③ Encourage client to use a bedside commode.
④ Prevent foot drop by placing a foot board to the bed.

14.45 Which assignment is most appropriate for the UAP?

① Doing a sterile dressing change on a 60-year-old male admitted for skin grafts.
② Obtaining a temperature on a 70-year-old client receiving the final 40 minutes of a blood transfusion.
③ Assisting a client newly diagnosed with a CVA to eat his dinner.
④ Completing the initial vital signs on an 80-year-old who has just returned to her room after having abdominal surgery.

14.46 What should be the primary goal of nursing interventions for a client who has Multiple Sclerosis with a progressive disability?

① Maintain a cheerful, positive outlook.
② Remain physically active and independent.
③ Maintain good personal hygiene.
④ Remain in a quiet environment to decrease stimuli.

14.47 A client is admitted to the emergency room after an acute asthmatic attack. Vital signs on admission include:

• Pulse 98 bpm

• Respiratory rate 40 with substernal retracting.

Immediate care should include placing the client in which position?

① High Fowler's
② Supine position
③ Trendelenburg
④ Sim's position

14.48 A young adult client is seen in the emergency room for an overdose of acetylsalicylic acid. Which plan represents correct care in the Emergency Room?

① If aspirin was ingested within the last two hours, administer activated charcoal powder.
② Initiate an intravenous infusion and administer protamine sulfate.
③ Since aspirin overdose will cause bleeding, AquaMephyton should be given.
④ Obtain an arterial blood gas and request respiratory therapy to begin respiratory support.

14.49 Which client condition could precipitate a toxic reaction to Phenytoin?

① Impaired liver function
② Decreased hemoglobin and hematocrit
③ White blood count of 10,000/mm³ and serum sodium of 140 mEq/L (140 mmol/L)
④ Depressed neurological functioning

14.50 An infant is admitted for vomiting and diarrhea. The anterior fontanelle is depressed and a fever of 103.2°F (39.6°C) is noted. What should be the initial plan to assist with rehydration?

① Determine daily weights and evaluate weight loss.
② Evaluate child's ability to take in oral fluids.
③ Place a full bottle of Pedialyte at bedside.
④ Document I & O.

14.51 What is the priority nursing action while assisting the physician with the spinal tap on a 4-month-old?

① Restrain the child appropriately.
② Instruct parents about procedure.
③ Provide support to the child.
④ Elevate the head of the bed.

14.52 Which of these nursing actions by the licensed practical nurse (LPN), when working with a client with a nasogastric tube, requires intervention by the charge nurse?

① The tube is flushed after an enteral feeding is given.
② The tube is secured by taping the tube to the client's cheek with a short length of tubing looped on the nose.
③ When the gastric residual was 150 mL, the feeding was held and rechecked residual in 1 hour.
④ The client is positioned in the semi-Fowler's position when residuals are high.

14.53 Which teaching is appropriate regarding wearing anti-embolism stockings following surgery?

① Wear them when legs are cramping.
② Wear them the entire time client is in the hospital.
③ Put stockings on in the evening prior to going to bed.
④ Put stockings on after client has been out of bed and walked around.

14.54 An infant is in Bryant's traction. During the neuro-vascular assessment, the nurse notes that the foot of the uninjured leg feels warmer to touch than that of the broken leg. What action should the nurse implement now?

① Recognize that as long as the foot of the injured leg is warm to touch, circulation is doing well.
② Encourage child to move his foot by playing a toe-moving game with him.
③ Cover the colder foot with a sock and check its temperature in one hour.
④ Recognize that the strapping may be too snug and notify the physician.

14.55 Which nursing action indicates an understanding of how to administer AquaMephyton to a neonate?

① Administers an injection into the vastus lateralis.
② Mixes it in the formula.
③ Applies drops into the inner canthus.
④ Administers a subcutaneous injection into the anterior thigh.

14.56 Which plan is a priority in an emergency wound evisceration?

① Maintain moisture to the wound.
② Start an IV and begin antibiotics.
③ Keep a sterile dressing over the wound.
④ Irrigate the wound with normal saline.

14.57 During chemotherapy of an outpatient who is lethargic, weak, and pale, which intervention is most important for the nurse to implement?

① Establish emotional support.
② Position for physical comfort.
③ Maintain respiratory isolation.
④ Hand washing prior to care.

14.58 Which response to mannitol is desired for decreasing the intracranial pressure of a client with a closed head injury?

① The blood pressure increases to 150/90.
② Urinary output increases to 175 mL/hour.
③ Decrease in the level of activity.
④ Absence of fine tremors of the fingers.

14.59 A young adult client, gravida 2, para 1, in her third trimester of pregnancy has had diabetes since age 14. Which statement made by the client indicates an understanding regarding the insulin requirements during the third trimester?

① "I cannot continue to exercise as this will increase my insulin needs."
② "I understand my insulin requirements will increase as my pregnancy progresses."
③ "Since the baby has a normal pancreas, my insulin needs will not change."
④ "The more weight I gain, the more insulin I will need to take."

14.60 Which observation indicates the client has an understanding of appropriate crutch walking?

① Weight bearing is under the arm on the axillary area.
② The crutches are placed about 18–20 inches (46–50.8 cm) in front of him with each step.
③ The weight of the body is being transferred to the hands and the arms.
④ Leather sole shoes are worn to increase the smooth motion across the floor.

14.61 Which of these instructions is most important to include with the discharge teaching for a client who is going to be discharged on simvastatin?

① "Return to the office in 7 days to determine if the lipids have decreased."
② "Take the medication on an empty stomach to assist with absorption."
③ "Review the importance of taking with food and at bedtime."
④ "Discuss the importance of decreasing the fiber in diet when taking this medication."

14.62 A client is currently hospitalized with renal failure and has 3+ pitting edema of the lower extremities. Which nursing observation indicates a therapeutic response to therapy for the edema?

① Potassium level of 4.0 mEq/L (4.0 mmol/L)
② Serum glucose of 140 mg/dL (7.77 mmol/L)
③ Increased specific gravity of the urine
④ Weight loss of 5 lbs. (2.3 kg) over last 2 days

14.63 Several days after a myocardial infarction, a client was placed on a 2 Gm sodium diet. Which selection indicates compliance with the diet?

① Scrambled egg, orange slices and milk
② Instant oatmeal, toast, and orange juice
③ Poached egg, bacon, and milk
④ Biscuit, fruit cup, and sausage

14.64 Which actions should be implemented for a client admitted with left ventricular heart failure who is presenting with a sudden onset of dyspnea, breathlessness, moist cough, and a rapid and weak heart rate while lying in the bed? **Select all that apply.**

① Administer morphine sulfate 4 mg intravenously (IV) as prescribed.
② Prepare to administer cyclosphosphamide as prescribed.
③ Prepare to administer furosemide IV as prescribed.
④ Initiate oxygen via a high-flow rebreather mask per protocol.
⑤ Reposition client to the left side to facilitate cardiac contractility.

14.65 Which would be most responsible for prolonging wound healing in the older client?

① Depression
② Increased social contacts
③ An increase in the adipose tissue
④ An intake of 20 to 35 g. of fiber per day

14.66 In the immediate postoperative period, which nursing assessment is a priority in a client with a pneumonectomy?

① Presence of breath sounds bilaterally
② Position of trachea in sternal notch
③ Amount and consistency of sputum
④ An increase in the pulse pressure

14.67 What is the priority nursing assessment for a client who is a primipara in early labor with newly ruptured membranes?

① Determine the pH of the amniotic fluid.
② Evaluate the mother's blood pressure.
③ Check the monitor for an early deceleration with the next contraction.
④ Observe the perineal area for evidence of a prolapsed cord.

14.68 Which diet selections should be included in the teaching plan of the client with osteoporosis?

① Steak and baked potato
② A glass of skim milk and a toasted cheese sandwich
③ Chicken and salad
④ Fish and French fries

14.69 A client is in labor and is receiving magnesium sulfate IV. Which assessment is most important to report to the nurse on the next shift?

① Respiratory rate change from 13/min. to 15/min
② Increase in anxiety and hyperactivity
③ Presence of nausea and refusal to take clear liquids
④ Urine output change from 60 mL/hr to 40 mL/hr

14.70 Which of these statements made by the nurse indicates an understanding of the reason a client with chronic renal failure is receiving calcium carbonate?

① "This medication will minimize the complications with constipation."
② "This medication will prevent the development of osteoporosis."
③ "Calcium carbonate will prevent the development of ulcers."
④ "Calcium carbonate will bind with phosphorus to decrease concentrations."

14.71 Which of these clinical assessment findings should be reported to the provider of care for an older adult who has been vomiting and had diarrhea for the last 32 hours? **Select all that apply.**

① Heart Rate—68 bpm
② Blood Pressure—156/88
③ Furrowed dry tongue
④ Confusion
⑤ Increase thirst

14.72 What is the priority nursing assessment(s) after a client returns from having a liver biopsy?

① Urine output—50 mL/hr
② HR—105 bpm; RR—32 breaths/min; BP—100/68
③ Evaluate pretest prothrombin time and INR
④ Evaluate peripheral pulses

14.73 In the crowded hospital cafeteria, a nurse over-hears an unlicensed assistive personnel (UAP) openly discussing a client with her peers. Which nursing action has the highest priority?

① Report the UAP's behavior to the Director of Nursing.
② Complete an incident report regarding the behavior.
③ Discuss the importance and implications of client confidentiality with the UAP.
④ Report the incident to the evening charge nurse.

14.74 The charge nurse is making the morning assignment for a group of clients including several who are HIV positive, or who have AIDS. There are three unlicensed assistive personnel (UAPs) to assist with morning care. One of the UAPs states: "I am not going to take care of anyone who has AIDS." What is the best nursing action for the charge nurse to take regarding the assignment of the morning?

① Tell the UAP that when she was hired she was advised about HIV-positive clients, and she does not have a choice in the type of assignments she receives.
② Respect the UAP's request and assign all of the HIV-positive clients to the other two UAPs.
③ Determine what type of education the UAP received regarding standard precautions, and evaluate her ability to follow the precautions.
④ Discuss with the UAP in private that it is necessary for her to provide care to these clients and attempt to determine the source of fear.

14.75 What information is important for the nurse to explain to the mother whose child has been discharged on Tylenol?

① Acetaminophen is the generic name for Tylenol; any acetaminophen product in the children's strength is okay for her to use.
② The mother may purchase Tylenol in the children's or infant's strength for her child.
③ Determine if the mother has any acetaminophen at home either in the adult strength or in the children's strength for her child.
④ Tylenol is the generic name for the brand names of Advil or Motrin. Either of these in the children's strength may be used.

14.76 What would be most important to have at the bedside of a 36-month-old client with a fever of 103.4°F (39.7°C), respirations at 49/min. with suprasternal retractions present, drooling, and an enlarged epiglottis?

① Defibrillator
② Tracheostomy set-up
③ Tongue blade
④ IVAC pump

14.77 A client is given Aminophylline capsule 4 hours too early. This incident is discovered 30 minutes after administration. Which plan would be the most appropriate?

① Document the event on an incident report, and notify the healthcare provider (HCP).
② Change time for next medication administration.
③ Assess for bradycardia and lethargy, and notify physician.
④ Skip the next dose of medication.

14.78 A client at 38 weeks gestation is admitted in active labor. The nursing assessment reveals a decreased blood pressure to 90/50 and the FHR is 130 and regular. Which nursing action is the most important?

① Call the physician and advise of the decrease in blood pressure.
② Elevate the head of the bed to facilitate respirations.
③ Check the client's blood pressure and FHT every 30 minutes for the next 2 hours.
④ Place the client on her left side and reevaluate the blood pressure.

14.79 The client has an order for IV fluid of D5.2 Normal Saline, 1000 mL to run from 9 AM to 9 PM. The drip factor on the delivery tubing is 15 gtts/mL. The nurse would adjust the IV to infuse at what rate?

① 21 gtt/min
② 12 gtt/min
③ 25 gtt/min
④ 31 gtt/min

14.80 After a right radical mastectomy, which position is the most appropriate for a client?

① Left side with right arm protected in a sling
② Right side with right arm elevated
③ Semi-Fowler's position with right arm elevated
④ Prone position with right arm elevated

14.81 Which nursing assessment is a priority for an elderly client who is very confused and disoriented when admitted from a long-term care facility?

① Determine level of mobility regarding safe walking.
② Evaluate teeth and determine appropriate diet.
③ Determine if a family member can remain at bedside.
④ Assess the respiratory status and evaluate for hypoxia.

14.82 A client is admitted to the Emergency Room with second and third-degree burns to the anterior chest, both arms, and right leg. What should be the priority information to determine at the time of admission?

① Percentage of burned surface area.
② Amount of IV fluid necessary for fluid resuscitation.
③ Any evidence of heat inhalation or airway problems.
④ Circumstances surrounding the burn and contamination of the area.

14.83 Which nursing action is correct regarding the initial infusion of oxytocin?

① Mix oxytocin in D5W, begin at 5 mg/mL as primary IV to gravity flow.
② Decrease the rate/flow of oxytocin if fetal heart rate is below 150.
③ Piggyback the oxytocin into mainline IV and maintain flow by gravity.
④ Start an IV line and piggyback the oxytocin with an infusion pump.

14.84 The nurse is caring for a client who vigorously follows several rituals daily, including frequent hand washing. The client's hands are now reddened and sensitive to touch. Which nursing action would be least helpful initially?

① Provide special skin care.
② Give positive reinforcement for nonritualistic behavior.
③ Limit the amount of time the client may use to wash hands.
④ Protect the client from ridicule by other clients on the unit.

14.85 A client is admitted for a total abdominal hysterectomy. When the nurse gives the client the operative consent, client refuses to sign it. Which documentation in the chart is appropriate?

① The surgeon was notified and stated he/she would return to speak with the client.
② The client was informed about the importance of signing the consent, and advised to call the physician.
③ The husband was notified and gave a telephone consent.
④ The operating room was notified and surgery was canceled.

14.86 During a well-baby check-up on a 6-month-old, what would the nurse expect on assessment?

① Pincer grasp
② Sit with support
③ Birth weight tripled
④ Presence of the posterior fontanelle

14.87 Which nursing assessment is indicative of a positive tuberculin skin test reaction?

① Induration of 10 mm at the site
② A pruitic rash of 5 mm at the site
③ High fever and congested cough
④ Erythema and inflammation at the site

14.88 To assess the right middle lobe (RML) of the lung, the nurse would auscultate at which location?

① Posterior and anterior base of right side
② Right anterior chest between the fourth and sixth intercostal
③ Left of the sternum, midclavicular at fifth intercostal space
④ Posterior chest wall, midaxillary right side

14.89 1000 mL 5% dextrose in 0.45 saline is to be administered IV over 8 hours using an infusion pump for an adult client. What is the correct rate setting on the IV infusion pump?

_____mL/hr

14.90 The parents of a newborn with a meningocele have been grieving the loss of their perfect child. After 3 days of grieving, progress in their emotional status would be indicated by which comment made by the parents?

① "When will it be safe for us to hold our baby?"
② "We would rather you feed our baby."
③ "What did we do to cause this problem?"
④ "When do you anticipate our baby going home?"

14.91 The nurse is assigned to work with the parents of a retarded child. With regard to the parents, which nursing action should be included in the care plan?

① Need to interpret the grieving process for the parents.
② Discuss the reality of institutional placement.
③ Assist the parents in making decisions and long-term plans for the child.
④ Perform a family assessment.

14.92 The provider of care prescribes Lactated Ringer's 50 mL IV to be infused over 20 min. What should the nurse set the IV flow rate to deliver how many mL/hr?

_____mL/hr

14.93 A woman being evaluated for infertility is given clomiphene citrate 50 mg daily to take for 5 days. The client asks the nurse the purpose of the medicine. What should the nurse instruct the client about regarding the action of clomiphene citrate?

① Clomiphene citrate will induce ovulation by changing the hormone effects on the ovary.
② Clomiphene citrate will change the uterine lining to be more conducive to implantation.
③ Clomiphene citrate will alter the vaginal pH to increase sperm motility.
④ Clomiphene citrate will produce multiple pregnancies for those who desire twins.

14.94 During the initial prenatal visit, the physician orders an iron supplement to be taken throughout the client's pregnancy. What information is important for the nurse to tell the client regarding the iron?

① The medication should be taken with orange juice.
② Take the medication with antacids to decrease gastric distress.
③ Drinking 8 ounces of water will enhance absorption of the medication.
④ Notify the physician if stools become dark or loose.

14.95 A client with Addison's disease has been placed on Prednisone. Which comment by the client indicates an understanding of how to take the medication?

① "I should take the medication one hour before meals."
② "It is important to take the medication with my meals."
③ "I will take the medication on an empty stomach."
④ "I will not drink milk right after I take my medicine."

14.96 A client has an order for a low-sodium, low-cholesterol diet. Which selection reflects the client's compliance?

① Vegetable soup, applesauce, and hot chocolate
② Cheeseburger, French fries, and milk
③ Tomato and lettuce salad, and roasted chicken
④ Tuna fish sandwich, cottage cheese, and a Coke

14.97 What is the priority of care for an elderly client who is taking amitriptyline?

① Monitor urine output every 12 hours.
② Stand up slowly from sitting or lying positions.
③ Provide oral care every 12 hours.
④ Review foods that are low in fiber.

14.98 Which evaluation indicates a therapeutic response to volume replacement in hypovolemic shock?

① Urine output increased to 50 mL per hour.
② Blood glucose of 180 mg/dL (9.99 mmol/L), serum potassium of 4.0 mEq/L (4.0 mmol/L).
③ CVP of 2 mm Hg, pupils equal and reactive.
④ Pulse rate of 110 with no arrhythmias.

14.99 A postoperative client has returned to the room from the surgical recovery area. The client is sleeping and is disoriented when aroused. What is a nursing action to promote the client's safety?

① Placing the call bell within the client's reach.
② Staying with the client until totally oriented.
③ Restraining all four extremities until client is oriented.
④ Placing the side rails up until the client is fully awake.

14.100 Which nursing action is most appropriate for an infant who is post operative for cleft lip and palate repair and is presenting with upper airway congestion and slightly labored respirations?

① Elevate the head of the bed.
② Suction the infant's nose.
③ Position the infant on his side.
④ Administer oxygen until breathing is easier.

14.101 An American Indian client is scheduled for a joint replacement. Upon admission for surgery, the client says to the nurse, "I need to have the tissues that are removed, so they can be buried with me when I die. Without them, I will not be whole in my afterlife." What action should the nurse take?

① Inform the client this request violates protocol.
② Inform the client this request does not make sense.
③ Inform the surgeon of the client's request.
④ Inform the operating room staff to save the tissue removed.

14.102 An unaccompanied client, who is six months pregnant, is admitted to the nursing unit with vaginal bleeding. Which comment made by the client indicates a need for the nurse to assess the adequacy of the client's emotional support?

① "My husband will be so angry with me if I lose this baby."
② "I'm afraid I am going to lose my baby."
③ "I can't stay here. I don't have any insurance."
④ "I feel so guilty. I didn't want to get pregnant."

14.103 On a home health visit, an elderly client states, "This neighborhood has really gone down. I feel like a prisoner in my own home with all the trouble out there." Which nursing response would be priority?

① "Have you and your neighbors formed a Neighborhood Watch?"
② "It must be very difficult for you to live in this neighborhood."
③ "I see a lot of police cars. You should be pretty safe."
④ "Tell me what has happened to make you feel that you are not safe."

14.104 A client is experiencing septic shock and the provider wants dosing of medications to be regulated so that a mean arterial pressure (MAP) between 65 and 75 mm Hg is maintained. Which of the client's blood pressure readings meet this goal?

① 135/90
② 125/80
③ 115/70
④ 105/60

14.105 A client on the psychiatric unit was observed crying in her room following a visit from the healthcare provider (HCP). Which nursing docmentation is the most appropriate regarding this observation?

① Depressed following visit with healthcare provider (HCP).
② Appeared depressed after the visit from healthcare provider (HCP).
③ Crying in her room following visit by healthcare provider (HCP).
④ Upset with the healthcare provider (HCP) after his visit.

14.106 Which of these clients should the nurse question the new prescription for sildenafil citrate?

① A client with a history of headaches
② A history of shingles
③ A history of bronchitis
④ Heart failure and hypotension

14.107 A recently widowed elderly client has been hospitalized following a suicide attempt. Which behavior most clearly indicates the client remains a suicide risk?

① He admits having vague suicidal ideas in the past.
② His history indicates difficulty forming relationships with caregivers.
③ He becomes emotional and cries when talking about his late wife.
④ He begins to give away some of his most prized possessions.

14.108 Which of these clinical assessment findings should be reported to the healthcare provider for a client who has a nasogastric tube with suctioning? **Select all that apply.**

① Spiked T waves
② Hyperactive bowel sounds
③ Positive Chvostek's sign
④ Muscle cramping
⑤ Syncope when getting up out of bed

14.109 The nurse is administering Desmopressin Acetate (DDAVP) to a client diagnosed with diabetes insipidus. Which of the following assessments indicates the desired outcome of treatment?

① BP was 189/101 and is now 160/90.
② Blood glucose was 140 mg/dL (7.77 mmol/L) and is now 110 mg/dL (6.11 mmol/L).
③ Client intake of meal increased from 50% to 75%.
④ Urine output was 300 mL hr and is now 65 mL hr.

14.110 Which of the following actions is appropriate for the nurse to delegate to the UAP for a client who is one day post-operative choleycystectomy?

① Empty the T-tube drainage bag and report the amount of drainage noted.
② Instruct the client to avoid broccoli, fried chicken, and cheese.
③ Obtain vital signs and monitor for changes.
④ Assist the client to ambulate in the hall.

14.111 An LPN is caring for a client who has acquired third-degree full thickness burns, and is experiencing an excessive fluid loss. Which nursing action indicates the LPN understands how to provide appropriate care?

① The LPN is administering PO pain medications.
② The LPN assists the client to elevate extremities.
③ The LPN is administering hypotonic IV fluids.
④ The LPN assists the client to dangle his legs.

14.112 After a client is started on haloperidol 5 mg TID, which would be a priority for the nurse to discuss with the client?

   ① Stay away from foods high in tyramine.
   ② Move slowly to a standing position.
   ③ May experience a dry mouth.
   ④ Limit salt intake.

14.113 An elderly client in the Rehabilitation Department was evaluated to determine at what risk the client was for developing a pressure sore. How would the charge nurse intervene with a score of 21 points on the Braden Scale?

   ① A multidisciplinary client care meeting would be held to develop a plan for prevention, since the client is high risk.
   ② Since this client is high risk, review with staff that a Stage II ulcer involves the partial thickness skin loss involving epidermis and/or dermis. This ulcer may present clinically as an abrasion, blister, or shallow crater.
   ③ Interpret this score as an excellent one, and continue with protocol for skin care to prevent any complications.
   ④ Review with the UAPs how to move client up in bed since a major cause of pressure sores are secondary from friction and shear.

14.114 A client with chronic bronchitis is receiving supplemental oxygen via nasal cannula and orders state that the SpO_2 should be maintained at 90 percent or higher. During the nursing assessment, the nurse notices that the oxygen delivery is set at 7 liters per minute with an SpO_2 of 88 percent. What should be the priority nursing action?

   ① Reduce the oxygen delivery to the client no more than 2 liters per minute and stay with the client.
   ② Change the method of oxygen delivery to a simple mask or face tent.
   ③ Validate the SpO_2 value and further assess the client for possible causes of hypoxemia.
   ④ Investigate if the client, a significant other or a staff member set the oxygen at 7 liters.

14.115 After a client has returned to the floor from thyroidectomy surgery, which nursing intervention has the highest priority?

   ① Monitor vital signs every four hours.
   ② Monitor for hemorrhaging by observing frequent swallowing.
   ③ Monitor signs of respiratory distress frequently.
   ④ Position client in supine position.

14.116 The nurse is preparing a client to be discharged and who will be going home with crutches. The following are instructions for going down the stairs. Put the steps in order. Use all of the options.

① Shift weight to the unaffected leg.
② Transfer weight to the crutches and move the unaffected leg to that step.
③ Assume tripod position at the top of the stairs.
④ Move crutches and the affected leg down onto the next step.

14.117 Which of these nursing actions by the LPN when performing nasopharyngeal suctioning requires intervention by the charge nurse due to the standard of practice not being followed?

   ① Applying suction only when withdrawing the catheter and rotating it with the thumb and forefinger.
   ② Allowing the client 10 to 15 seconds for recovery between suctioning sessions.
   ③ Advancing the catheter the approximate distance from the tip of the nose to the base of the earlobe.
   ④ Suctioning client for 10 to 15 seconds.

14.118 A home care nurse is caring for a 70-year-old client that is taking docusate sodium. Which of these clinical assessment findings indicates an undesirable effect from this medication?

  ① Orange urine
  ② Abdominal distention with absent bowel sounds
  ③ HR of 72 bpm
  ④ Abdominal cramps

14.119 Which of these documentations by the RN indicates an understanding of how to safely provide care for a peripherally inserted central catheter?

  ① Flushed port with 10 mL 0.9% sodium chloride as per facility protocol for intermittent medication administration.
  ② Applied a gauze dressing over site and changed gauze dressing every 24 hours.
  ③ Cleansed the insertion port with betadine for 10 seconds and allowing it to dry completely prior to accessing it.
  ④ Informed client that after 24 hours a shower can be taken with no precautions to site.

14.120 The nurse is caring for a client in labor. The nurse palpates a firm round form in the uterine fundus. On the client's right side, small parts are palpated, and on the left side, a long, smooth curved section is palpated. Which location should the nurse auscultate the fetal heart?

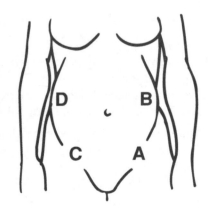

Category Analysis—Practice Exam

1. Management of Care
2. Physiological Adaptation
3. Safety and Infection Control
4. Pharmacology
5. Basic Care and Comfort
6. Management of Care
7. Physiological Adaptation
8. Safety and Infection Control
9. Management of Care
10. Physiological Adaptation
11. Physiological Adaptation
12. Physiological Adaptation
13. Basic Care and Comfort
14. Management of Care
15. Physiological Adaptation
16. Reduction of Risk
17. Pharmacology
18. Reduction of Risk Potential
19. Pharmacology
20. Reduction of Risk Potential
21. Management of Care
22. Basic Care and Comfort
23. Reduction of Risk Potential
24. Reduction of Risk Potential
25. Safety and Infection Control
26. Safety and Infection Control
27. Safety and Infection Control
28. Pharmacology
29. Pharmacology
30. Physiological Adaptation
31. Reduction of Risk Potential
32. Reduction of Risk Potential
33. Pharmacology
34. Basic Care and Comfort
35. Reduction of Risk Potential
36. Health Promotion
37. Physiological Adaptation
38. Pharmacology
39. Pharmacology
40. Pharmacology
41. Pharmacology
42. Safety and Infection Control
43. Basic Care and Comfort
44. Reduction of Risk Potential
45. Management of Care
46. Reduction of Risk Potential
47. Physiological Adaptation
48. Pharmacology
49. Pharmacology
50. Basic Care & Comfort
51. Reduction of Risk Potential
52. Basic Care and Comfort
53. Basic Care & Comfort
54. Reduction of Risk Potential
55. Pharmacology
56. Basic Care & Comfort
57. Safety and Infection Control
58. Pharmacology
59. Health Promotion
60. Basic Care & Comfort
61. Pharmacology
62. Physiological Adaptation
63. Basic Care and Comfort
64. Physiological Adaptation
65. Psychosocial
66. Physiological Adaptation
67. Health Promotion
68. Basic Care and Comfort
69. Pharmacology
70. Pharmacology
71. Physiological Adaptation
72. Reduction of Risk Potential
73. Management of Care
74. Management of Care
75. Pharmacology
76. Physiological Adaptation
77. Pharmacology
78. Health Promotion
79. Pharmacology
80. Reduction of Risk Potential
81. Psychosocial

82. Physiological Adaptation	95. Pharmacology	108. Physiological Adaptation
83. Pharmacology	96. Basic Care and Comfort	109. Physiological Adaptation
84. Psychosocial	97. Basic Care and Comfort	110. Management of Care
85. Management of Care	98. Physiological Adaptation	111. Basic Care and Comfort
86. Health Promotion	99. Safety and Infection Control	112. Pharmacology
87. Safety and Infection Control	100. Physiological Adaptation	113. Basic Care and Comfort
88. Physiological Adaptation	101. Psychosocial	114. Physiological Adaptation
89. Physiological Adaptation	102. Psychosocial	115. Physiological Adaptation
90. Psychosocial	103. Health Promotion	116. Safety and Infection Control
91. Psychosocial	104. Physiological Adaptation	117. Physiological Adaptation
92. Pharmacology	105. Psychosocial	118. Pharmacology
93. Pharmacology	106. Pharmacology	119. Pharmacology
94. Basic Care and Comfort	107. Psychosocial	120. Reduction of Risk

Directions

1. Determine questions missed by checking answers.
2. Write the number of the questions missed across the top line marked "item missed."
3. Check category analysis page to determine category of question.
4. Put a check mark under item missed and beside content.
5. Count check marks in each row and write the number in totals column.
6. Use this information to:
   - identify areas for further study.
   - determine which content test to take next.

We recommend studying content where most items are missed—then taking that content test.

Number of the Questions Incorrectly Answered

Pretest	Items Missed																						Totals
C Management of Care																							
O Safety and Infection Control																							
N Health Promotion and Maintenance																							
T Psychosocial Integrity																							
E Physiological Adaptation:Fluid Gas																							
N Reduction of Risk Potential																							
T Basic Care and Comfort																							
Pharmacology and Parenteral Therapies																							

Answers & Rationales

14.1 ③ Option #3 is correct. Morphine should be contraindicated since this will mask the neurological assessment for this client. Option #1 is incorrect since the medication should be contraindicated for this client and should not be administered. Option #2 is incorrect due to the same rationale as #1. The client should not be receiving this medication, so there would be no need for the antidote at the bedside. Option #4 is not consistent with the standard of care for clients with increased intracranial pressure. Coughing will increase the ICP.

14.2 ① Option #1 is correct. Based on the clinical findings, the client is presenting with an acute episode of hypoxia. The key statement is "*suddenly becomes anxious and very SOB.*" This may be from heart failure, but with the current clinical data provided the nurse must make a clinical decision based on this limited information. There is a need for further assessments and an immediate intervention. Of course, part of this clinical decision making strategy is to compare and contrast the options in order to make a clinical judgment. Option #2 is not a priority over #1. The client in Option #2 is septic and the body is responding physiologically like it should with a WBC count of 20,000 mm^3 and a diagnosis of pneumonia. In contrast, however, Option #1 has a client presenting with a "*sudden onset of hypoxia.*" Option #3 is a concern due to the saturation and temperature, but is not a priority over Option #1. A key to answering this question would be to review the similarity between Options #2 and #3. Remember, this is not a question evaluating "*select all that apply.*" Option #4 is also a concern. This client is presenting with intermittent claudication which is secondary to arterial insufficiency. Yes, the nurse needs to see this client, but this client still is not as acute as the client in Option #1.

14.3 ③ Options #3 and #4 are correct. Protective
       ④ isolation is used to protect clients who have an increased susceptibility to infection such as if they are receiving chemotherapy or are immuno-suppressed or neutropenic. Clients who have had a renal transplant are immuno-suppressed. Option #3 is included in the standard of care for these isolation guidelines. Option #4 is reinforced to minimize exposure to microorganisms found on the outer layers of fresh flowers. This also applies to fruits and vegetables. Option #1 is incorrect. The nurse is not concerned with protecting self from the client's secretions as a result of being splattered. The goal is to prevent the client from getting infected. If the question, however, did indicate that the nurse was going to engage in nursing care that would require the nurse to come in contact with the client's body secretions such as with entubation, suctioning, etc., then the goggles would be required based on the standard/universal precautions outlined by CDC. Option #2 is incorrect. The client should be placed in a ventilated positive pressure room for maximum protection. Negative-pressure airflow would be appropriate for a client with tuberculosis. Option #5 is not within the standard of care for this type of infection control precaution.

14.4 ① Option #1 is the priority to report to the provider of care, since client could be bleeding in the brain which could result in confusion and inability to remember daughter's name. Option #2 is the reason the client is receiving the medication. This does not indicate a complication from the medication. Option #3 would not be a priority over #1. Option #4 is incorrect, since this is not a lab that is drawn for this medication.

14.5 ③ Options #3, #4, #5 are correct. This question
④ is evaluating "*How to communicate with*
⑤ *the client with sensory deficits.*" Looking at
the client directly during communicating,
speaking slowly, and giving instructions one at
a time will result in effective communication.
Additional nursing actions may also include:
remaining in the client's field of vision if
possible; using a warm, pleasant voice and not
speaking loudly; explaining procedures prior
to starting them; and keeping background
noise to a minimum. When a subject is
changed, it is imperative to slow down or
to use key words to indicate the change.
Option #1 is incorrect since this may have
an effect on the self esteem of the client,
and does not assist in a development of
independence. Option #2 is incorrect since
the communication board is another devise
to assist with communication, but is not the
ONLY method. The entire distractor must be
complete for it to be a correct answer.

14.6 ① Option #1 is correct. When confronted with a
fire, the most important response from a nurse
is to rescue the client. In order of priority, the
proper responses are: 1) rescue; 2) alarm; 3)
confine the fire; and 4) evacuate.

14.7 ① Option #1 is correct. Option #2 would
be appropriate position to auscultate the
pulmonic heart sound. Option #3 would be
the appropriate location to auscultate the
PMI. Option #4 is incorrect.

14.8 ④ This is being a client advocate. The observed
nurse may need some assistance, and this
would be an excellent opportunity to provide
education regarding this procedure. Options
#1 and #3 do not address the problem. Option
#2 is unsafe practice and can lead to infection.

14.9 ① Options #1, #2, and #3 are correct.
② Options #4 and #5 are not necessary for
③ this procedure.

14.10 ④ Option #4 is correct. Option #1, alcohol or
healer acetone pads in place of the electrode
paste or gel may impair electrode contact with
the skin and diminish the transmission quality
of electrical impulses. In Option #2 the client
should be instructed to lie in a supine position.
Option #3 is incorrect. Client should breathe
normally.

14.11 ④ Option #4 is correct. The client is getting
hypoxic and needs oxygen. Options #1 and
#2 are incorrect. Option #1 is unsafe.
Option #3 is partially correct. Stopping
procedure is correct, but evaluating breath
sounds is not a priority in this clinical
situation over Option #4.

14.12 ③ Option #3 is the correct answer. The client
is experiencing hypoglycemia, but is still
arousable. Diaphoresis and lethargy are
symptoms of hypoglycemia. Additional
symptoms of hypoglycemia may be shakiness,
anxiety, nervousness, nausea, chills, headache,
weakness, and confusion. The guidelines for
this hypoglycemic client would be to treat
with 15 to 20 Gm carbohydrates. Examples
of this amount of carbohydrates may include:
4 oz. (118.3 mL) orange juice, 2 oz. (59 mL)
grape juice, 8 oz. (237 mL) milk, glucose
tables per manufacturer's suggestion to equal
15 GM. Option #2 is incorrect. Option #2
is part of the standard of care for the diabetic
client, but is not the priority for this clinical
situation. The HbA1c is the best indicator
of the average blood glucose level for the
past 120 days. This lab assists in evaluating
treatment effectiveness and compliance. This
option does not answer the question which
requires immediate intervention. Option #4
should be done after an intervention, based
upon the outcomes from the nursing action.
It is, however, not the priority over treating
the hypoglycemia.

I CAN HINT: One of the key words in this
question is "arousable". If, however, the client
was unconscious or unable to swallow, the
home health nurse would need to administer
(Option #1) glucagon SC or IM (repeat
in 10 min if still unconscious), and notify
the healthcare provider. Since the client is
arousable, Option #3 is the priority.

14.13 ④ Option #4 is correct. Option #1 is incorrect. Betadine is an inappropriate option. Option #2 is incorrect. Avoid using alcohol because it causes pain and tissue dehydration. Hydrogen peroxide may be used. The foaming action facilitates debris removal. However, peroxide should never be instilled into a deep wound because of the risk of embolism from evolving gases. Option #3 is incorrect when irrigating a traumatic wound, avoid using more than 8 psi of pressure. High-pressure irrigation can seriously interfere with healing, kill healthy cells, and allow bacteria to infiltrate the tissue.

14.14 ① The sickle cell crisis would be a priority due to the need to start IV fluids for hydration purposes. The hypoxia must be corrected immediately with IV fluids and oxygen. Option #2 would only be a preparation prior to surgery. Options #3 and #4 are important but not priorities to Option #1.

14.15 ④ Options #4 and 5 are correct. Option #4 will
⑤ bind with phosphates to decrease phosphates and assist with increasing calcium level. Option #5 is correct due to the problem with fluid excess due to the chronic renal disease. Option #1 is incorrect due to the complication that can occur is hyperkalemia which would result with a peaked T wave. Option #2 is incorrect because these are high in potassium. Option #3 is incorrect due to NSAIDs needing renal function for safety.

14.16 ① All are appropriate interventions for trouble
③ shooting ventilator alarms with the exception
④ of Option #2, silencing alarms. Alarms should
⑤ never be turned off for the protection of the client. When in doubt of the cause of the alarm, the nurse should manually ventilate the client with an ambule bag while another nurse or respiratory therapist determines the functioning of the ventilator. High pressure alarms frequently indicate a need for suctioning or a kinked/compressed ET tube. Low pressure alarms indicate a leak or possible disconnection.

14.17 ④ Correct answer is Option #4. Vasotec is an ace inhibitor used to treat hypertension. If given upon return from dialysis, this will prevent a hypotensive effect. Vasotec should not be given because the client could experience a hypotensive episode. If given the day after dialysis, this would disrupt the way that the medication is to be taken/administered to the client.

14.18 ③ Option #3 is the priority due to potential risk of compartmental syndrome. This is a sign of potential nerve involvement which can result in permanent damage. Option #1 presents no problem. Option #2 makes no comparison to the right foot. Option #4 is no problem.

14.19 ③ The client is presenting with signs of an infection. The cultures should be completed prior to antibiotic therapy in order to determine what organism the client is growing. If the antibiotic is started prior to getting the cultures, then the report will not be valid. This will not assist the healthcare provider in determining if the antibiotic is effective. While Option #1 is important to have to assist the HCP in calculating the antibiotic dose, the question reads "*after the HCP has been called for the order.*" Option #2 has already been evaluated based on the stem of the question. Option #4 is not specific to this case.

14.20 ② This is indicative of an alteration in the circulation from the cast being too tight causing an unsafe evaluation that could result with the client losing part of his extremity. Option #1 is irrelevant. Option #3 is important, but is not the priority as Option #2. Option #4 is partially acceptable. The capillary refill can lead to Option #2. Therefore, Option #2 is the priority of concern with alteration in perfusion.

14.21 ④ Option #4 is correct. Options #1, #2, and #3 are dangerous for a maternity client since these diseases are communicable. Infection control is the priority concern here.

14.22 ② This is a priority due to the possibility of aspiration. While it is important to complete Options #1, #3, and #4, they are not a priority over Option #2.

14.23 ① This is the priority evaluation since the signs of drug withdrawal are more frequently associated with central nervous system alterations, gastrointestinal disturbances, and tachypnea. Options #2, #3, and #4 are secondary.

14.24 ③ It is important to monitor the beginning, the behaviors during the seizure, and the duration of the seizure. This will assist the neurologist in determining a more specific location and cause of the seizures. Option #1 is incorrect because the client should be positioned on side to facilitate the draining of oral secretions and minimize aspiration. Option #2 is incorrect since this is not an automatic protocol, and there is not enough data to substantiate this action. Option #4 is incorrect after the seizure is over.

14.25 ① Options #1 and #5 are correct. Standard
⑤ precautions are to prevent any contact with any blood or body secretions. Option #2 would be appropriate if the client had tuberculosis. Option #3 is never appropriate. Options #4 is not necessary unless the nurse is going to come in contact with client's blood or body secretions, and this would need to be indicated in the stem of the question.

14.26 ② Option #2 is the only appropriate option for this active 4-year-old. Play ground activities that are fun and promote bronchial drainage will engage the child in the intervention as well as meet his developmental needs. Option # 1 is wrong. The best position to target the lung bases for cystic fibrosis is reverse Trendelenburg not sitting. Option #3 is incorrect. Avoid performing CPT immediately after eating to prevent vomiting and aspiration. Option # 4 is incorrect. Client should have a lightweight layer covering their skin to get the most of the percussion effects.

14.27 ③ This is the safest plan for the radioactive material. Safety is a priority when dealing with implants—the client's, the nurse's, and the visitor's. Option #1 is inappropriate. Option #2 does not clarify how to remove it from the bed. Option #4 is incomplete and is unsafe for any radioactive material.

14.28 ② Hypotension is a significant side effect of nitroglycerin. While the effect may be transient, the client's blood pressure needs to be closely observed to assure that it does not continue to fall. Options #1 and #3 are not relevant to this medication. Option #4 is an expected outcome.

14.29 ② Humulin N insulin is an intermediate insulin that peaks from 8-12 hours after onset. This is when signs and symptoms of hypoglycemia occur. Options #1, #3, and #4 are signs of hyperglycemia.

14.30 ④ Rales and tachycardia would indicate a cardiovascular fluid overload. Option #1 is a normal CVP reading. Options #2 and #3 do not contain information relevant to fluid overload.

14.31 ③ These are signs and symptoms of hypofunction of the thyroid. Some other assessments would include dry hair, facial expression mask-like, thickened skin, enlarged tongue, and drooling. Options #1 and #4 contains signs of hyperfunction of the thyroid. Option #2 contains signs of hyperthyroidism.

14.32 ① These are accurate assessments of the position of a fractured hip prior to repair. Option #2 occurs with foot drop. Option #3 is incorrect because the leg will not appear longer. Option #4 occurs with injury to the lumbar disc area.

14.33 ② Option #2 is correct. Green, leafy vegetables are high in vitamin K, and this is the antidote for coumadin. Options #1, #3 and #4 are correct instructions. Option #1 would be indicative of bleeding. Option #3—client will need to have pT and/or INR evaluated. Option #4—Ginseng and Coumadin will increase the risk for bleeding.

14.34 ① As with hemodialysis, hypotension is most likely to result from rapid removal of fluid from the intravascular space. Options #2, #3, and #4 are not complications associated with this procedure.

14.35 ② Option #2 is correct. The scope of practice for the UAP is if the activity delegated is performed according to an established routine sequence of steps (*that do not require clinical decision making*), then this is most likely within the scope of practice for the UAP. Other aspects of care that may be delegated to the UAP include: tasks that frequently recurs in the daily care of a client or group of clients; tasks that involve little to no modification from one client care situation to another; task may be performed with a predictable outcome; task does not inherently involve ongoing assessment, interpretation, or decision making which cannot be logically separated from the procedure(s) itself; and the task does not endanger the client's life or well-being. Option #1 is incorrect since this involves assessment of the injection technique, and this is not within the scope of practice for the UAP. Option #3 is incorrect since this is not a routine task, and will require some teaching regarding the process for the task of obtaining the 24-hour diet recall. Option #4 requires evaluation which is not within the scope of practice for the UAP.

14.36 ② The extrusion reflex disappears between 3–4 months of age. Option #1 disappears at approximately 1–2 years of age. Options #3 and #4 are normal occurrences at this age level.

14.37 ① The first action is to establish an airway. If there is no airway, any other resuscitation will not be helpful. Since the client hasn't had a cardiac arrest, Option #2 is inappropriate. Option #3 does not deal with the problem of the severe dyspnea. Option #4 is not a priority.

14.38 ④ The highest priority is to prevent tissue damage and promote tissue absorption of the medicine which is accomplished through rotation of the injection sites. Option #1 is ineffective. It is important to have seizure precautions and emergency respiratory equipment available. Option #2 is important to implement but is not a priority. Option #3 contains incorrect information.

14.39 ① Decreased hearing and vertigo occur as a result of involvement of the 8th cranial nerve which is caused from gentamycin (Garamycin) toxicity. Options #2, #3, and #4 are not toxic effects of this antibiotic.

14.40 ③ Allergic reaction is characterized by wheezing, urticaria (hives), facial flushing, and epiglottal edema. Options #1, #2, and #4 are indicative of a hemolytic transfusion reaction.

14.41 ① Option #1 is correct. When clients take beta blockers concurrently with cardiac glycoside and/or calcium channel blockers, there is an increased risk for bradycardia. Options #2, #3, and #4 are not correct for this situation. Option #4 is a therapeutic lab value.

14.42 ② Clients with a low WBC count are susceptible to infection. Option #1 contains incorrect information. The RBC's are not decreased. Option #3 is not correctly stated as a nursing diagnosis since it uses the disease versus the concept, but the reality is even if it were stated correctly it would still not be a priority over Option #2 due to the risks involved with infection. Option #4 is a potential, but not a priority. In reality, this option is not addressed in the stem of the question. For this to be correct, it would be important to have labs indicating a complication with fluid volume deficit such as the urine specific gravity, BUN, Hct or even clinical findings indicting dehydration such as weight loss, decrease in the skin turgor, dry lips and mucous membranes, dry skin, vomiting etc.

I CAN HINT: If the stem of the question gives you lab reports, assessments, vital signs, etc., PAY ATTENTION. The key here is to know the normal values for the following: WBC's: 4,800–10,800 mm³; RBC: 4,200–5,400 mm³; and Calcium: 8.5–10.5 mg/dL (2.12– 2.62 mmol/L).

14.43 ③ With the client complaints, WBCs and RBCs should be present. WBCs are a response to the inflammation process and irritation of the urethra. RBCs are increased when the bladder mucosa is irritated and bleeding. Option #1 is not a primary component in determining urinary tract infections. Option #2 is not as complete a response as Option #3. Option #4 indicates the concentration of the urine for this specimen and is not specifically associated with a urinary tract infection.

14.44 ① Immobility is a leading cause of problems with Buck's traction. It is important to turn client to the unaffected side. Option #2 is incorrect because the head of the bed can be elevated 15 to 20 degrees, since the supine position can increase problems with immobility. Option #3 is incorrect because the client is on strict bed rest. Option #4 would interfere with the traction.

14.45 ② Option #2 is correct since it is in final time of transfusion. Option #1 is not appropriate. Option #3 is newly diagnosed. Option #4 is initial and would be inappropriate.

14.46 ② The goal of care for this disease is to maintain independence as long as client is able. Options #1 and #3 are not primary goals, but are included in the care plan. Option #4 is inappropriate for this client.

14.47 ① This will facilitate maximum expansion of the lungs and will decrease the pulmonary workload. Options #2, #3, and #4 would not improve the quality of respirations and would increase client anxiety.

14.48 ① The charcoal, if given within two hours, will absorb the particles of salicylate. Option #2 is an antidote for Heparin. Option #3 is an antidote for warfarin (Coumadin). Option #4 may be necessary later after evaluating the response to charcoal.

14.49 ① Phenytoin (Dilantin) is metabolized and excreted by the liver. Elderly clients frequently have some degree of liver impairment and are a high risk for the toxic reaction. Options #2 and #3 are not affected by Dilantin. Option #4 is incorrect.

14.50 ② This will assist in determining if hydration can be done through oral fluids alone. Option #1 is done, but is not to assist with rehydration. It evaluates rehydration. Option #3 does not solve the problem, since it doesn't guarantee the child is taking fluids. Option #4 evaluates the amount of fluid taken in, but does not actually assist with rehydration.

14.51 ① The safest objective is to prevent trauma to the child during the procedure, so the child must be restrained. Option #2 would be done prior to obtaining consent and performing the procedure. Option #3 should be done before and/or after the procedure. Option #4 will not expose the spinal column of a 4-month-old necessary for this procedure to be performed safely.

14.52 ② Option #2 is correct. This action needs intervention since this is not the standard of care for this procedure. The tape should be secured from the client's nose to the nasogastric tube in order to secure placement. The tube is too bulky for the nurse to create a loop. Options #1, #3, and #4 are all correct and safe nursing care for this client.

14.53 ② The stockings should be worn the entire time the client is in the hospital. They should be removed with the bath and replaced after the skin is dry and prior to the client getting out of bed. Option #1 is incorrect because the stockings should be worn to prevent any discomfort and to increase the blood flow. Option #3 is incorrect because the stockings should be worn during the day and when the client is non-ambulatory. Option #4 is incorrect because the stockings should be applied prior to getting out of bed.

14.54 ④ The assessment indicates that the ace is too tight and it needs readjusting. Option #1 ignores the possibility of the ace being too tight. Options #2 and #3 do not relieve the circulation problem.

14.55 ① AquaMephyton is given in the vastus lateralis. Options #2, #3, and #4 are not correct routes of administration of this medication.

14.56 ① The priority is to maintain moisture to prevent the wound from drying out and becoming necrotic prior to returning to surgery. Option #2 is inappropriate. Option #3 needs to be moist in order to be correct. Option #4 needs to be continuous to be correct.

14.57 ④ Chemotherapy can lead to immuno-suppression which predisposes the client to infection. Hand washing is one of the most effective means of decreasing the infection transmission. Options #1 and #2 are appropriate but not a priority. Option #3 is not the correct isolation during chemotherapy.

14.58 ② Mannitol (Osmitrol) is an osmotic diuretic, thus increasing the urinary output. The diuresing effects facilitate the decrease in the intracranial pressure. Options #1, #3, and #4 are not indications of desired effects of the medication.

14.59 ② During both the second and third trimester, the need for insulin will increase due to insulin antagonism by the placental hormones. Option #1 is incorrect because the client is encouraged to continue to exercise. Option #3 is incorrect because the baby's pancreas is normal. However, the mother's insulin needs will increase. Option #4 is incorrect because weight gain in pregnancy and insulin needs do not correlate.

14.60 ③ The arms should be bent at 35 degree angle and weight should be placed on the hands and arms. Option #1 is incorrect because pressure placed on the axillae can damage the brachial plexus. Option #2 is incorrect because crutches should be placed 8-10 inches in front with each step. Option #4 is unsafe. Shoes should be non-slip soles.

14.61 ③ "Statins" should be taken at bedtime and with food. Option #1 is incorrect since it will take several weeks before the lipids decrease. Option #2 is incorrect. Option #4, clients should be instructed to increase fiber in their diet (whole grain cereals, fruits, and vegetables).

14.62 ④ Edema is a result of sodium and fluid retention. Weight loss should occur if therapy is effective. Options #1 and #2 do not relate to edema. Option #3 is inappropriate for this client.

14.63 ① All are low in sodium, and milk is allowed on a salt-restricted diet. Option #2 is incorrect because instant oatmeal is high in sodium. Option #3 is incorrect because bacon is high in sodium. Option #4 is incorrect because all baked breads are high in sodium along with the sausage.

14.64 ①③④ Options #1, 3, and 4 are correct. Option #1 will reduce peripheral resistance and venous return. This will result in a redistribution from the pulmonary circulation to other body systems. It will cause a pooling of blood in the peripheral blood vessels, resulting in a reduction of the amount of blood returning to the heart which will decrease the work of the heart. Option #3 is correct because furosemide (Lasix) will facilitate the excretion of water and sodium and decrease the amount of blood returning to the heart. Option #4 is correct because a high-flow rebreather mask should be used for oxygen therapy in pulmonary edema to relieve the feeling of breathlessness and support the signs of hypoxemia the client is experiencing. Option #2 is incorrect. This is an alkylating agent used for chemotherapy. There is no need for this agent with this client's clinical assessment findings. Option #5 is incorrect. The client should be positioned upright, preferable with the legs dangling over the side of the bed, to reduce venous return to the heart.

14.65 ① Depression is a frequent cause of malnutrition in the older client. Psychological, sociological, and economic factors, chronic disease, and polypharmacy all contribute to the potential or actual problem of malnutrition which will prolong wound healing. Option #2 could be a contributing factor if said decrease in social contacts. Option #3 is a normal process with aging and is not responsible for prolonging wound healing unless it is an extreme increase. Option #4 is the recommendation from the American Cancer Association for dietary fiber. This may improve the intake of vitamins and minerals as well as being beneficial for glucose tolerance.

14.66 ② The position of the trachea should be evaluated. With a tracheal shift, an increase in pressure could occur in the operative side and cause pressure against the mediastinal area. Option #1 is incorrect because on the surgical side, breath sounds will be absent. Option #3 is important to observe, but not as high a priority as Option #2. Option #4 does not relate to the situation.

14.67 ④ The initial assessment is to check for a prolapsed cord. Option #1 is a useful assessment, but not the priority assessment over Option #4 due to safety. It will determine if the fluid is urine (acidic) rather than amniotic fluid, but this can be assessed later. Option #2 is incorrect because the mother's blood pressure is not affected by rupture of the membranes. Option #3 would read variable decelerations for a cord compression or prolapse versus early deceleration.

I CAN HINT: The book *Nursing Made Insanely Easy*, has great images to simplify these decelerations. Just remember, *Early decelerations = Head compression; Variable decelerations =Cord compression; Late decelerations = Uteroplacental insufficiency.*

14.68 ② The calcium intake is important in minimizing the development of osteoporosis. Both of these contain calcium. The other options are not focused on calcium intake.

14.69 ④ Magnesium sulfate is a central nervous system depressant. A side effect is oliguria. Option #1 is not a concern because the respirations are increasing. Options #2 and #3 are not relevant for the medication.

14.70 ④ Option #4 is correct. Clients with chronic renal failure have hyperphosphatemia. Calcium carbonate will bind with the phosphorus to assist with the phosphorus excretion. Some examples of these calcium-based phosphate binders include calcium acetate, calcium carbonate, or aluminum hydroxide gel. The other options are not correct for this client with chronic renal failure.

I CAN HINT: Remember it is important to focus on what information is in the stem of the question. The key here is the diagnosis with the medication.

14.71 ③ Options #3 and #4 are correct. Older
       ④ clients are at greater risk than young people for dehydration and hypovolemia. If hypovolemia is present which is a risk from vomiting and diarrhea, they may present with tachycardia, hypotension, tachypnea, a furrowed dry tongue, and sunken eyeballs, and confusion. Option #1 is a normal rate and Option #2 would typically be decreased with this clinical presentation. Option #5 is not a reliable assessment in the older client, since this is typically decreased with age.

14.72 ② Option #2 is the priority since the client is at high risk for hemorrhaging or shock due to the liver being a vascular organ. Option #1 is WNL. Option #3 is pretest, and Option #4 would become an issue if the bleeding continued and client was to progress into shock.

14.73 ③ The unlicensed assistive personnel (UAP) needs to be re-educated about the importance of maintaining client confidentiality. Options #1, #2, and #4 are avoiding the current situation. If the behavior continues, then this must be communicated to a different level of authority.

14.74 ④ The charge nurse should discuss standard precautions (universal precautions) with the unlicensed assistive personnel (UAP) and determine the nature of her problem. It may be easily solved with education, or the UAP may need to be transferred to another unit. Option #1 may cause the UAP to resign when she may be retrained. Option #2 does not show respect for other UAPs. Option #3 is not an issue.

14.75 ① The generic children's strength acetaminophen is less expensive than the brand names (Tylenol) and may be used. Options #2 and #3, the mother should be instructed to use only the children's strength. The infant's strength of Tylenol is more concentrated. Option #4, acetaminophen is not the generic name for Advil or Motrin. These are Ibuprofen.

14.76 ② An airway is a priority. Epiglottitis can cause a sudden total airway obstruction. Option #1 is not appropriate to this situation. Option #3 is incorrect because this client has airway problems, not a seizure problem, plus a padded tongue blade is no longer recommended. Option #4 is not specific for the potential emergency of airway obstruction.

14.77 ① Document the error on an incident report, assess for side effects, and notify the healthcare provider (HCP). Options #2 and #4 are unsafe, incorrect nursing interventions. Option #3 is incorrect information. Tachycardia and hyperactivity are signs of aminophylline overdose.

14.78 ④ The decrease in blood pressure is most likely due to pressure on the inferior vena cava which occurs in the supine position (vena-caval syndrome). By positioning the client on her side, the pressure is relieved and the blood pressure will increase. Option #1 may be necessary, but Option #4 should be done first. Option #2 does not address the problem of low blood pressure. Option #3 is incorrect because the problem needs to be addressed immediately.

14.79 ① The IV is to run in 12 hours, or 720 minutes. The formula is: volume to be infused is divided by 720 times 15. Another calculation may be used to determine the number of mL's per hour, then per minute and multiplied by the drip factor. Options #2, #3, and #4 are incorrect calculations.

14.80 ③ This position will facilitate the removal of fluid from the venous pathways and lymphatic system through gravity. The arm is elevated to enhance circulation and prevent edema. Option #1 is incorrect because a sling is not necessary; the arm needs to be elevated. Option #2 is incorrect because the right arm cannot be elevated from this position. Option #4 is incorrect because the prone position is inappropriate.

14.81 ④ The presence of hypoxia needs to be addressed immediately. The hypoxia also contributes to the confusion. Once hypoxia is ruled out, then the confusion could be from being in a new environment. Always start with assessing physiological issues! Options #1, #2 and #3 are important to consider but are secondary to Option #4.

14.82 ③ The priority of care is to determine if any heat inhalation has occurred that would cause airway problems. Option #1 is secondary. Option #2 will be done as soon as Option #1 is completed. Option #4 will also be done, but Option #3 remains the priority.

14.83 ④ The Pitocin should always be a secondary infusion and the infusion controlled by an IV pump. Option #1 is incorrect because Pitocin should be a secondary infusion. Option #2 contains incorrect information. Normal range for fetal heart tones is 120 to 160 per minute. Option #3 is incorrect because the rate should be maintained by an infusion pump.

14.84 ③ Placing a limit on the ritual initially will only increase the client's anxiety and need for the rituals. Limits must be gradually instituted. Options #1, #2, and #4 are appropriate nursing actions.

14.85 ① The client and/or family must be informed about questions or concerns about the surgery prior to signing the consent. After notifying the physician, the physician's response should be documented. Options #2, #3, and #4 do not protect the client's rights.

14.86 ② A 6-month-old should sit with help. Option #1 is present at 9 months of age. Option #3 is present at 1 year. Option #4 is closed by 2–3 months.

14.87 ① A positive skin test is determined by the area of induration (raised) rather than the area of inflammation. This correctly describes a positive reaction to the skin test. Options #2 and #4 describe other types of inflammatory responses. Option #3 does not have anything to do with reading the skin test.

14.88 ② The RML is found right anterior between the fourth and sixth intercostal spaces. Options #1 and #4 are incorrect because the RML cannot be auscultated from the posterior. Option #3 is the point of maximum impulse or apical pulse.

14.89 __125__ mL/hr

Pump rates are always set in mL's per hour. 1000 mL divided by 8 hours equals 125 mL/hour.

14.90 ① This comment indicates a desire to begin stroking and cuddling this baby. This must happen before parents can actually provide physical care. Option #2 indicates a fear or a sense of insecurity with the feedings. Option #3 indicates some feeling of guilt. Option #4 is a request for information and does not address the question.

14.91 ④ This will help the nurse know where the family is in regards to grieving, coping, etc. Options #1, #2, and #3 are inappropriate before the assessment. Actions can be taken only when the circumstances are known.

14.92 __150__ mL/hr

Step One: What is the volume to be infused? 50 mL

Step Two: What is the time for the infusion? 20 min.

Step Three: Set up the equation and calculate:

$$\frac{\text{Volume (mL)}}{\text{Time (min)}} = \frac{x\,\text{mL}}{60\,\text{min}}$$

$$\frac{50}{20} = \frac{x\,\text{mL}}{60\,\text{min}}$$

$$20x = 3{,}000$$

$$x = 150\,\text{mL/hr}$$

150 mL IV pump to deliver 150 mL/hr

I CAN HINT: Reassess to review if the answer makes any sense. It does make sense to infuse 50 mL over 20 min to administer 150 mL/hour.

14.93 ① Clomiphene Citrate (Clomid) induces ovulation by altering the estrogen and stimulating follicular growth to produce a mature ovum. Options #2 and #3 are infertility problems, but Clomid does not affect them. Option #4 is not an appropriate use of the medication.

14.94 ① Vitamin C facilitates the absorption of iron. Option #2 is incorrect because antacids will decrease the absorption of the iron. Option #3 is incorrect because although the client needs increased fluids, fluids will not affect absorption. Option #4 is incorrect because dark stools are characteristic of iron therapy, and there is no need to notify the physician.

14.95 ② Prednisone (Deltasone) can cause ulcers. Administering it with meals or with milk will assist in protecting the GI mucosa. Options #1 and #3 do not protect the stomach. Option #4 is incorrect because the drug is recommended to be given with milk.

14.96 ③ Fresh fruits and vegetables are low sodium, and roasted chicken is low cholesterol. Option #1 is incorrect because canned foods contain increased salt, and milk contains cholesterol. Option #2 is incorrect because breads contain sodium, and frying increases the cholesterol. Option #4 is incorrect because bread and carbonated beverages contain sodium.

14.97 ② Option #2 is correct due to the risk for falling from orthostatic hypotension. This is a safety issue, and the number one injury to older adults is falls. Options #1, and #3 are correct, but not frequent enough, so would not be a priority over "*safety with the risk for falling.*" Option #4 is incorrect, since the foods should be high in fiber.
I CAN HINT: Amitriptyline (Elavil) has anticholinergic effects and can result in a few complications such as with low blood pressure, constipation, urinary retention, and dry mouth.

14.98 ① The primary objective of fluid replacement is to perfuse the vital organs. The increase in urine output to a normal range indicates that the kidneys are adequately perfused. Therefore, other major organs are being perfused also. Option #2 does not give any indication of adequate fluid replacement. Option #3 is incorrect because although the CVP is an indicator of fluid balance, a CVP at 2 mm Hg is in the low range and does not indicate tissue perfusion. Option #4 is incorrect because the client is tachycardiac, and the absence of arrhythmias does not indicate tissue perfusion.

14.99 ④ Side rails should be up for any disoriented client. Option #1 is appropriate, but is not the safety priority. Option #2 is incorrect because it is not necessary to stay with the client, especially while sleeping. Option #3 is incorrect because restraints are not necessary at this time.

14.100 ② Suctioning the nose will help open the airway. Option #1 will not promote adequate drainage from the upper airway. Option #3 will facilitate drainage of mucous from the upper airway and will assist the adjustment to breathing through the nose, but is secondary to Option #2. Option #4 does not relieve the congestion.

14.101 ③ Option #3 is the correct answer. It is imperative the nurse notify the physician of the client's request to assure the wishes of the client will be met. Options #1 and #2 disregard the client's request. Option #4 does attempt to make the staff aware, but does not ensure accountability. By notifying the surgeon of the client's request, and documenting the process, the nurse is covering themself from liability if this request is not met.

14.102 ① The client's concern about her husband's feelings indicates that he may not be able to support her emotionally at this time. Option #2 reflects a reality-based concern. Option #3 indicates an economic concern. Option #4 indicates she needs to talk about her current feelings. It does not give any indication of level of emotional support.

14.103 ④ Assessing the basis for the client's fears and encouraging discussion about those fears are the first positive steps. Option #1 jumps to solutions without adequately defining the problem. Option #2 is an empathetic response but does not gain any more information, or encourage the client to continue. Option #3 provides false reassurance.

14.104 ④ Option #4 is correct. The formula for mean arterial pressure (MAP) is SBP + 2 DBP divided by 3. The blood pressure with mean arterial pressure between 65 and 75 is 105/60 (MAP = 75).

14.105 ③ An objective description of the client's mood and documentation of what actually occurred is the most appropriate nursing action. Options #1, #2, and #4 interpret the behavior, or make assumptions regarding the behavior, rather than describing the behavior.

14.106 ④ Option #4 is correct. Due to the action of this drug which produces smooth muscle relaxation of the corpus cavernosum, this drug should be given with caution in clients with a history of CHF or hypotension. The other options are not correct for this medication.

14.107 ④ Giving away prized possessions is an indication that he does not intend to be using them in the future and is considered a sign of suicidal intentions. Option #1 is of concern, but does not imply active suicidal ideation at the present time. Option #2 may be true but is not a sign of suicidal intent. Option #3 is a normal expression of grief.

14.108 ④ Options #4 and #5 are correct. Nasogastric
⑤ losses are isotonic, containing both sodium and potassium. Option #4 would be a finding from hypokalemia, and Option #5 would be from hyponatremia due to hypotension. Option #1 is incorrect since this would occur from hyperkalemia, and Option #2 would occur from hypernatremia. Option #3 is a finding from hypocalcemia which is not a complication from the NG suctioning.

14.109 ④ Option #4 is correct. Desmopressin Acetate (DDAVP) is an antidiuretic replacement agent. This is used as a synthetic posterior pituitary hormone that causes an increase in water absorption from the kidneys and a decrease in the urine output. This option clearly evaluates this outcome. Option #1 is incorrect. This BP has actually decreased, but still remains elevated. This is not the desired outcome of this treatment. Actually, one of the side effects of this medication could be excessive fluid retention. Option #2 is inaccurate for this medication. Option #3 is not a desired outcome.

14.110 ④ Option #4 is correct. Following a choleycystectomy, it is important to get the client up ambulating in order to decrease risk for pneumonia, DVT, etc. This question is not just evaluating your understanding of the standard of practice for this client, but also the scope of practice for the UAP. UAPs can ambulate clients. Option #1 is incorrect because they must evaluate the characteristics of the drainage when the bag is emptied, and this is not within the scope of practice for the UAP. Option #2 is incorrect because teaching is not within their scope of practice. Option #3 is incorrect because it reads that the UAP would be monitoring for changes in the vital signs, and this is not within their scope of practice.

14.111 ② Option #2 is correct. The LPN demonstrates an understanding of appropriate positioning to facilitate an increase venous return due to the hypotension. Option #1 is incorrect. During this time, the majority of the meds will be administered through the IV. Option #3 is incorrect since the client will require a large amount of fluid replacement, so the fluid administered will be isotonic crystalloid solutions, such as 0.9% Sodium Chloride, or Lactated Ringer's solution. Option #4 is incorrect since this will facilitate arterial perfusion, and may result in a further decrease in the blood pressure.

14.112 ② A side effect of Haldol is hypotension. Moving slowly to a standing position will decrease the problem with orthostatic hypotension. Option #1 would be appropriate for a monoamine oxidase inhibitor (MAO). Option #3 is incorrect because this side effect of a dry mouth, from the anticholinergic effect, is not a priority to safety which could result in a fall. Option #4 is incorrect because salt does not have any effect on the medication.

14.113 ③ Option #3 is the correct answer. Out of 23 points, this client scored 21 which was excellent and requires prevention to continue to be the priority of care. There are six subscales rates factors within the schema from 1 (least favorable) to 4 (most favorable), for a total of 23 points. A score of 16 points or less is the critical cutoff for predicting risk. The six subscales include: sensory perception, moisture, activity, mobility, nutrition, and friction and shear. Each of these scales go from 1–4 with the exception of friction and shear and it goes from 1-3. Option #2 is a correct statement about the Stage II pressure sore, but it not correct for this client who is not high risk. Option #4 is incorrect since there are 5 other subscales that are evaluated to determine the risk factor. This option also does not address the score of 21 in the question.

14.114 ③ Option #3 is correct. Because of the risk of inaccuracy in SpO_2 assessment, an abnormal SpO_2 should always be validated with a second reading. Once this is accomplished, the client should be assessed for other causes of hypoxemia such as airway congestion or narrowing that can be seen in bronchitis. Option #1 is incorrect. It is true that an oxygen delivery of 7 liters per minute is too high for a client with chronic bronchitis because of the risk for respiratory depression, but simply reducing the delivery to 2 liters does not address the client's hypoxemia. Option #2 is incorrect. This practice must be authorized by the provider and does not appropriately address the client's hypoxemia. Option #4 is incorrect. It is likely that the delivery of 7 liters per minute is an error, but this act is low priority in this clinical circumstance.

14.115 ③ After the surgery, swelling can occur which causes respiratory distress. Option #1 is not as specific to this surgery. Option #2 is for monitoring a postoperative tonsillectomy. Option #4 is unsafe. The head of bed should be elevated.

14.116

③Assume tripod position at the top of the stairs.
①Shift weight to the unaffected leg.
④Move crutches and the affected leg down onto the next step.
②Transfer weight to the crutches and move the unaffected leg to that step.

14.117 ② Option #2 is correct. This does not follow the standard of care for nasopharyngeal suctioning. The client should be allowed 20 to 30 seconds for recovery between sessions. The LPN needs to review the standard in order to improve the care delivered to clients. Options #1, #3, and #4 are correct and do not require intervention by the charge nurse.

14.118 ④ The correct answer is Option #4. Silace is a stool softener that is used to treat occasional constipation. Some of the undesirable effects include abdominal cramps, diarrhea or a sore throat. Option #1 is incorrect. In Option #2, client could have urinary retention or may be distended from the use of opioid medications or an accumulation of gas in the GI tract; however, bowel sounds should not be absent. Option #3, HR of 72, is within the normal range of 60–80 beats per minute.

14.119 ① Option #1 is correct. Option #2 is incorrect. Part of this statement about the gauze dressing is correct for the initial dressing, but this should be changed and replaced with a transparent dressing within 24 hours. Option #3 is incorrect. The insertion port should be cleaned with alcohol for 3 seconds and allowed to dry completely prior to accessing it. Option #4 is incorrect. The client should be advised not to immerse arm in water. When taking a shower, cover dressing site to avoid water exposure.

14.120 The fetal heart rate with the LOA position would be ausculated at point A. LOP-point B; ROA-point C; ROP-point D.

CHAPTER 15

Human nature is the same all over the world.
– EARL OF CHESTERFIELD, 1747

CGFNS™

The certification of Graduates of Foreign Nursing Schools has many steps. This chapter is provided for international nurses who are preparing for the CGFNS™ Qualifying Exam. This chapter has been written as a result of many requests from international nurses who have attended our review sessions.

Many of you have been practicing nursing for years in your home country. Now you are preparing for the CGFNS™ Qualifying Exam to assess your chances of passing the U.S. nurse licensing exam, the NCLEX-RN® examination. Due to our extensive experience in preparing international nurses for the NCLEX-RN®, we are very aware of your unique issues when preparing for both the CGFNS™ Qualifying Exam and the NCLEX-RN®.

The items in this book, and specifically in this chapter, have been written to prepare you to be successful and PASS the CGFNS™ Qualifying Exam by providing you the current information on the NCLEX-RN® exam.

Those preparing for NCLEX® can utilize these practice questions as a bonus.

NURSING PRACTICE IN THE USA

Registered nurses in the United States often have a more comprehensive role in client care than some countries outside the U.S. They are particularly responsible for safe patient care and being a client advocate. Being a client advocate means that a nurse will question a medication or procedure if in the nurse's professional opinion it is unsafe for the client. Just because it is ordered, does not mean that we as nurses will give it or perform the task. It also means that that the nurse will communicate with the health team on the client's behalf and will provide the client information so that an informed decision can be made. In this country, the client is responsible for making decisions about their own healthcare.

We have developed this acronym of SAFETY to assist you to remember the crucial points to nursing care in the United States. Refer to www.cgfns.org for specific questions.

S   **SYSTEM-SPECIFIC FOCUSED ASSESSMENTS.** The nurse cannot make a clinical decision unless an assessment has been made. This means going to the bedside for the assessment.

A   **ACCURACY OF ORDERS/ASSIGNMENTS.** Is this a safe medication/treatment for the nurse to administer? Even though it is ordered by the physician, nurse practitioner or physician assistant (healthcare provider = HCP), the nurse who administers the medication/treatment is responsible for clarifying, amplifying, or questioning the order if it is not appropriate for that client. For example, if the client has a medication diagnosis such as asthma, an order for propranolol is unsafe and needs to be verified with the HCP. An understanding of the scope of practice for nursing personnel is imperative for answering questions about assignments and delegating. Refer to "RISK" below for scope of practice.

F   **FIRSTS.** Which action should the nurse take first? What is the priority for performing treatments? Which clients should be assessed FIRST? PRIORITY is a very important concept when making clinical decisions.

E   **EVALUATE OUTCOMES (i.e., PHARMACOLOGY, CARE, etc.)** Evaluate client response to the medication, the medical treatment, nursing care, etc. Was the care successful? For example: How did the client present following an albuterol treatment? Breath sounds? HR? RR?)

T   **TEACH AND PRACTICE INFECTION CONTROL.** Infection is a huge problem in this country. Hospital-based infections cause many deaths, worsen illnesses and promote extended stays in hospitals. ALL actions taken by the nurse should have the priority of practicing infection control!

Y   **YOU MUST MANAGE CARE TO PREVENT "RISK" TO THE CLIENT.**

   Recognize standard of practice and scope of practice; identify limitations of staff members (scope of practice, wrong orders, interactions, etc.). The question may be asking if the standard of practice was implemented, if the nurse needs to intervene due to the nurse not following the standard of practice, or what care is most appropriate to delegate.

   Identification of client. Informed consent, Interisciplinary team collaboration.

   Safe medication administration is an important step in prioritizing.

   Keep client/environment safe (falls, equipment, etc.); ensure client safety. Reduction of hazards in the environment may include fall/accident prevention such as bed position, use of assistive devices, rugs, cords, etc.; or may include a client who is at risk for suicide. Clinical and/or questions may ask about safety situations in both the home and the acute-care setting. Know how to admit, transfer, and discharge a client.

15.1   What is the priority assessment for an older adult client who is presenting with delirium?

①   Agitation and confusion.
②   Frequent hand washing.
③   A gradual decline in memory.
④   A recent change in medication.

15.2   What should be documented for a client who is found on the floor next to the bed in a puddle of urine, and states: "I've been ringing to go to the bathroom and no one would come"?

①   Client states: "I needed to go to the bathroom and no one would answer call button."
②   Client found lying on floor with no shoes on after falling out of bed.
③   Client found lying on floor next to bed.
④   Client states an inability to reach the call button and had to use the restroom.

15.3   Two days after admission to the hospital, an elderly client reports that her hands are shaking, she cannot relax, and she feels "things moving around in her bed." The nurse assesses her pain level to be a 4 on a 10 scale. Which would be the best follow-up response from the nurse?

①   "This hospitalization is causing you to be anxious."
②   "What pain medication do you normally take at home?"
③   "Can you attribute your hands shaking to a particular event?"
④   "I'd like to review your drug and alcohol history with you."

15.4   Which statement by a client with gastroexophageal reflux disease (GERD) suggests an understanding of the teaching?

①   "I usually drink a small glass of water before bed."
②   "I avoid food such as celery and bran cereal."
③   "I changed from butter to margarine."
④   "I quit drinking coffee and cola drinks."

15.5   A terrorist attack on a public building has resulted in several injured clients arriving at the ER simultaneously for treatment. Which victim is highest priority for immediate treatment?

①   A toddler with his forehead wound bleeding profusely.
②   A pregnant woman with a fetal heart rate of 120 bpm.
③   An adolescent with a painful rigid abdomen.
④   A client with bilateral fractures of the forearms.

15.6   Which question is most appropriate for the nurse to ask clients before a blood sample is drawn for a middle-aged male client who is offered a psotrate-specific antigen test?

①   "Are you allergic to iodine or radiopaque dyes?"
②   "Have you had rectal penetration in the last 48 hours?"
③   "Do you strain when you void or have a bowel movement?"
④   "Have you eaten red meat within 24 hours?"

15.7   A client with Parkinsonism is having problems with ambulation and is experiencing wavering and stumbling. Which client teaching would be most beneficial in preventing the client from falling?

①   Keep the arms as still as possible when walking.
②   Walk with the feet spaced at hip width.
③   Maintain a slightly forward-leaning position.
④   Focus eyes on the level of the horizon.

15.8   A client's thrombocyte count is 510,000/mm^3. Which nursing intervention is the highest priority?

①   Observe for nosebleeds.
②   Use a manual sphygmomanometer.
③   Encourage fluid intake.
④   Minimize physical activity.

15.9 Which behavior by the client indicates a need for further teaching when changing the dressing on the left deltoid following an incision and drainage of an abscess?

① Using clean gloves to remove the dressing
② Removing the tape by pulling away from the wound
③ Cleansing the wound with saline
④ Measuring the wound's length and width

15.10 Which information should be included in the variance report for a client who received the wrong medicine?

① The nurse's opinion of why the incident occurred.
② The name of the staff member who was to blame for the incident.
③ A statement that a copy of the report was filed in the client's chart.
④ An objective account of the incident and when it occurred.

15.11 A client diagnosed with a lower GI bleed has an order for 1 unit of packed red blood cells. What information is most important to be documented during this procedure?

① Vital signs prior to procedure
② Confirmation that the nurse alone verified the blood label information
③ The total volume that is to be infused
④ Vital signs before, during, and after procedure, date and time started and completed

15.12 Which plan is the most appropriate for a 34-week-pregnant woman who is being treated with magnesium sulfate and bed rest for preeclampsia?

① Assessing the equality of the pedal pulse
② Assessing the abdominal circumference
③ Assessing for an increase in the urine output
④ Obtaining the client's daily weight

15.13 What plan is the highest priority for a client who is 24 hours post-operative following a renal transplantation and begins presenting with hematuria?

① Reporting discomfort at the transplant site and T—102.1°F (38.9°C).
② Advising the provider that fluid intake should be increased.
③ Continuing to monitor the urine's volume and appearance.
④ Using a urine dipstick to check for proteinuria.

15.14 Which client should be delegated to the RN?

① A client who started her menses within the last 24 hours.
② A client whose family insists she get the "best care available."
③ A client who is arriving as a transfer from a skilled nursing facility.
④ A client who has a diagnosis of Type I diabetes with a blood sugar of 180 mg/dL (9.99 mmol/L).

15.15 Which behavior by the client demonstrates an understanding of how to take cyclosporine?

① Client mixes it in a citrus juice and stirs it well.
② Client waits at least 30 minutes to take the drug after mixing it in a solution.
③ After taking the medication, client adds water to the container and drinks that, too.
④ Client uses a plastic or Styrofoam cup to mix the medication solution.

15.16 Six months after her vaginal hysterectomy, a client tells the nurse, "Sex with my husband is painful." Which is the most appropriate response from the nurse?

① "Are you using a water-soluble lubricant during intercourse?"
② "Tell me what aspect of sex is painful to you."
③ "It may be too early after surgery to be having sex."
④ "I will advise your surgeon to talk to you about this."

15.17 What is the priority of care for a client who is one day post-operative following an abdominal hysterectomy and is presenting with edema in the left leg?

① Instruct the client to increase the frequency of post-op leg exercises.
② Consult the client's chart for a history of renal or heart failure.
③ Elevate the foot of the client's bed at least thirty degrees.
④ Measure both legs at mid-thigh and mid-calf.

15.18 Which client can be discharged to make room for an emergency admission?

① A young-adult client, post-op bowel obstruction with nasogastric tube in place.
② The client admitted today in heart failure.
③ An older-adult client with bronchial asthma and oxygen saturation on room air of 95%.
④ A client with a fractured femur and possible fat embolus.

15.19 What is the priority plan for a licensed practical nurse (LPN) who documented one hour prior to turning client there was "No skin breakdown"; and when turning the client, the registered nurse notices a first-degree pressure sore on the client's coccyx area?

① Talk to the practical nurse about the assessment when client returns to the unit.
② Correct the practical nurse's charting to address the pressure sore.
③ Document that there has been a change in the client's skin assessment.
④ Ask the client to state a time when the practical nurse did the skin assessment.

15.20 What is the priority of care for a client who has a right radius and ulna fractures with an external fixator and develops loss of two-point discrimination in the fingers on right hand?

① Elevate the right arm on pillows.
② Place the right arm at heart level.
③ Put the right arm in a dependent position.
④ Vary the right arm position every 15 minutes.

15.21 What is the priority of care for a client who sustained a closed-head injury, is being monitored for increased intracranial pressure, and has a $PaCO_2$ of 33 mm Hg?

① Encourage the client to slow his breathing rate.
② Auscultate the client's lungs and suction if indicated.
③ Advise the healthcare provider (HCP) that the client needs supplemental oxygen.
④ Report the results and continue to monitor for signs of increasing intracranial pressure.

15.22 What is the priority plan for a client who presents with a positive Brudzinski sign and has a recent history of sinusitis?

① Control intracranial pressure.
② Administer prescribed antibiotics.
③ Add pads to the side rails of the bed.
④ Hydrate the client with 0.45% saline.

15.23 When correcting a documentation made in the wrong chart, which of the following best describes the appropriate action by the nurse?

① Mark through the error with one line and write above it "error" along with the nurse's initials.
② Mark through the statements with one line and write "wrong chart."
③ Write: "Late note. This was entered in error on the wrong chart."
④ If an instance occurs where a late entry is needed, it is better to start that day over on a fresh sheet by copying what had taken place prior to it, and therefore record it in the correct order.

15.24 The nurse observes that a fire has started in the nursery. Which action should the nurse take first?

① Confine the fire to the nursery.
② Extinguish the fire.
③ Pull the fire alarm.
④ Rescue the babies.

15.25 A city council person is admitted to the hospital after experiencing chest pain at a ribbon-cutting ceremony. A journalist from the newspaper contacts the hospital's nursing supervisor and asks her for a report on the client's status. What should be the next nursing action?

① Advise the journalist of HIPAA guidelines.
② Contact the hospital's chief executive officer.
③ Ensure the journalist is authorized to receive such information.
④ Obtain signed authorization from the client.

15.26 Which assignment would be appropriate for the Labor and Delivery (L&D) nurse who will be working for one shift on the Medical Surgical unit?

① A 3-year-old with croup
② A 30-year-old with malignant hypertension
③ A 40-year-old with unstable angina
④ A 50-year-old with congestive heart failure

15.27 After establishing IV access, what would be the best for the nurse to document immediately after procedure?

① The type of catheter used and number of venipuncture attempts.
② The type of IV fluid hung and equipment used.
③ The date, time, venipuncture site, type and gauge of catheter, and IV fluid hung.
④ Type, amount, and flow rate of IV fluid, condition of IV site.

15.28 What question would be most important to ask a male client who is in for a digital rectal examination?

① "Have you noticed a change in the force of the urinary stream?"
② "Have you noticed a change in tolerance of certain foods in your diet?"
③ "Do you notice polyuria in the AM?"
④ "Do you notice any burning with urination or any odor to the urine?"

15.29 Which statement made by the new mother indicates an understanding of screening for PKU for her newborn son who she is breastfeeding?

① "I will have him tested 24 hours after birth."
② "I will return to the clinic in 48 hours for the screening."
③ "I will return in 1 week to obtain blood samples."
④ "I will return in 1 month for the screening."

15.30 Which of these schedules would be the most appropriate to recommend to a pre-menopausal woman regarding her self breast exam?

① One week prior to the monthly period
② One week after the menstrual period
③ During every shower
④ The same day monthly

15.31 During the history, which information from a 20-year-old client would indicate a risk for devel-opment of testicular cancer?

① Genital Herpes
② Hydrocele
③ Measles
④ Undescended testicle

15.32 Which plan is least appropriate for meeting the needs of a family after a loved one has died?

① Allow the family to wash the body.
② Allow the minister to touch the body.
③ Allow chanting to be done during the "last rites."
④ Call the funeral home immediately to remove the bad spirit.

15.33 What is the priority clinical assessment finding indicating a common side effect for a client who receives a positive end expiratory pressure (PEEP) at the end of the ventilator respiration cycle?

① Increased blood pressure
② Decreased cardiac output
③ Decreased lung compliance
④ Increased venous return to heart

15.34 Organize the following steps to suctioning in chronological order (with 1 being the first step in this procedure).

①Put on sterile glove.
②Lubricate catheter with normal saline.
③Apply suction for 5–10 seconds.
④Explain procedure to client.
⑤Wash hands thoroughly.

15.35 Which findings would indicate that a client with Adult Respiratory Distress Syndrome (ARDS) is deteriorating?

① PaO_2—88%; R—24
② PaO_2—87%; HR—80
③ PaO_2—58%; HR—108
④ PCO_2—47 mm Hg; R—32

15.36 Which of the clinical assessment findings requires further evaluation due to risk of a potential complication with appendicitis?

① Sharp pain with extreme gastric distention.
② Rebound tenderness in the right lower abdominal quadrant, with decreased bowel sounds.
③ Growing pain, radiating to the lower back.
④ Pain on light palpation in epigastric area with diarrhea.

15.37 Which clinical assessment finding indicates a complication resulting in a low volume alarm on a volume-cycled positive pressure ventilator?

① Client is biting on the tubing.
② Excessive fluid is in the ventilator tubing.
③ A leak in the client's endotracheal tube cuff.
④ Client is lying on the tubing.

15.38 Which of these documentations indicate the nurse understands how to accurately evaluate the client's stool for occult blood?

① Collect stool placed in a clean container to examine for pathological organisms.
② Remained on regular diet prior to test being done.
③ Stool sample obtained from one area of the stool.
④ Guaiac testing—positive for occult blood. Paper turned blue.

15.39 What is the priority of care after the urinary catheter is removed?

① Encourage client to eliminate fluid intake.
② Document size of catheter and client's tolerance of procedure.
③ Evaluate client for normal voiding.
④ Documentation of client teaching.

15.40 The client is admitted to ER with severe discomfort and an inability to urinate after today's A&P repair. The nurse inserts the Foley catheter all the way up to the collecting tube without urine return. Which nursing action should be next?

① Leave the catheter in place and wait for an hour to determine if it is in the correct position.
② Change the position of the catheter in an attempt to get urine flow.
③ Acquire a new catheter and attempt to place in the appropriate orifice.
④ Try an alternate method to get the client to urinate.

15.41 Which of these statements made by a female client who has been abused by her spouse indicates the counseling has been effective?

① "I know my husband will never hurt me again."
② "I know it is my fault that he hits me."
③ "I promise I will get him to promise that he will not do it again."
④ "I have made arrangements to go to the battered women's shelter the next time he hits me."

15.42 Which clinical findings indicate a complication from diabetes insipidus?

① Urine specific gravity—1.001
② Serum sodium—135 mEq/L (135 mmol/L)
③ Urine output greater than 200 mL/hr
④ Weight loss of 2 lbs. (0.9 kg)

15.43 Which nursing action is most appropriate for a client receiving a tube feeding around the clock?

① Rinse the bag and change the formula every 4 hours.
② Rinse the bag and change the formula every shift.
③ Change the bag and formula every shift.
④ Rinse the bag and change the formula every 2 hours.

15.44 A 17-year-old is beginning chemotherapy for her malignancy. Which statement indicates she has a realistic perception of her health status?

① "I will be cured after my therapy is completed."
② "I may lose my hair during chemotherapy."
③ "I will be able to continue my current school schedule."
④ "I must have done something to cause this illness."

15.45 What nursing action is most appropriate when inserting a vaginal suppository?

① Remove the suppository from the wrapper and lubricate it with Vaseline.
② Instruct client to place in tampon after inserting the vaginal medication.
③ With an applicator on the forefinger of your free hand, insert the suppository about 2" (5 cm) into the vagina.
④ Direct the applicator up initially and then down and forward.

15.46 Which statement made by the client with a cast on his right leg indicates he understands how to safely walk up stairs with his crutches?

① "I will put my right leg up first."
② "I will put my left leg up first."
③ "I will put both of my crutches up first."
④ "I will put both of my legs up first."

15.47 Which statement made by the nurse while teaching the client about the purpose of a continuous bladder irrigation (CBI) for the first-day postoperative TURP indicates an understanding of the procedure?

① Prevents urinary stasis and infection.
② Maintains urinary dilution to prevent irritation.
③ Keeps urine flowing by preventing clot formation.
④ Delivers medication directly to operative area.

15.48 What would the nurse ask the client to do when evaluating the cranial nerve 1?

① Ask client to smell and identify different odors.
② Ask client to shrug the shoulders.
③ Ask client to read a Snellen chart.
④ Ask client to stick out tongue and move from side to side.

15.49 Which plan is most appropriate for a client in septic shock?

① Position client with head down and feet up.
② Place in Sims position.
③ Restrict dietary protein.
④ Increase flow rate of IV fluids.

15.50 A client with a closed-head injury has a nasogastric tube in place and begins to vomit. What is the highest priority?

① Check the nasogastric tube for appropriate placement.
② Reposition client in bed to a side-lying position.
③ Notify the healthcare provider (HCP).
④ Remove the tube immediately.

15.51 The client has had an acute myocardial infarction and is on a cardiac monitor. She is beginning to have premature ventricular contractions (PVCs) at 10/minute. The nurse will administer which of these ordered drugs?

① Atropine
② Nitroglycerin
③ Propanolol
④ Lidocaine

15.52 Organize these steps in chronological order with #1 being the first step for a client who is having a nasogastric tube removed.

| ①Assist client into semi-Fowler's position. |
| ②Ask client to hold her breath. |
| ③Assess bowel function by auscultation for peristalsis. |
| ④Flush tube with 10 ml of normal saline. |
| ⑤Withdraw the tube gently and steadily. |
| ⑥Monitor client for nausea, vomiting. |

| |
| |
| |
| |
| |
| |

15.53 Prior to administering Atenolol and Digoxin, which assessment is most important to report and document?

① HR—56 bpm
② HR—92 bpm
③ BP—140/92
④ Serum potassium—3.8 mEq/L (3.8 mmol/L)

15.54 A psychiatric client with the diagnosis of schizophrenia tells the nurse that he is Elvis Presley. What would be the priority action for the nurse?

① Confront the client regarding this delusion and bring him back to reality.
② Reflect this statement back to the client to encourage therapeutic communication.
③ Respond with an open-ended response to get client to further discuss his thoughts.
④ Verify identify of the client prior to administering his medication.

15.55 A client is experiencing septic shock and the provider wants dosing of medications to be regulated so that a mean arterial pressure (MAP) between 65 and 75 mm Hg is maintained. Which of the client's blood pressure readings meet this goal?

① 135/90
② 125/80
③ 115/70
④ 105/60

15.56 What would be most important to monitor on a client who is taking Lisinopril?

① Serum potassium
② Serum pH
③ Serum calcium
④ Heart rate

15.57 Following an automobile accident, a client is admitted to the hospital with a head injury. Which clinical finding would indicate the cerebral edema is increasing and the client is deteriorating?

① Increase in pain
② Irregular respiratory pattern
③ Narrowing of the pulse pressure
④ Increase in heart rate

15.58 The physician orders heparin 7,000 U S.C. q8h for a client with deep vein thrombosis. The heparin available is 20,000 units per 1 mL. How many milliliters of heparin should the nurse administer?

① 0.2 mL
② 0.3 mL
③ 0.35 mL
④ 3.5 mL

15.59 Which interventions would be most appropriate for a 3-month-old infant in a right hip spica cast?

① Palpate the left radial artery and compare it to the right.
② Check cast for tightness by inserting fingers between skin and cast.
③ Blanch the skin of areas proximal to the casted right leg.
④ Medicate frequently for pain.

15.60 The nurse is caring for a female client in the ER who was attacked and raped 6 hours ago. What initial nursing action would be most important?

① Clean wounds immediately.
② Obtain written informed consent for examination.
③ Determine if the woman has bathed or douched.
④ Obtain laboratory specimens.

Category Analysis—CGFNS™

1. Psychosocial
2. Management of Care
3. Pharmacology
4. Basic Care and Comfort
5. Management of Care
6. Physiological Adaptation
7. Reduction of Risk Potential
8. Basic Care & Comfort
9. Basic Care & Comfort
10. Management of Care
11. Pharmacology
12. Basic Care & Comfort
13. Basic Care and Comfort
14. Management of Care
15. Pharmacology
16. Health Promotion
17. Basic Care and Comfort
18. Management of Care
19. Management of Care
20. Basic Care and Comfort

21. Reduction of Risk Potential
22. Reduction of Risk Potential
23. Management of Care
24. Safety and Infection Control
25. Management of Care
26. Management of Care
27. Pharmacology
28. Health Promotion
29. Health Promotion
30. Health Promotion
31. Health Promotion
32. Psychosocial
33. Physiological Adaptation
34. Physiological Adaptation
35. Physiological Adaptation
36. Basic Care and Comfort
37. Physiological Adaptation
38. Basic Care and Comfort
39. Basic Care and Comfort
40. Basic Care and Comfort

41. Psychosocial
42. Basic Care & Comfort
43. Basic Care & Comfort
44. Psychosocial
45. Pharmacology
46. Reduction of Risk Potential
47. Basic Care and Comfort
48. Reduction of Risk Potential
49. Physiological Adaptation
50. Basic Care and Comfort
51. Pharmacology
52. Basic Care and Comfort
53. Pharmacology
54. Psychosocial
55. Physiological Adaptation
56. Pharmacology
57. Reduction of Risk Potential
58. Pharmacology
59. Reduction of Risk Potential
60. Management of Care

Directions

1. Determine questions missed by checking answers.
2. Write the number of the questions missed across the top line marked "item missed."
3. Check category analysis page to determine category of question.
4. Put a check mark under item missed and beside content.
5. Count check marks in each row and write the number in totals column.
6. Use this information to:
   - identify areas for further study.
   - determine which content test to take next.

We recommend studying content where most items are missed—then taking that content test.

Number of the Questions Incorrectly Answered

Pretest	Items Missed																								Totals
C Management of Care																									
O Safety and Infection Control																									
Health Promotion and Maintenance																									
N Psychosocial Integrity																									
T Physiological Adaptation:Fluid Gas																									
E Reduction of Risk Potential																									
N Basic Care and Comfort																									
T Pharmacology and Parenteral Therapies																									

Answers & Rationales

15.1 ④ Option #4 is correct. Alcohol and drug use is a common unrecognized problem in the elderly in the United States. This client may be exhibiting manifestation of substance withdrawal; and in recognizing this should gather more data from the client. Option #1 is incorrect because it makes an unfounded assumption and ignores the client's symptoms, Option #2 is incorrect as it is a symptom of Obsessive Compulsive Disorder, not delirium. Option #3 in incorrect as there is a difference is suspected delirium and slow onset memory loss as in Alzheimer's.

15.2 ③ Option #3 is correct.

15.3 ④ Option #4 is correct. Alcohol and drug use is a common unrecognized problem in the elderly in the United States. The client may be exhibiting manifestation of substance withdrawal; and in recognizing this, the nurse should gather more data from the client.

15.4 ④ Option #4 is correct. Coffee and cola drinks are discouraged in GERD because the increased gastric motility and the likelihood of reflux. Drinking before bed is discouraged because it is preferred that the stomach be empty when reclining. High fiber and low fat diets are recommended in cases of GERD.

15.5 ③ Option #3 likely has a severe injury that is causing hemorrhaging internally. Option #1 should be seen next as children lose volume rapidly. #2 should be seen as soon as possible the FHR should be around 140 and the fetus is under stress. #4 may be the last one to be seen. There are no good options, they are all terrible as is the terror attack that caused this situation.

15.6 ② Option #2 is correct. Rectal penetration such as a digital exam or rectal intercourse can cause a false high PSA result. If this has occurred, 48 hours must pass before the test can be done. Allergies to iodine or radiopaque dye, straining with voiding or defecation, and eating red meat are not contraindications for testing.

15.7 ④ Option #4 is correct. Focusing on the horizon level helps maintain the balance of a client with Parkinsonism who is having ambulation difficulties. The client should be taught to swing the arms when walking, not to keep them still. The feet should be widely spaced at shoulder width or greater. The client should try to maintain an erect posture, not a forward-leaning one.

15.8 ③ Option #3 is correct. The client has thrombocytosis, which predisposes him to thrombus formation. Fluid intake reduces the risk of thrombus by maintaining an adequate amount of water in the serum. The other measures identified are associated with thrombocytopenia.

15.9 ② Option #2 is correct. When removing a dressing, the tape should be removed toward the wound, not away from it, as pulling away from the wound may disrupt healing. Home care of an abscess wound requires medical asepsis so clean gloves are acceptable during the procedure. It is standard practice to clean wounds with saline. Measuring the wound can give the provider information regarding the progress of the healing.

15.10 ④ Option #4 is correct. Just the facts ma'am. Other options are not inclusive.

15.11 ④ Option #4 is correct. Option #1 is not as inclusive as #4. In Option #2, blood should be verified with another nurse. Option #3 should be actual volume versus projected amount since the infusion may need to be discontinued prior to total amount being infused.

15.12 ④ Option #4 is correct. This is a primary concern since it provides a baseline and an ongoing record of potential increase in the weight. Options #1, #2, and #3 are incorrect. Option #1 should read the patellar reflexes since they are more indicative of neurological problems with PIH or magnesium sulfate toxicity. Option #2 is not routinely done. Option #3 would be a decrease in urine output if assessing magnesium sulfate toxicity

15.13 ① Option #1 correct. The highest priority is to report evidence of transplant rejection such as hyperacute which occurs within 48 hours after surgery and would include symptoms such as: fever, hypertension, and pain at the transplant site. The acute rejecton occurs 1 week to 2 years after surgery and would include symptoms such as oliguria, anuria, low-grade temperature, hypertension, tenderness over the transplanted kidney, lethargy, azotemia, and fluid retention. This question is asking about the hyperacute rejection since it is within 24 hours following the renal transplantation. Option # 2 is incorrect since fluids should only be administered as prescribed and not increased. While Option #3 is important, the assessment of the urine appearance and odor hourly (initially pink and bloody, gradually returning to normal in a few days to several weeks, is not a priority over Opton #1. This hematuria is an expected finding following this surgery. Option #4 is incorrect. While the daily urine tests are important, they would not be a priority over Option #1 since signs or rejection must be reported immediately.

15.14 ③ Option #3 is correct. Of the four clients described, the only one that must receive an assessment from the RN is the newly arriving client. An RN must perform the initial assessment of a client.

15.15 ③ Option #3 is correct. To ensure getting the full dose of the drug, after the dose has been taken, water should be added to the container, swished around to mix with the residue of the drug, and the water should then be drunk. Option #1 is incorrect because not all citrus juices should be mixed with the drug. Grapefruit juice is contraindicated. Option #2 is incorrect because the drug should be taken immediately after mixing. Option #4 is incorrect because the drug will adhere to the sides of a plastic or Styrofoam cup. Only a glass container should be used.

15.16 ② Option #2 is correct. The nurse needs more information, more assessment, before optimal help can be given to the client. Therefore, it is ideal for the nurse to ask for clarification of the client's statement. Options #1, #3, and #4 are all incorrect because these responses bypass the necessary assessment. The client did not state that intercourse is painful so #1 is making an assumption. Option #3 is incorrect because in most cases, intercourse after a vaginal hysterectomy does not need to be postponed for 6 weeks. Option #4 is incorrect because it undervalues the nursing role and overlooks the opportunity to help the client in her dilemma.

15.17 ④ Option #4 is correct. One of the most reliable physical finding of deep vein thrombosis, a post-op complication, is edema of the affected leg. When discovered, a nurse should measure both legs at midthigh and midcalf so that the nurse's report to the provider is complete and accurate. Option #1 is incorrect because increased activity of the leg without concurrent treatment for deep vein thrombosis may actually dislodge the clot. Talk to the provider before instituting this strategy. Option #2 is incorrect because it does not address the immediate need of the client, and in renal failure and heart failure, edema is bilateral. Option #3 is incorrect because it does not address the immediate need of the client and will not help to resolve the problem of a deep vein thrombosis.

15.18 ③ The client in Option #3 is in the least distress and should be discharged. We would like to see the N/G removed before going home, but Option #1 could be the second to go if an emergency and appropriate discharge instructions were given. Options #2 and #4 could have life threatening emergencies and should remain hospitalized if possible.

15.19 ① Option #1 is correct. There is a significant difference in the skin assessment of the practical nurse and the registered nurse. The registered nurse is obligated to discuss the matter with the practical nurse. Option #2 is incorrect. One nurse should not alter the charting of another nurse. Option #3 is incorrect. The nurse should not make this assumption without talking to the practical nurse first. Option #4 is incorrect. As a matter of professional respect, it is preferred that the registered nurse speak to the practical nurse before involving the client in the matter.

15.20 ② The client has a symptom of compartment syndrome which is a complication of trauma and fractures. In this case, the best position for the arm is neutral or at heart level. Option #1 is incorrect because it reduces arterial flow to the arm and increases tissue ischemia. Option #3 is incorrect because it can increase swelling and further impair circulation to the extremity. Option #4 is incorrect because it both reduces arterial flow and increases swelling of the extremity.

15.21 ④ Option #4 is correct. A lower-than-normal $PaCO_2$ can actually benefit the client because it reduces intracranial pressure by preventing cerebral vasodilation. The results should be reported to the physician, and monitoring for signs of increased intracranial pressure should continue. Option #1 is incorrect. Instructing the client to slow his breathing rate is inappropriate because it could elevate the $PaCO_2$ which could increase intracranial pressure. Option #2 is incorrect. There is no evidence that suction is indicated. Suctioning elevates intracranial pressure and therefore should be avoided. Option #3 is incorrect. There is no evidence that supplemental oxygen is needed. An abnormal $PaCO_2$ does not indicate the need for supplemental oxygen.

15.22 ② Option #2 is correct. The Brudzinski sign indicates bacterial meningitis, a complication of sinusitis. The client's greatest need is a regimen of antibiotics to which the causative agent is sensitive. Option #1 is incorrect. Bacterial meningitis causes increased intracranial pressure, and it is important for the nurse to monitor for manifestation of increased intracranial pressure. However, in this circumstance, it is not the highest priority. Option #3 is incorrect. Because of the risk for seizures in bacterial meningitis, padded side rails are an important nursing intervention. However, this intervention does not have priority over instituting the client's antibiotic therapy. Option #4 data does not indicate the use of a hypotonic solution for hydrating the client

15.23 ② Option #2 is correct. This is the most accurate form of documentation. Option #1 is incorrect due to the word "error." Options #3 and #4 contain unnecessary information.

15.24 ④ Option #4 is correct. Just remember, "RACE." (Rescue, Alarm, Confine, and Extinguish).

15.25 ④ Option #4 is correct. Maintaining client confidentiality/privacy is most important to this situation. Options #1, #2, and #3 do not address this concern with privacy. These answers focus on the journalist and hospital. The correct answer is the answer that is client-focused.

15.26 ② Option #2 is correct. The L&D nurse provides care for clients with pregnancy induced hypertension. These assessments and plans of care would correlate with the nurse's skills. Options #1, #3, and #4 would not be appropriate for this nurse. L&D nurses do not routinely provide care for children. Options #3 and #4 require an understanding of cardiology.

15.27 ③ Option #3 is the most correct answer. Options #1 and #2 are appropriate but not as inclusive as Option #3. Option #4 should be included in the once-per-shift documentation. This question states "after establishing IV access."

15.28 ① Option #1 is correct. This change would be most indicative of a potential complication with (BPH) benign prostate hypertrophy. Options #2, #3, and #4 are incorrect. Option #4 would be indicative of an infection.

15.29 ③ Option #3 is correct since the newborn is only getting colostrum for the first few days. This screening may have a possible false negative result with the initial screening. Options #1, #2, and #4 are inaccurate and would not provide valid information.

15.30 ② Option #2 is correct because this is when the breasts are least congested. Option #1 is when the breasts are most congested. Option #3 is unnecessary. The recommended frequency is monthly. Option #4 is for post-menopausal women.

15.31 ④ Undescended testicles make the client high risk for testicular cancer. Mumps, inguinal hernia in childhood, orchitis, and testicular cancer in the contra lateral testis are other predisposing factors. Options #1, #2, and #3 are not factors that contribute to testicular cancer.

15.32 ④ Families of most cultures choose to "say good-bye in their own ways."

15.33 ② Option #2 is correct. As a result of the PEEP, the cardiac output may decrease. Options #1, #3, and #4 are incorrect for PEEP.

15.34

④Explain procedure to client.
⑤Wash hands thoroughly.
①Put on sterile glove.
②Lubricate catheter with normal saline.
③Apply suction for 5–10 seconds.

15.35 ③ Option #3 is correct. ARDS is a form of pulmonary edema that is characterized by dyspnea, labored respiration, and low PaO_2. Option #3 indicates client's deterioration. Options #1 and #2 are incorrect. In Option #4, increasing levels of CO_2 are generally not a problem.

15.36 ② Option #2 is correct. Rebound pain is manifested by pressing firmly over the area known as McBurney's point. The rebound pain, decreased bowel sounds, tender abdomen, and fever, are all characteristic of appendicitis. Options #1, #3, and #4 are incorrect.

15.37 ③ Option #3 is correct. When the low alarm sounds, this usually indicates a leak. Options #1, #2, and #4 would result in a high volume alarm.

15.38 ④ Option #4 is correct. Options #1, #2, and #3 are incorrect. Option #1 should be in a sterile container. In Option #2, client may be on a specific type of diet prior to test being done to minimize false results. Option #3 should be collected from various areas of stool.

15.39 ③ Option #3 is a priority. Within 24 hours client should be voiding normally. Options #1, #2, and #4 are incorrect. Option #1 should be increased. Option #2 is not totally correct. The size of the catheter should have been documented when it is placed. Option #4 is important but is not a priority for this question.

15.40 ③ Option #3 is correct. The bladder is not as deep in the body cavity as the full length of a Foley, The catheter is obviously in the wrong orifice. Option #1 will leave the client in pain for another hour and is not acceptable. Option #2 can be dangerous if the old catheter is pulled from the vagina and placed into the uretha. Option #4 is too late as client is in pain.

15.41 ④ Option #4 is correct. Most abused women eventually leave the situation. Interventions may not produce quick outcomes, but they can begin to facilitate the process of healing. Options #1, #2, and #3 are incorrect. In Option #1, the husband will not change without identifying cause of anxiety and altering the manner he deals with it. Options #2 and #3 do not indicate counseling was effective.

15.42 ④ Option #4 is correct. Clinical manifestations from diabetes may result in severe dehydration. These manifestations may include: dry skin and mucous membranes; weight loss; decrease in blood pressure; decrease in central venous pressure; weakness; confusion; or speech difficulty in elderly. Options #1 and #3 are clinical manifestations of diabetes insipidus but not complications. Option #2 is normal range.

15.43 ① Research indicates there is an increased growth of organisms after four hours. Options #2 and #3 are inappropriate due to increased organism growth. Option #4 is not a necessary action to maintain asepsis.

15.44 ② This statement reflects the client's understanding of the side effects of chemotherapy. Option #1 may or may not occur. Option #3 is not realistic. It may be possible at times, but the question requests a "realistic perception." Option #4 is inaccurate and may reflect blame and guilt.

15.45 ③ Option #3 is correct. Option #1 is incorrect. It should be lubricated with a water-soluble lubricant. Option #2 should not be done because the tampon would absorb the medication and decrease its effectiveness. Option #4 should read to direct the applicator down initially (toward the spine), and then up and back (toward) the cervix.

15.46 ② Option #2 is correct. The unaffected leg moves up first, followed by the crutches, and the affected leg. Options #1, #3, and #4 are incorrect. When going downstairs, affected leg and crutches move down first.

15.47 ③ Continuous bladder irrigation prevents the formation of clots which can lead to obstruction and spasm in the postoperative TURP client. Option #1 refers to a possible preoperative complication of infection due to the enlarged prostate. Option #2 will be ineffective. Option #4 is incorrect because medicine is not routinely administered via CBI in a first-day post-op TURP.

15.48 ① Option #1 is correct for the CN1 (olfactory). Option #2 would be correct for CN11 (spinal accessory). Option #3 is still correct for CN2 (optic). Option #4 is correct for CN12 (hypoglossal).

15.49 ④ Option #4 is correct. Due to dilation of blood vessels from the overwhelming infection, the client experiences a decrease in venous return. To maintain adequate circulation, IV fluid replacement is essential. Position should be supine with legs elevated.

15.50 ② Option #2 is correct. It is done to decrease risk of aspiration. Options #1, #3, and #4 are incorrect. While the nurse may implement Option #1, it is not a priority to Option #2.

15.51 ④ Lidocaine decreases cardiac irritability and is the first line drug for treatment of PVCs. Option #1, atropine, is an anticholinergic drug used to treat bradycardia and heart block effect. Option #2, nitroglycerin, is primarily given for anginal pain. Option #3, Inderal, is used (primarily) to treat supraventricular dysrhythmias.

15.52

③Assess bowel function by auscultation for peristalsis.
①Assist client into semi-Fowler's position.
④Flush tube with 10 mL of normal saline. Flushing will ensure that the tube doesn't contain stomach contents that could irritate tissues during tube removal
②Ask client to hold her breath. This is to close epiglottis.
⑤Withdraw the tube gently and steadily.
⑥Monitor client for nausea, vomiting. For 48 hours, monitor client for GI dysfunction including nausea, vomiting, abdominal distention, and food intolerance.

15.53 ① Option #1 is correct. When clients take beta blockers concurrently with cardiac glycoside and/or calcium channel blockers, there is an increased risk for bradycardia. Options #2, #3 and #4 are not correct for this situation. Option #4 is therapeutic.

15.54 ④ Option #4 is correct. Safety is a priority in the clinical situation. Client identification is imperative since he is delusional. Option #1 is not a priority to #4. Options #2 and #3 include strategies for effective communication.

15.55 ④ Option #4 is correct. The formula for mean arterial pressure (MAP) is SBP + 2 DBP divided by 3. The blood pressure with mean arterial pressure between 65 and 75 is 105/60 (MAP = 75).

15.56 ① Option #1 is priority. This medication may cause retention of potassium. Options #2, #3, and #4 are incorrect.

15.57 ② Clients with increased intracranial pressure have Bradycardia, an irregular respiratory rate, and a widening of the pulse pressure. Option #1 is not a sign that a client with a head injury is deteriorating. The earliest sign of a change in the client's neurological status is an alteration in the level of consciousness. In Option #3 there is a widening of pulse pressure with increased intracranial pressure. Narrowing of the pulse pressure indicates hypovolemic shock. Option #4, Bradycardia, is a sign of increasing intracranial pressure.

15.58 ③ Option #3 is correct.

$$\frac{20{,}000 \text{ U}}{1 \text{ mL}} = \frac{7{,}000 \text{ U}}{X}$$

$$20{,}000 \text{ X} = 7{,}000 \text{ U}$$

$$X = \frac{7{,}000 \text{ U}}{20{,}000 \text{ U}}$$

15.59 ② Option #2 is correct. Check the cast to make sure it is not constricting circulation. The child is not in traction; the arms are not part of the treatment; and the circulation is checked distal to the cast, not proximal. Medicating frequently is inappropriate.

15.60 ② Option #2 is correct. Consent must be a priority action before obtaining laboratory specimens and completing a specific interview or calling the police.

Books Published by I CAN Publishing®, Inc.

NCLEX-RN® 101: How to Pass!

NCLEX-PN® 101: How to Pass!

Nursing Made Insanely Easy!

Pharmacology Made Insanely Easy!

Medical Surgical Nursing Concepts Made Insanely Easy! A New Approach to Prioritizing Nursing!

Concepts Made Insanely Easy for Clinical Nursing! A New Approach to Prioritizing Nursing!

Pathways to Teaching Nursing: Keeping It Real

The Eight-Step Approach to Teaching Clinical Nursing

The Eight-Step Approach for Student Clinical Success

We Do not Die Alone: "Jesus is Coming to Get Me in a White Pickup Truck"

★ ★ ★ ★ ★ ★ ★ ★ ★ ★ ★ ★ ★ ★ ★ ★ ★ ★ ★

CDs for Educators

Nursing Made Insanely Easy! Images on CD

Pharmacology Made Insanely Easy! Audio CD Review; Images on CD

★ ★ ★ ★ ★ ★ ★ ★ ★ ★ ★ ★ ★ ★ ★ ★ ★ ★ ★

I CAN
PUBLISHING®, INC.

1-866-428-5589
www.icanpublishing.com